Sheila Jansen grew [...] mid-twenties she moved to London, where she spent ten years before going to America. There she read English and French and now teaches English in California, where she lives with her husband, a professor of wilde-land sciences.

Mary Maddison

Sheila Jansen

HEADLINE

First published in 1991
by HEADLINE BOOK PUBLISHING PLC

First published in paperback in 1992
by HEADLINE BOOK PUBLISHING PLC

10 9 8 7 6 5 4 3 2 1

ISBN 0 7472 3741 7

Typeset on 10/11 pt Times
by Colset Private Limited, Singapore

Printed and bound in Great Britain by
HarperCollins Manufacturing, Glasgow

HEADLINE BOOK PUBLISHING PLC
Headline House
79 Great Titchfield Street
London W1P 7FN

ACKNOWLEDGEMENTS

To my friend and mentor, Clark Brown, in whose creative writing class many years ago this book was born as a short story. My thanks also to my husband, Henricus, and my sister, Shirley, without whose prodding it would never have reached novelhood.

Chapter One

'Please tell me another, Grandpa,' the child begged, squirming like a tadpole on the old man's lap and winding her small arms round the large, wrinkled neck. Her auburn curls glinted in the firelight as she screwed up her green eyes and pursed her small mouth, planting a kiss on the gnarled cheek.

'You mean you haven't had enough yet?'

'No, I'll never have enough of your stories, Grandpa.'

'That's what you think now, but you'll soon be grown up and then you'll find your old grandpa's tales boring,' he said wistfully.

'But I'm only nine, Grandpa. It's ages away before I'll be grown up, and I don't want to be grown up anyway; I'll be too big to sit on your lap any more.'

The old man stroked her pale cheek and tweaked the turned-up nose. 'You'll never be too old for that but, all right, just one more and then *bed*, young Mary, or your mother will be after me for keeping you up,' he sighed in resignation. 'What would you like now?'

'The one about the queen who saved her baby from Rumpelstiltskin,' she said eagerly.

'Don't you ever get tired of that one?'

'No! I'll never get tired of it; it's my very favourite.'

The old man settled his large frame more comfortably in the winged chair by the study fireplace, his faded blue eyes twinkling in his heavy jowled face, and his resounding voice causing his huge, round belly to vibrate, as he began: 'Once upon a time . . .'

The rugged north-east coast weather had wrinkled and ruddied his skin, bleached his remaining fringe of grey hair to a pure white, and given him a colourful, healthy air. But he felt tired tonight as he stroked the young head nestling on his chest while he told the familiar story with the familiar ending: '. . . and they all lived happily ever after.' He then lifted the child from his knee and said with mock firmness: 'All right, that's enough. If you go off to bed now and go straight to sleep, I'll take you for a ride after breakfast.'

'Oh, thank you, Grandpa, I will. I promise.' With that Mary skipped across the landing to her bedroom, slipping under the warm satin eiderdown and settling her head in the soft feather pillow. She'd be riding Strawberry tomorrow; Grandpa had bought the pony for her seventh birthday, and it was the best birthday present she'd ever had.

She was asleep even before her mother tiptoed in to kiss her goodnight. The woman gazed fondly at the pale, sleeping face and tucked the eiderdown more snugly round the little figure. 'Goodnight, sweetheart,' she whispered, tiptoeing out.

It had rained overnight and the ground was muddy when Mary in her riding habit and her grandfather in his jodhpurs and hacking jacket made their way to the stables. The groom greeted them: 'Mornin', sir, mornin', Miss Mary. I expect you'll be wantin' Strawberry, and you'll be takin' Blackie, sir. He's been a bit restless this mornin'; a good run's what he needs.'

'Yes, good morning, James. I need a good run myself . . . getting a bit stiff in my old age. How's your back doing?'

'Can't complain, sir. This damp weather doesn't help.' The old man rubbed his aching back as he spoke.

'You're not stiff, Grandpa,' Mary said. 'You're still the best rider in the county. But one of these days *I* will be,' she added with a grin.

The groom arrived with Strawberry and helped the child mount. She bent down to nuzzle the warm, sweet-smelling brown mane and laughed with delight – two whole hours to ride with Grandpa before her piano lesson was due. She pulled a face at the thought; she wished her teacher would let her play pieces instead of just scales and arpeggios.

'Let's away then,' said the old man, now mounted on Blackie, who was tossing his black head and snorting. 'This fellow's in fine form. Let's just trot them down to the river to warm up and then I'll race you back across Larkin Meadow.'

'Whoopee!' Mary yelled, slapping the reins and urging Strawberry to a trot. She knew Grandpa would let her win.

She won by a nose and, laughing with delight, admonished her grandfather. 'I saw you pulling in Blackie, Grandpa. You cheat!'

'No, I don't cheat; I just give you an even chance. It's called a handicap. Strawberry isn't as big as Blackie, so she needs a little help. As soon as you're big enough I'll buy you one like Blackie.'

'Oh, that would be lovely. But I could never give up Strawberry.'

'Well, you wouldn't have to; you could keep them both. Now let's just trot back slowly. That's enough excitement for one day.' The old man was breathless and his face had been whipped by the wind to a bright red. Mary's face was glowing.

Miss Winston, the music teacher, was waiting in the drawing room when they arrived.

'Sorry, Miss Winston, I didn't know it was so late. It'll only take me a few minutes to change.'

'That's all right, Mary. I was early today, so take

your time.' The middle-aged, bespectacled woman was round everywhere except for her hands, which were long and slender and simply floated over the keyboard. Mary wanted to play like Miss Winston one day.

Back in five minutes, dressed in her blue day dress and black buttoned boots, Mary seated herself at the grand piano.

'Let me hear the scales and arpeggios I gave you last week and then I've got a surprise for you. I've got a little piece I'd like you to learn. I think you're ready for it.'

'Oh, wonderful! What is it?' She skipped to the piano stool and seated herself next to her teacher.

'It's called "The Little Drummer Boy". But first, your exercises.'

The lesson was barely over when the gong sounded for lunch; Mary just had time to wash her hands and run to the dining room. She was surprised to see only her mother and grandmother seated at the table. 'Hello, Mother, Grandma, sorry I'm late; I played my first piece today. I like music now. Where's Grandpa . . . and Uncle Joseph?' she added as an afterthought, taking her seat at the long oval dining table.

'Uncle Joseph had to go to town today and Grandpa is having a nap. He was very tired after the ride; you shouldn't tire him out so, Mary. And now let's eat before lunch gets cold.' The old woman bent her white head and clasped her long, wrinkled hands in prayer: 'For what we are about to receive, may the Lord make us truly thankful, amen.'

As soon as she could, Mary raised her bowed head. 'But Grandpa was fine this morning; we rode for two whole hours.'

'That's just what Grandma means, Mary. Your Grandpa's not as young as he was, you know. Next time, one hour's ride is enough, and no racing.' Her

4

mother's pale, pretty face was smiling, but her green eyes were troubled. She had passed on her good looks to her daughter, even the auburn curls. 'Now why aren't you eating? Your salmon will get cold,' she said, daintily dabbing at her mouth with her white napkin.

'Yes, Mother,' Mary answered, picking up her knife and fork and attacking the plate of poached salmon with boiled potatoes and vegetables from the garden. The ride had made her hungry.

Elizabeth gazed fondly at her daughter. 'After lunch, would you like to help me cut some flowers from the conservatory? Uncle Joseph is giving a big dinner party this evening for some business associates. I'll show you how to make flower arrangements. Would you like that?'

'Yes, please, and then I want to practise my new piece,' she said, stabbing a carrot with her fork. They were her least favourite vegetable, but she knew she had to eat them or she wouldn't be allowed dessert. 'What's Cook making for the dinner party, Mother?'

'We're starting with oysters, then sole, rack of lamb, and your favourite, sherry trifle, followed by Stilton.'

'Ugh! I can't stand the oysters and the Stilton but I'll have the rest.'

'I know, dear. You don't have to eat everything, and anyway you'll be having yours in the nursery. I'll sit with you and keep you company. Dinner won't be till nine and that's too late for you. In any case, Uncle Joseph's business friends would just bore you.'

Mary grimaced. 'I'd rather eat upstairs with you, and can we play draughts afterwards?'

'I don't see why not, but I'll have to leave at eight to change. I'm wearing my new green velvet gown; I'll come and show you when I'm dressed.' Elizabeth sipped water from the crystal goblet before continuing: 'Oh, and I've been thinking: it's time we had some of your school friends to tea again. Would you like to invite them for next Sunday and I'll get Cook to make some angel cakes and currant scones. And what else would you like?'

'Ooh, almond surprises and meringues, please.'

'I knew you'd say that. All right, almond surprises and meringues it shall be.'

'Can Grandpa come and visit? He always does his tricks at my parties,' Mary pleaded.

'We'll see, dear.'

'I shall invite Anne and Vera and Maude and Jane and Rosemary but not Angela. She eats too much and last time she took two meringues and I didn't get one.'

Her mother laughed. 'She *is* a little glutton. After we've done the flowers, I'll give you some of my best pink scented stationery and you can write your invitations . . . and invite Angela; I'll tell Cook to make extra meringues.'

Her grandmother smiled. 'And don't count how many Angela eats; it's not polite.'

The following Sunday the girls arrived for the party, dressed in their best party dresses – an array of pinks, blues, violets and yellows. Mary's was blue silk, with a frill round the hem and a wide sash tied in a bow at the back.

'That's a smashing dress, Mary,' said Maude, a plain, thin girl in yellow poplin, as Roseanne, the maid, led the gang upstairs to the nursery.

'Yes, Miss Mary, and you see you keep it clean this time; it's the devil for me to wash and iron,' Roseanne admonished. Her young, pretty, though slightly coarse-featured face, with its full red mouth and slightly pouting underlip, bore an expression of boredom and annoyance as she opened the nursery door. Pushing back the dark brown curls that tumbled out defiantly from her white starched cap, she stood stiffly in attendance as the young ladies entered. She hated these parties because she had to supervise the brats and pour their tea and watch them stuffing themselves, when what she'd really like to do was give them each a clout across the ear for being so snooty.

Mary poked out her tongue behind the maid's black-uniformed back and the others smothered giggles.

After Roseanne had seated them at the table, she went out to get the tea.

'Poker face,' said Mary, pulling down her mouth to imitate Roseanne's expression. 'I know she doesn't like me, or anyone much for that matter, except Uncle Joseph. She always smiles at him, and she even waits on him in the middle of the night when she's supposed to be off duty. I saw her one night when I had to get up to go to the you-know-what.'

'Do you mean she serves him *food* during the night? I wish our maid would do that for me,' sighed plump, freckled Angela, her round grey eyes fixed on the meringues.

'I don't know what she served him. She wasn't even in uniform, just a dressing gown, and her hair was all messy and hanging down her back. I couldn't hear what he said to her, but she was actually laughing as she closed the door. I think that's the only time I've seen her laugh; she always goes around with her face tripping her up.'

The others laughed. 'Where did you learn that, Mary? It's very good. I could say the same about my nanny; her face could trip her up too,' said Angela, her eyes now scanning the other delicacies on the table. She wished Roseanne would get a move on.

'I heard Mother say it to Grandma about Uncle Joseph; she wouldn't dare say it to his face though,' said Mary importantly, pleased that she'd made her friends laugh.

Then Jane piped in, looking longingly at the table and impatiently pushing back a lock of red hair that had fallen over her face: 'I hope the maid's face doesn't trip her up while she's carrying the teapot. I'm dying to start.'

They all laughed again and Vera, who was always top of the class and always boasting about it, said seriously in her squeaky voice: 'My mother says that life would be much easier if we didn't have to deal with servants, that sometimes they're more trouble than they're worth. But I don't think so. Who would scrub the floors and do the washing and the cooking? I'd rather put up with servants than have to do all that.'

Mary quickly defended the rest of the staff: 'But some of them are nice. Cook's fun and I like James, the groom, and sometimes the gardeners let me help them plant things . . .' Her voice trailed as she heard a sound on the landing. 'Look out! Here comes sourpuss,' she warned, as the door opened and Roseanne entered with the silver teapot and hot water jug on the matching tray.

The group was silent as she poured tea into the delicate china teacups. 'Ring the bell when you want some more, Miss Mary,' she said, plunking the pot down on the dresser. 'I don't want none o' you pourin' it and scaldin' yourselves.'

The girls each politely took a quarter of bread and jam; they knew they must watch their manners and eat at least one piece of bread before setting to work on the cakes.

After tea they played hunt the thimble and charades, and then the door opened and Grandpa came in, leaning on Elizabeth's arm. His face looked thinner than it had the previous week, and his ruddy complexion had changed to a pasty white, except for two bright spots on his cheekbones, but his eyes still twinkled.

'Grandpa was feeling a little better today so he's come to join you,' Mary's mother said, leading him in.

'Oh, Grandpa, you *did* come. Thank you!' Mary was joyful.

'Well, I couldn't miss a party, could I?' He sat down slowly at the table. He usually stood up for his tricks but today they all joined him at the cleared table.

'Now, would you believe that this young lady here has a sixpence in her ear?'

'No,' they chorused as usual, but then, miraculously, he lifted back Rosemary's long, blonde hair and, sure enough, he took a sixpence out of her ear.

'Ooh!' they all gasped, as though it were the first time they'd seen the trick.

'And now, where did I put my handkerchief?' he asked, absentmindedly fumbling in his pockets. 'Ah, here it is!' Triumphantly he pulled out one handkerchief, followed by another and another – six of them, all miraculously attached to one another. 'Now I only need one, don't I?' he said, placing them in a bundle on the table and waving his hands over the heap. 'Abracadabra!' And he picked a single handkerchief from the pile. The applause was deafening.

Next he took from his other pocket a pack of cards and shuffled them slowly. Why was he so slow? Mary wondered. He always shuffled with two flicks of his hands.

'Now, Anne, you pick a card, please.' Anne's almond-shaped hazel eyes screwed up in concentration as she took one from the middle. 'Look at it and show everyone while I close my eyes, and then you put it back anywhere in the deck.' Anne did so very carefully. Again he shuffled the cards slowly, but this time some of them slipped out of his hands and landed on the table. 'Oops! Well, never mind, we'll just put them back carefully, like this,' he said, his hands fumbling with the deck, 'and voilà! This is your card, Anne.' But it wasn't. There was a gasp of disbelief from the girls; they'd seen him do this trick a hundred times.

'Oh, Grandpa, you made a mistake!' Mary said, distraught.

Her mother broke in: 'I think perhaps Grandpa is a little too tired for tricks today after all. But it was very good of him to do what he did, don't you think? And now, I think that's enough excitement for one day. It's Grandpa's nap time.'

'Yes, I bungled that one, didn't I? I am feeling tired. Goodbye, young ladies. I'll see you next time.' With that, Mary's mother helped the old man up from the chair and walked slowly with him to the door.

'Is your Grandpa not well?' Jane asked Mary, who sat staring at the door her mother had just closed.

'He hasn't been very well for a week but the doctor's treating him and he's getting better. Mother says he just needs to have lots of rest and to get his appetite back to keep his strength up.'

The door opened again, framing Roseanne's curvaceous young form. 'The car's just arrived for the young ladies, Miss Mary. I'll take them down.'

'Oh, rats, we've got to go,' grumbled Angela. But they all got up obediently.

'Thank you, Mary, for a lovely party,' they each said as they hugged her goodbye.

Chapter Two

The child didn't understand the change gradually coming over the old man: the stories became fewer and fewer and he spent more and more time in his room, no longer accompanying her on her rides. His eyes, too, were different; they didn't twinkle any more. But she would sneak into his room at bedtime, whenever she was sure he was alone, and beg for a story.

Tonight, as she did every night, she peeked through her bedroom door and waited for her grandmother to leave – now was her chance. Opening the door silently she stole out of the room and crossed the wide landing to the large room with the red velvet curtains and matching bedspread, careful to keep her bare feet on the red oriental rug – the polished wooden floor was cold and slippery. She tiptoed up to the old man's chair and climbed on to his knee.

'Please, Grandpa, just one, I promise, and then I'll go to bed.'

He raised his head. 'What's that, young lady? What's that?' Then he just sat in his chair and said nothing. It was strange, sometimes he would say nothing, while at other times he would babble on about things she didn't understand. He must be too tired to talk, she thought, and kissed him. 'Goodnight then, Grandpa. I'll come again tomorrow.' She closed the door gently and hung her head guiltily as she saw her mother standing on the landing. She would be in for trouble now.

'Mary, how many times have I told you, you're not to bother your grandfather? From now on you may visit him only when Grandma or I take you.' Yet it wasn't an angry voice.

'Yes, Mother, I'm sorry,' she said, relieved at her mother's tone. 'But I wasn't bothering him much; I only wanted one story.'

The visits with her chaperones proved to be even less fruitful than her illicit ones. Often they would lead her out after only a few short minutes; there wasn't enough time for him to tell her a story even if he'd wanted to.

'What's wrong with Grandpa, Mother? Is he very ill?' she asked after one such visit. 'He never wants to see me any more.' The troubled round eyes were narrowed and close to tears.

'He's just very tired, dear, and needs a good rest. And you know you shouldn't bother him by asking for stories.' Her mother bent and placed her slim white hand on the child's shoulder, kissing her cheek. The identical green eyes met before Elizabeth straightened to her full five feet three inches, but Mary had noticed that her mother's eyes were wet.

'He's not going to die, Mother, is he?' she almost shrieked.

'Of course not, silly. You know your grandfather's always been a healthy man. He's just tired, I told you. The doctor's medicine will perk him up again. Now, why don't you go for a walk in the garden before lunch; it will be served in half an hour.'

'It's no fun in the garden without Grandpa,' the child grumbled as she wandered aimlessly towards the french doors leading to the spacious grounds of the large stone house. 'Would Grandma come for a walk with me?'

'She would, I'm sure, dear, but she's going to sit with Grandpa to keep him company. You be a good

girl and run along.' Elizabeth smoothed down the skirt
of her long, green gown. 'I'm off to the kitchen to see
what Cook is doing about lunch.' The delicate face
turned thoughtfully after the little figure. It's going to
be hard for her, she thought.

On 9 June 1910, just one month before Mary's tenth
birthday, the old man died. Her mother and grandmother cried as they led her to kiss his cold lifeless
lips on the day they carried him out.

'Why couldn't I say goodbye to him before he died?'
she sobbed.

'Because it's proper to say your last goodbye after
he's gone, dear. He's in heaven now and he'll feel your
kiss.' Her mother, looking elegent in her black mourning gown and black hat and veil, ushered Mary gently
with her suede-gloved hands towards the still figure in
the brass-trimmed mahogany box.

The child's trembling lips unwillingly grazed the
ice-cold mouth and recoiled in horror. 'Goodbye,
Grandpa,' she stammered, her lips feeling as frozen as
those she had just touched.

Uncle Joseph sat in her grandfather's chair at the
table that day and every day after that. It had been two
weeks now and Mary still hadn't become accustomed
to the change that had come over the house.

'Grandma,' she said excitedly as she seated herself
at the dinner table, 'guess what Beth Armstrong said
to Sister Maria today. She . . .'

Her voice trailed as her uncle, his six-foot, narrow
body standing erect behind his chair, wagged his right
forefinger and admonished: 'Now, now! We'll have
no nonsense at the table, Mary.'

His was a totally different face from the rest of
the family's: long, thin, sombre under the thick black
hair; bushy black eyebrows joining above the long,
narrow nose, creating the impression of a permanent
frown; and, above the thin-lipped mouth that rarely

laughed, a bushy black moustache, which hardly moved as he said Grace: 'Thank you, Lord, for what we are about to receive, amen.'

'Amen,' they all repeated.

'But Grandpa always asked me how my day at school went,' ventured Mary, with a touch of defiance.

'I'm not your grandfather and I didn't ask about your day at school. Remember, young ladies speak only when they're spoken to.'

'Yes, Uncle.'

As was his custom, he shook out his napkin as a signal for the meal to commence. Her grandfather had always winked at Mary after Grace, and meals had been cheerful and full of chatter. Now all that was different.

'How did the day go, Joseph?' Elizabeth asked in her refined voice, putting an end to anything Mary might have continued to say. The candlelight seemed to set fire to her swept up hair as she inclined her head towards her brother.

'Not so well. I think I'm going to have to get rid of one of the gardeners if we're going to make ends meet.'

'But I thought the market took all the carrots and potatoes last week.'

'So they did, but at half the price we got the week before. They said they'd got a glut.' He neatly severed a piece of roast lamb from the thick slice on his plate and, almost with reverence, placed it in his mouth, chewing thoughtfully. 'I'm going to have to concentrate on the greenhouse stuff; the lettuce and cucumbers bring in more money, despite the lower demand.'

Mary played with her food, remembering the times when the greenhouses had all been conservatories, which she'd loved to walk through with her grandfather, both delighting in the delicate carnations and

14

roses. But he had been forced to convert all but one to nurseries to house the seedlings for the market garden. The flowers sold poorly, but vegetables – even the more expensive salad items from the nurseries – usually sold quite well. The majority of customers at the markets, the coal miners and factory hands of Newcastle and its surroundings, could afford flowers only for weddings and funerals.

'I'm thinking of getting rid of George,' Uncle Joseph said matter-of-factly, deftly pronging a roast potato with his fork. 'He's getting too old to be of much use anyway.'

'Oh, Joseph!' Mary's grandmother's voice was horrified. 'You can't do that; he's been with us for over fifty years.' She clattered down her knife and fork and held her napkin to her quivering mouth. Her faded eyes were stricken and her head, the white hair neatly knotted at the nape of her neck, was shaking in disbelief. Her shoulders slumped as her hands fell to her lap. She had lost interest in her meal.

'Afraid I have no choice, Mother, and anyway, under the law he'll get some sort of a pension when he's seventy. I've got to cut every corner I can to get the estate back on its feet; we can't go on operating at a loss.'

'But he's barely sixty-five; he'd probably be dead of starvation before he got a pension even if he were due one – he's worked for us all his life.' Her grandmother was on the verge of tears, and Mary's mother took the thin old hand under the table to comfort her.

Joseph was unmoved. 'That's not our problem, Mother. We've paid him enough over the years; if he hasn't saved some of it for his old age, that's his problem.'

'Let's not discuss finances at the table, Joseph,' Elizabeth cut in, squeezing her mother's hand again. 'Let's have some cheerful talk. Mary and I are going to town tomorrow for an outing. Is there anything you need?'

'Yes, I need some new embroidery silks,' the old lady replied, relieved not to have to discuss George and estate problems for the moment. She'd have to think of what she could do about George.

'I'm going to get some new white gloves and a new hat,' Mary volunteered excitedly, forgetting the rule of silence, 'and Mother says I can wear my new white dress and white buckskin boots tomorrow if it's a nice day like today.'

Her uncle shot her a look of disapproval, but before he could say anything her mother broke in protectively: 'So don't forget to leave them out to be cleaned tonight and leave your black ones, too, so they'll be ready for school on Monday.'

That night Mary left out both pairs of boots, but the next morning only the black ones occupied their usual place outside her bedroom door. Puzzled, she went down to the kitchen in her nightgown to question Roseanne. The white buckskins were sitting on the kitchen floor, still dirty, and Roseanne was sipping tea and chatting with Cook. At any other time Mary would have been pleased to see the good-natured cook, who looked like one of her own dumplings – fat and suety and lumpy, with a pale, round, soggy face and hands like balls of dough. She reminded Mary of an undercooked pastry doll, except that she was round instead of flat. But she hardly noticed Cook today.

Roseanne's face was half hidden by the teacup she held to her mouth. Her dark, deep eyes, which never seemed to be looking at you even when they were, didn't even turn in the child's direction as she entered. Mary's rare temper flared: 'Roseanne, why didn't you clean my white boots? I'm going to town today and now they won't be dry in time – that Blanco paste takes hours.'

'I did your black ones, miss; I thought your whites was for Mass the morrow.' Her brown eyes remained deep and impassive and, continuing to sip her tea, she resumed her conversation with Cook, turning her back to Mary. It was a gesture of dismissal.

The maid's deliberate lack of response kindled Mary's fire and, her eyes flashing, she let her words fly: 'You're paid to *work*, Roseanne, not *think*. Now look what you've done! I'll have to wear my black school boots to town with my new white dress.'

On hearing the commotion, Mary's mother rushed into the kitchen. 'Roseanne simply made a mistake, Mary. Now, apologise to her for losing your temper and never let me hear you raise your voice like that again.'

Her mother's tone warned Mary that she must do as she was told.

'Sorry, Roseanne,' she muttered as ungraciously as she dared and ran from the kitchen, stamping her bare feet on the cold grey flagstones. She longed to take one of the copper pots hanging on the whitewashed walls and fling it at Roseanne, right in the middle of that pink and white insolent face.

Although still angry at having to wear her black boots to town, the impending trip soon helped her to forget her grievance. In the train they passed green fields with munching cows and frolicking lambs. As they neared Newcastle, that vast sea of coal mines and shipyards, they passed the familiar rows of grime-covered pit cottages and, closer to the town and the factories, the red-brick terraced houses, clinging together desperately for support. It seemed to Mary that if one were moved, the rest would topple, just like her dominoes. The entrances to the tiny houses were directly off the street – one and a half identical stone steps leading to each identical brown-painted front door. Strangely, though the paintwork was shabby and the bricks discoloured with soot and smoke from the factories, the steps were always meticulously scrubbed and coloured a sort of mustard yellow. Mary was always fascinated by the housewives tending their front steps on hands and knees, the uniform mobcaps on their heads, dipping the yellow coloured rubbing stones into buckets of water and applying them vigorously over the freshly scrubbed steps.

She knew the people in town were different from her family. They were shabbily dressed and the children were pale and neglected looking, many wearing oversized hand-me-downs, and most with basin haircuts and running noses. A crowd of such children were playing on the pavement as they left the station.

'Ha'penny for me ma, me da's been laid off,' several of them shouted, converging on the well-dressed pair.

Mary's mother threw a handful of halfpennies on the pavement, and the little mob scrambled for them as if for life.

'Thanks, missus, you're a right lady.'

'I don't like to throw them,' sighed Elizabeth, 'but if I tried to dole them out one at a time we'd get knocked over in the scramble. Poor little mites.'

'Ugh! Why don't they use their handkerchiefs, Mother?' Mary twitched her nose in distaste as they made their way to the town centre.

'They most likely haven't got handkerchiefs, Mary. Not all children are as fortunate as you.'

'I suppose you're right, Mother; I've got nice clothes and toys and, best of all, I've got Strawberry. And I like my friends at the convent, and I'm glad I don't have to live in, like some of them. But I haven't got a father like the other girls at school, and now I haven't got Grandpa.'

'What nonsense are you talking, child? You can't miss your father when you never knew him. I know it was sad to lose Grandpa, but you must instead consider yourself lucky to have had him for so long; I never knew mine. And you've still got Grandma and me . . . and Uncle Joseph,' she added.

'I don't count him,' Mary said, vehemently kicking at a loose stone on the cobbled street.

'Mary, you mustn't talk about your uncle like that. He loves you; he just shows it differently from Grandma and I. He's the only man in the house now and he feels he must be a responsible guardian to you.'

'He was always like that, even before Grandpa died, but he knew he couldn't get away with it so much then. I hate him!'

'That's quite enough, young lady. I'll not hear you use that word again.'

Mary didn't dare retort, so she kicked another stone instead. Although it hurt her toe, it was worth it, for she pretended it was her uncle. And this one's for Roseanne, she thought, this time kicking one of the fixed cobblestones. Now she'll have to work extra hard on these boots to get the scuffs out.

'Mary, any more nonsense like that and we go straight home.'

Mary knew her mother would carry out the threat and, bending her head, said contritely, 'I'm very sorry, Mother. I promise I'll be extra good for the rest of the day.'

'And tomorrow, I hope,' her mother laughed.

On their return from town, Mary ran excitedly past Roseanne who opened the door and took their packages. 'Grandma! Grandma! Come and see what we've bought.'

But Roseanne, stacking the purchases on the hall table, addressed her mistress: 'She's in bed, ma'am, and the doctor and the master are with her.'

'Oh, dear Lord,' Elizabeth moaned as she ran up the stairs.

The white-haired family doctor, who looked too frail and old to be practising, took her hand and shook his head. 'She's had another bout with her heart and she's very weak. I don't think she has the strength to pull through. To tell the truth, I don't think she wants to; I've watched her going downhill since Edward died.'

And so, only three short months after Mary's grandfather's death, her grandmother followed him. It was an unhappy time and, after the funeral, things began to worsen. Mysterious looking lawyers constantly visited Uncle Joseph, who became even more preoccupied with the estate business. Even Cook went about with a long face. There was no one left to have fun with any more, Mary thought; she'd have a better time staying with the boarding girls at the convent.

One day, while she and her mother were having tea and scones with strawberry jam in the nursery, her mother broke the news. 'It's nothing to worry about, Mary, but you're going to find out soon anyway that the estate now belongs to Uncle Joseph. Your grandfather left it to both of us in his will, but the lawyers claim it's not valid because he wasn't well in his mind when he made it. The law says the estate goes to the eldest son, so Uncle Joseph inherits everything.'

'Do you mean we can't live here any more . . . this will be *Uncle Joseph's* house?' She almost spat as she pronounced the name and then she shook with fear at the thought.

'Of course we'll live here, silly,' her mother laughed. 'Everything will be just the same as always; we're still part of the family. You'll understand more about the legal side when you're older.'

However, life didn't go on as before. There was a different feeling about the house, and Mary noticed that her mother and her uncle never seemed to talk to each other except at the table, and then it was usually only about the housekeeping and spending less. But one day, while passing the study door, she heard them arguing inside and halted to listen.

'It's none of your damned business anyway.' Her uncle's voice was louder than she'd ever heard it. 'It's *my* life!'

'As you say, Joseph, it's *your* life, but it's also Mary's and mine. I knew when Mother and Father were alive what was going on but never dreamed it would come to this.'

'If I were in your position I should keep my mouth shut about other people's "goings on ".'

'That's enough, Joseph! The past is the past. So when is the wedding to be?'

'Roseanne wants it to be as soon as possible, probably three weeks, as soon as the banns have been read.'

'And I suppose she wants us out before then?'

'Yes, just as soon as you can get fixed up somewhere else.'

'Don't worry! I'll start looking tomorrow. She's the mistress now, I suppose, or at least she will be soon enough.' Her mother was shouting, but there was a slight quaver in her voice.

After a pause, Uncle Joseph cleared his throat and muttered awkwardly, 'Look here, Elizabeth, I can lend you a few pounds to help you get started and you can pay me back when you get a job.'

'Thank you, no, Joseph! You can keep your conscience money. Roseanne is probably right in one respect: if it's going to be a family split, then it's better to make it final. I just hope you're happy with her – little upstart! I don't know how she managed to get you of all people under her thumb.'

'That's not fair, Elizabeth.'

'Can you truly say you're being fair, Joseph?'

As the sound of light footsteps approached the

door, Mary remained transfixed in the hall, her face white and incredulous.

'I see you've already heard,' her mother said, but instead of scolding her for eavesdropping, she put her arms round her. 'Don't worry, my precious. We'll do fine on our own; we'll find a cosy little place to live and I'll find work. You'll see, everything will be all right.' Though her voice sounded cheerful, there were tears in her eyes.

Chapter Three

'I'm coming, I'm coming.' Mary answered her mother's call reluctantly, dragging her feet to the taxi waiting to take them to the station. Her sharp white teeth cut into her underlip and her eyes were lowered. She was determined not to look back at the house. 'I've just been saying goodbye to Strawberry,' she said, tears streaming down her face.

'I know, my darling, it's very hard for you.' Elizabeth's eyes were wet as she put her arms round her daughter to comfort her. 'But you know you always enjoy the trip into town,' she said briskly, turning her back for an instant and dabbing her own eyes with a handkerchief. Then she ushered Mary into the black shiny car and followed quickly. They held hands and neither looked back as the car started.

After a moment's silence, Mary grumbled, 'But this isn't like the other trips; we're never coming back.'

'No, but we're going to our *new* home. Don't you find that the tiniest bit exciting?'

Mary wasn't convinced by her mother's tone. 'But I want to stay here. I'll miss Strawberry and my friends at the convent and I don't want to *live* in town anyway; I just like to visit and go shopping.' The lower lip was pouting now.

'Would you rather stay here and live with Roseanne and Uncle Joseph or live in town with me?' This time her mother's voice was sharp.

'You know I couldn't *bear* to live with those two. I *hate* them, and anyway I want to be with you.'

'Well, then, the matter is settled and there's no point in pouting about it. You'll make new friends at your new school and we'll have our own home, just the two of us. I was very lucky to find a flat, and soon I'll find a job.'

'Yes, it will be nice to be just the two of us with no Uncle Joseph and no Roseanne,' Mary answered vehemently, gripping her mother's hand more tightly. In such a short time so much had happened; now her mother was the only person she had in the world.

The train journey passed quickly and then they took another taxi to their new home.

'This is our road,' Elizabeth announced.

Mary was dismayed: it was just like any other mean little street of terrace houses.

'But you said it was called Beauchamps Street, and my French teacher said that Beauchamps means beautiful fields, but there aren't any fields, not even a tree.' Her lower lip trembled and tears of disappointment tumbled down her cheeks.

'A name is just a name,' her mother sighed. 'We'll make the flat nice inside and the outside won't matter. This is our number, driver. Please pull up here.'

As the taxi came to a stop at number twenty-six, Mary was surprised to see bits and pieces of furniture heaped on the pavement in front of the house.

'Is that our furniture, Mother? I didn't know you'd bought things already.'

'I haven't yet. This must belong to the people moving out. Maybe we're too early to move in. I'd better tell the driver to wait a few minutes, just in case,' she said, getting out of the car and exchanging words with the driver through the window.

The two-storeyed, red-brick buildings each had two doors, one for the upstairs and one for the downstairs tenants. From number twenty-six emerged two police-en and two men with drooping moustaches. They were wearing brown suits and pork pie hats and were followed by a woman wearing a soiled floral pina-re and a white mobcap. She held a small baby in her arms and two toddlers clung to her skirts. The woman was crying, and neighbours with grim faces were standing on their mustard-yellow doorsteps watching the scene. A man in dirty blue overalls and a workman's cap was the last to leave the house; he was shouting at the men with the drooping mous-taches: 'I might be out o' work, but I'd rather be honest without work than gettin' paid for turfin' folks out o' their homes.'

Mary had heard Cook and Roseanne talking about bailiffs and knew what was happening.

Her mother approached the policemen: 'Please, can't they stay?' she implored. 'We can find some-where else; I couldn't possibly push these people out of their home.'

'No, missus. It won't make no difference whether *you* move in or somebody else does; the landlord's got an order to get them out and that's that, and there's plenty would jump in afore you if they could. I'd get in while you can if I was you.'

'I suppose you're right, Constable, but I'll come back tomorrow. Let them at least move out with some dignity.'

She quickly ushered Mary back into the taxi, briskly informing the driver to take them back to the station to deposit their luggage and then on to the nearest cafe, where they would have lunch.

Mary was appalled by the scene she had witnessed but the main horror for her was the sight of the mean little house in the equally mean, narrow, cobbled street. She was ashamed of herself, for she knew her mother considered herself lucky to have found a flat so quickly. But despite her efforts to stem them, the tears rolled down her cheeks.

Her mother took her hand. 'Don't worry, my little flower; that will never happen to us, we'll never fall behind with the rent. I'm very sorry for those poor people, but there's nothing we can do.' She sighed as the taxi spluttered off. 'So that's why we were lucky enough to get the flat. I never thought I should be forced to benefit from another's misfortune. Dry your eyes, Mary. You must be hungry by now; let's first have a good lunch and then shop for some furniture. We'll just pick up a few essential pieces at the Sale Rooms this afternoon. It's probably too late for delivery today anyway, so we'll find a hotel for tonight. Would you like that?'

'Yes, Mother, that would be nice,' Mary muttered, rubbing her eyes with her handkerchief. 'When will we move into the flat?'

'Oh, tomorrow will be soon enough; by then we should have enough furniture for our immediate needs.' But her mother averted her face as she looked out of the taxi window, and her voice sounded choked.

They lunched at a little cafe near the station. All her life Mary would remember every single course they had, especially the dessert.

'Would you like a cream horn, Mary?'

'Yes, please,' said Mary with little enthusiasm, although they were one of her favourite cakes. Such unhealthy sticky confections were normally allowed only on special occasions, like birthday parties and tea parties with her friends. It was strange that a day could be special and miserable, she thought and, after that day, she lost her passion for cream horns.

The following morning was sunny and warm, a rare event and usually a topic for conversation. Although the sun never gained total victory over the ever-present haze of smoke and soot in the air, everyone was grateful for those times when it made the attempt.

'God's smiling on us today,' Mary's mother said as she looked out of the hotel room's grimy window that morning. 'You'd better clean your white boots before breakfast or they won't be dry in time.'

A strange emotion went through the child as she recalled the previous 'white boot day'. She thought of Roseanne. 'I wonder who's cleaning Madam Roseanne's boots now,' she pouted. The memory of the maid, now playing lady of the manor in *their* house, evoked in her a feeling of pure hatred.

'Now, Mary, I've told you before about using that tone of voice and, besides, Roseanne's affairs no longer concern you.' Although her mother's voice was firm, her tone was sympathetic, and she averted her face lest her expression give her away.

After breakfast they walked to the shops, but they didn't go back to the Sale Rooms as Mary had expected, for the previous day, although her mother had chosen with her usual care and good taste, they had ordered only a few second-hand pieces. This day they went to a dingy little shop with three brass balls above the door. This was the shop she'd heard her mother asking Cook about; she'd heard Cook describing the brass balls and saying something about 'pawning', whatever that was.

'What are we going to buy here, Mother?' she asked.

Her mother placed her small but exquisite collection of jewellery on the counter, keeping only a tiny gold pin that had belonged to Mary's grandmother. This she fastened onto her jacket lapel.

'You're not going to sell your jewellery, are you, Mother?' Mary was horrified at the possibility. 'You told me we had enough money to start with.'

'Well, we'll have enough now to last a little longer, in case it takes me a while to find a job. Don't worry, this is just a loan shop. I'm not selling them; I could never do that.' Elizabeth didn't tell her daughter that after having bought the furniture the previous day, their total capital had been reduced to a meagre five pounds. Then she bought some pots and pans and kitchen utensils from the pawn shop.

Mary was puzzled. 'But, Mother,' she queried, 'if this is just a loan shop, how can you buy things? What if someone buys your jewellery?'

'Stop worrying, Mary. That won't happen; it's only when people don't reclaim their possessions within the given time that they're put on sale.'

Mary was still only partially reassured, but the remainder of the day was so busy she had no time to brood on the incident. The furniture van was waiting at the door when they arrived at Beauchamps Street, and after the two burly men had arranged the pieces to her mother's liking, she thanked them and placed three pennies in each of their hands.

'Now we'd better go out and get some food and soap and scrubbing brushes. And we'll need a broom.' Mary's mother sat at the table and took her diary and a pencil from her handbag. 'I'd better make a list so we don't forget anything.'

Outside in the street they asked a grey-haired woman in a black dress the way to the nearest shops. She eyed them suspiciously before indicating with her head and replying: 'Just up the street an' turn left.'

'Thank you,' Elizabeth said, smiling. As they turned, the woman still stood staring suspiciously after them.

They went to the hardware shop first, where they bought a scrubbing brush and a broom. The man unscrewed the head from the broom and asked: 'Have you got a basket, missus? You'll just have to carry the handle.'

'Oh, dear, how foolish of me! I didn't think of that.

28

And we'll need something to carry the groceries in. Have you got any shopping baskets? I shall probably need two.'

The man disappeared into the back of the shop and returned with two large, round wicker baskets with sturdy handles. 'They're one and eleven pence each, missus. With the brushes, that'll be five an' six altogether. They'll last a lifetime.' The man fingered his chin as he scrutinised Elizabeth's elegant matching grey dress and jacket and tan crocodile-skin handbag.

'Oh! That much? Well, I suppose we have to have them.' She opened the bag and counted out the coins, laying them on the counter.

'Well, that's my first lesson,' she whispered to Mary as they left the shop. 'I should have looked for things like that at the second-hand shop or the pawn shop. Now we have to go to the greengrocer's, the grocer's, the bakery . . . oh, and the butcher's. Oh dear, there's such a lot to think about. How I'm missing Cook already.'

'Me too, I'm hungry.'

'Well, as soon as we get home we'll have some bread and cheese for lunch. I'll make a proper dinner this evening. I got some of your favourite recipes from Cook, but it will have to be something simple tonight. I shall have more time to practise with recipes after we're settled in.'

'Did you get her recipe for meringues?' Mary asked hopefully.

'I'm afraid not, dear. I don't think our budget or my cookery skills will stretch to meringues, though I did get her currant scone recipe.'

They trudged home, each with a laden basket, and heaved them up the stairs. Her mother almost dropped hers on the scullery floor. 'Oh, that's a relief,' she panted, leaning against the scullery bench for support. 'I think in future it'll be easier to do a little shopping every day. Would you please put the food in the larder while I light the fire and put the kettle on for tea, and we can have some of that nice cheddar and bread with it.'

'Tea, Mother! We didn't buy tea.' Mary stopped in the act of unpacking the baskets; she'd been looking forward to a cup of tea.

'Oh, my goodness! What an idiot I am. I hope I get the hang of this housekeeping business soon.' She sighed, 'Well, we'll just have to make do with milk for today. There's too much to do now to go out again.'

Feeling revived after the milk and bread and cheese, they prepared to clean and put the flat in order. After changing into their oldest dresses, her mother tucked her skirts up round her waist in readiness to scrub the scullery floor, and then let out a wail of dismay. 'Oh, no! I'm even more stupid than I thought.' Her voice sounded as if she were about to cry.

'What is it, Mother?' Mary asked, afraid something terrible had happened.

'How can I scrub the floor without a bucket? And I was sure I'd thought of everything.' Her voice still sounded tremulous.

'Isn't there anything we can use instead?' Mary asked anxiously, frightened as always when her mother was upset.

Elizabeth straightened her shoulders and forced a smile. 'Of course, dear, I can use the soup pan. Don't take any notice of me; I'm just angry at myself for being so useless. But one thing I am is a good learner, so it won't take me long, don't worry. And I suppose it would be a good idea if I put the fire on first and heated some water,' she laughed. 'Thank the Lord those poor people didn't take their coal with them, or that's something else I'd have forgotten. Now you get started sweeping the floors and when that's done we'll dust the furniture together. Let's think of it as playing a new game.'

'It's not the same as a game,' Mary grumbled. 'I'd rather be playing draughts or riding Strawberry.' Tears stung her lids as she thought of her pony. 'Oh, Mother, Uncle Joseph has probably sold him by now or, worse still, had him killed. He costs a lot of money to feed.'

'No! He wouldn't do that. Ponies are worth a lot of money. Don't worry, he's probably in a nice new home by now.' Elizabeth put her hand on Mary's shoulder and said coaxingly: 'It only makes it more painful to think about it, sweetheart. Come on now and let's get started cleaning. Keeping busy helps to keep your mind off your troubles.'

It took the whole afternoon before the flat began to take on a more shiny, cared-for appearance. Despite their awkwardness and inexperience, their efforts paid off.

The accommodation was enough for their needs: two tiny bedrooms, a front parlour and, at the back, a good-sized kitchen with a scullery leading off. Elizabeth had furnished the kitchen comfortably with a small round dining table and two bentwood chairs by the window, arranging two stuffed armchairs by the stove so that they had a cosy place to sit until they could afford to furnish the parlour. In the scullery was a large sink and a scrubbed wooden workbench hinged to the wall. Although the front parlour was bare to the floorboards, Elizabeth hung up the white lace curtains she'd bought at the second-hand shop. 'No sense in letting the whole world know we can't afford furniture yet, is there? We must keep up appearances.' But Mary thought her mother's voice sounded funny.

At six o'clock they flopped down, exhausted, in the armchairs by the fire. 'Oh, wouldn't a nice cup of tea be wonderful now.'

'I'm hungry; I'd rather have dinner,' Mary said ungraciously.

'I know, dear. I'm going to do some potatoes and carrots and fry that nice cod we bought. You sit there and rest.'

'Ugh, cod! I'd rather have sole,' she said, screwing up her nose in distaste.

'The sole was too expensive, Mary. You'll just have to eat what we can afford – at least until I get work.'

From her armchair in the kitchen, Mary watched her mother peel the vegetables in the scullery and set them to boil on the kitchen stove. She curled up in the chair, her eyes drooping from tiredness and the heat of the fire, as her mother cut off a small piece of the lard they'd bought from the butcher and melted it in the frying pan, adding the two slices of cod. 'While that's cooking, I have to go down to the privy, Mary, and while I'm down I'll get a bucket of coal. Keep an eye on those pans for me, will you?'

But when her mother returned, staggering under the weight of the heavy bucket, there was a sizzling sound from the stove and a smell of burning. Mary was fast asleep.

'Oh, Mary. I asked you to watch the dinner,' Elizabeth cried, quickly setting the bucket down and grabbing the kettle holder to rescue the smoking frying pan, which she placed on the hearth.

'Sorry, Mother, I fell asleep,' Mary muttered.

'Well, thank goodness, it's only burnt on one side; we can scrape that off. Now let's see how those vegetables are doing.' She lifted the lid and poked the carrots with a knife. 'Good, they're done, and now the potatoes. Oh, dear, they're still a bit hard. I suppose I should have cut them up smaller. Well, I shall know next time. We'll just have to wait a few more minutes till they're done.'

Dinner was awful. The burnt flavour carried right

through the fish, despite the black pieces having been scraped off, the carrots were soggy, and the potatoes still hard; worst of all, her mother had forgotten to add salt. Mary knew better than to complain; at least they'd remembered to buy salt. She sprinkled it heavily over the food and managed to wade her way through half the contents of her plate. At least her stomach had stopped rumbling now. Her mother also pushed her plate aside half eaten.

'Well, that was my first lesson. Next time will be better,' she smiled ruefully.

It was late August and school resumed for the autumn term the following week. The Mother Superior had given Mary a letter recommending her for entrance to grammar school, but an examination was still required and there had been no time to arrange it during their hasty move.

Her new school turned out to be an old, decaying building, surrounded by spiked iron railings with a high brick wall separating the boys' building from the girls'. It was hard for Mary at first; the other girls made fun of her 'posh' accent and expensive clothes and excluded her from their games.

On her first day, she couldn't find her classroom and so arrived late. She apologised to the teacher while the entire class glued their eyes to her, and at play time, a group of girls assailed her in the school yard.

'Why, what do you know! Listen to that toffee-nosed voice o' hers. Who does she think she is, the cat's whiskers? Tryin' to be teacher's pet – on her first day an' all.'

The speaker, Annie Hatty, a plump, dirty looking girl with short, thin, black hair and a cast in one eye, had been strapped on the hand in class for talking. She made up for her unfortunate appearance with a formidable personality; with looks like hers she had to be the boss if she didn't want to be the butt of the others' ridicule. She and her little troupe of shabbily dressed followers giggled and made faces at Mary.

After this, Mary kept her distance in the school yard and the others ignored her most of the time; when they did approach her it was usually to taunt her.

One day they pulled out her hair ribbons and chanted: 'Mary with the bow in the hair and the nose in the air. Mary snooty stuck-up, Mary snooty stuck-up. Nyah, nyah, nyah, mouth full o' blah.'

They went off tittering, very pleased with themselves, and Mary, being outnumbered, didn't dare retaliate but saved her vengeance for a more appropriate time. That afternoon, as class was dismissed, she sidled up to the blackboard and swiftly sneaked a piece of chalk from the ledge into her pocket. She looked around anxiously. No one had seen.

The next morning she arrived at school twenty minutes early and, stretching herself to her full four feet nine inches, wrote on the brick wall in the largest letters she could and as many times as she could till the chalk ran out: 'Fatty Fanny Annie Hatty is as ugly as she's batty.'

She was pleased with herself; she'd lain awake during the night composing the rhyme. Impatient to see the gang's faces when they read it, she hid in the lavatories until the first pupils arrived and it was safe to mingle with them.

She was rewarded. One of Annie's followers was the first to see it and her jaw dropped. 'Annie! Annie!' she yelled to the girl in question, who was just entering the yard. 'Come and see! Come and see!'

Annie's face went white as she laboriously read the print. 'Whoever done that's in for it,' she shouted, kicking the wall angrily and attempting to erase the words with her coat sleeve. 'Here, you lot, come and help,' she shouted at her followers, now closely encircled around her, wide-eyed in amazement. Who would dare do that to Annie? But she had so many enemies, it would be hard to find the culprit.

'I'll get the bugger,' Annie yelled, 'an' to make sure I get the right one, I'll get the lot o' them.'

She went berserk, kicking every one of her known enemies on their calves as high up as she could; there was no point in kicking them where their boots protected them. Mary was one of the last, but the kick was worth it. She limped into class feeling very pleased with herself.

'It'll be better next year when you go to grammar school,' her mother consoled Mary when she recounted the story of the writing on the wall and the kicks, though of course not admitting that she was the culprit. But Mary wondered if that day would ever come. She dreaded going to the dismal school every morning and it was really a waste of time because she was learning nothing; the lessons the teachers taught she had learned two years before at the convent. She always got the highest marks in the class and it was ruining her reputation even more.

The following week, Brenda Bingham, one of Annie's gang, approached her in the school yard after the teacher had just praised her for getting ten out of ten in an arithmetic test. 'Little Miss Know-it-all, think you're so clever. You get ten out of ten again an' you're in for big trouble. Annie sent me to tell you, and this is just a warning.' With that she pushed Mary, who almost lost her balance. 'You're just tryin' to make us all look stupid.'

'I don't need to *try*, you *are* stupid. Stupid, stupid!' Mary poked her face dangerously close to Brenda's as she hissed the word again, 'Stupid.' It was a mistake. Splat! Brenda spat in her face. It was too much for Mary. She grabbed Brenda by the shoulders and shook her. 'Don't you dare do that again. You're filthy and disgusting as well as stupid.'

One of the teachers happened to be crossing the yard and had witnessed the spitting. She grabbed Brenda by the scruff of the neck. 'Brenda Bingham, you apologise to Mary, or it's two hundred lines and no play time tomorrow.'

'Sorry,' the girl said reluctantly. Anything was better than two hundred lines.

'Come on, Mary; I'll take you to wash your face.'

The teacher's kindly tone made Mary feel even more sorry for herself, and she burst into tears.

'Don't cry, Mary. Just you come straight to me if any of them get on at you again. Little ruffians, I'll see to it that they're punished and they'll soon stop it.'

'Thank you, Miss James,' Mary sobbed. But she wondered if having a teacher to protect her wouldn't make matters worse. Perhaps she'd better put a couple of wrong answers in her tests in future.

'Oh, my precious,' her mother cried as Mary tearfully recounted the story of the day. 'Don't cry!' But she was crying with her. She blew her nose hard and took Mary on her lap. 'Aren't there *any* nice girls at school you can make friends with?'

'There's Joanne and Jean and Mabel; they're nice and quiet and we talk a lot in the playground, and they can't stand Annie Hattie either.'

'Then you just stay with them and form your own *good* gang.'

'But I haven't got any real friends there, nobody ever invites me home. I miss the girls at the convent.' Mary wailed again and her mother rocked her, her own eyes brimming. Dear God! What was He punishing them for?

Though highly educated, Elizabeth was untrained for any profession, and her attempts to find work in the offices and factories met with raised eyebrows and head-shakes. She was usually told that, even if they had an opening, it would not be her kind of work.

After many such refusals, Mary arrived home one day to find a new washing tub, boiler, and wringer installed in the scullery.

'I've decided to work at home,' her mother said, looking closely at Mary. She was sitting at the kitchen table writing advertisements on postcards to display in the windows of the corner grocer and the post office. 'It has several advantages over going out to work: I'll be at home when you get back from school and I shan't have to get up so early in the mornings. Once I've built up enough customers, it should pay enough to live on.'

So far, most of Mary's pity had been reserved for herself, yet on hearing this, she was overcome by a wave of pity for her mother. But it was mixed with a feeling of shame. *Her* mother – a washerwoman! 'Oh, Mother, let's go back to Uncle Joseph. Anything would be better than being a washerwoman.' But as she uttered the words, she wasn't so sure it would be better with Uncle Joseph.

'No, Mary, we can never go back there. And, anyway, what's wrong with taking in washing? It's an honest living,' her mother said in her special, forced, cheerful voice, not looking up from her writing task lest the child see the anguish in her eyes.

The false cheerfulness brought comfort. To Mary, her mother was omnipotent; as long as she was there, everything would be all right. She knew that the girls at school would taunt her about her mother's being a washerwoman, but she told herself she wouldn't care. It wouldn't be for ever.

She put her arms round her mother's shoulders. 'Oh, Mother, when I grow up I'm going to marry a rich, handsome man, with a deep voice like grandfather's. And he'll have a big house in the country, and you and I'll spend all our time reading, and walking in the grounds and conservatories.'

'That sounds delightful, dear. I certainly do hope you find your prince charming.'

The advertisements paid off. At first it was a small trickle, only two or three loads a week, but as word of Elizabeth's low rates spread, she was almost overwhelmed with customers. She charged little more than the public washhouse, where people paid simply to use the tubs and hot water.

Mary would come home in the late afternoon to the dank smell of wet clothes drying on lines strung in front of the stove and the distinctive, warm, singeing odour of the hot iron smoothing over the starched garments. Her mother now spent almost every evening ironing, and Mary never saw her read any more. Her beloved books remained in neat piles on the bare wooden floorboards of the empty parlour.

Occasionally Mary would help with the ironing so they could spend more time relaxing before bed. But it wasn't because she noticed how tired her mother looked nor how thin she was becoming. Nor did she notice that sometimes when she got home from school her mother's eyes were red. She was growing up fast, yet remained childishly oblivious of many things – those she didn't wish to know or was fearful of knowing.

One day she came home from school to find Mrs Moynihan, the downstairs tenant, scrubbing their front step.

'Hello, luv,' the woman said as Mary approached. 'I just thought I'd do your ma's step an' all, as I was doin' me own anyhow – save her a bit o' trouble, like. She had a little poorly turn this mornin', but she's sittin' up in bed there, right as rain now. Don't worry yoursel'. She'll be up an' about again the morrow. I gave her a nice cup o' tea an' told her to stay put an' rest a bit. I'll pop up in the mornin' again to see how she's gettin' on.'

Mary didn't even remember to thank her; she raced up the stairs two at a time. Her mother, sitting up in bed, turned as her daughter entered. 'There's no need to look so worried,' she said. 'I've just been overdoing things a little. I'll be back on my feet tomorrow after a good day's rest.'

'Oh, Mother! I didn't know you were so tired; why didn't you tell me? I could have helped you more with the washing and ironing.' She sat on the bed and fearfully kissed her mother's cheek.

'Yes, I think I'll have to let you do a bit more from now on. I hate to burden you with work after school but the business is getting too much for one person to cope with. And that's good news; at least we're making enough to live on.' In her weakened state her own misery, from which she'd always tried to protect the child, overwhelmed her and her tears suddenly flowed freely.

'Oh, Mother, please don't cry, don't cry,' Mary begged, burying her head in her mother's bosom and crying with her.

'Now, now! Dry your eyes, Mary, and don't take any notice of me. I was just feeling a little sorry for myself because I don't feel well,' but then she broke down and sobbed again, clinging to Mary. 'What have we done to deserve all this? Sometimes I feel I can't take much more, and I'm so worried about you.' They lay in each other's arms and let their misery take over, sobbing together until the sobs could come no more.

Elizabeth stroked Mary's hair. 'We mustn't give up hope, Mary; we can only struggle on and hope things will get better.' She dabbed at Mary's eyes with her handkerchief and then at her own, letting the roughened, reddened hands fall on the coverlet, and for the first time Mary noticed how pale and thin her mother's face looked and felt more frightened than she'd felt in her whole life.

That evening, following her mother's instructions, she did the washing. She hadn't realised what heavy work it was. Then, after seeing to her mother's needs, she fell into bed exhausted and cried herself to sleep. The following morning she missed school in order to do the ironing and keep an eye on her mother – not that she minded missing school. Her mother had tried to get up, but after an hour had gratefully returned to bed, persuaded by Mrs Moynihan, who had 'popped up' to see her, as promised.

Until then they hadn't made the acquaintance of their neighbours, except to greet one another in passing – mostly shy, self-conscious greetings, as the neighbours thought of them as 'nobs' and couldn't understand why they were living there. Mrs Moynihan turned out to be their life-support. She was a tall, spare woman who looked as if she'd never been young; wide, bony shoulders jutted out above pendulous breasts, as long and flat as razor straps from the prolonged sucking of numerous infants, and long muscular arms dangled beneath the rolled up sleeves of a grey workdress. Her brown hair was streaked with grey and clung tightly to her scalp, ending in a neat knot on the nape of the stringy neck; the long, narrow nose reached down between taut, broad cheekbones that looked as if they'd been carved out of stone. Yet the deep brown eyes were wide and kind, with a humorous glint, and the mouth was soft and generous, turning up at the corners as if in a permanent smile. It was a special face, a combination of force and gentleness, sadness and laughter. She had a husband who worked permanent night shift at the shipyard – 'Puttin' bolts in boilers,' she said – and she had five surviving children, out of eight born. Mary wondered where they all slept in that tiny, two-bedroomed flat.

After that first day, Mrs Moynihan 'popped up'

regularly to see Elizabeth, who had to spend more and more time each day resting between her chores. Mrs Moynihan cheered the ailing woman with her gossip and banter. One day she was talking about the night shift: 'Well, you know, hinny, it's a double blessin'. It pays more than the day shift and it's right useful fo' stoppin' the bairns comin'.'

Mary puzzled over this. How could working at night have anything to do with babies being born? She'd always believed that babies were a gift God gave to people who were married, that in some magical way the marriage ceremony made people able to have babies by simply being married in the eyes of God. The puzzle was beyond her, as was the riddle of a family of seven fitting into two bedrooms. But Mrs Moynihan became as essential to Mary's wellbeing as food and drink.

On arriving home from school some few weeks after her mother had first felt unwell, Mary saw a strange bicycle at the door. Upstairs, she discovered Mrs Moynihan talking to the local doctor and her mother lying in bed with her eyes closed, her face as white as the pillow she lay on. Mary ran to the still figure, her whole body trembling with fear. Mrs Moynihan took hold of her. 'Don't get yoursel' all upset, luv. She had a bad turn this mornin'.'

Mary's eyes filled with tears. 'What's wrong with her?' she managed to ask.

'Your mother has diabetes,' the doctor said in a kind voice, though, to Mary, it sounded thin and far away. 'Come on, lass, buck up,' he said, putting his hand on her shoulder. 'I'll look in every day to see her, and Mrs Moynihan's going to stay with you tonight. I'll give you a note for school telling them why you have to stay at home.'

'Aye, that's all right. Our Molly'll take the note in the mornin'.' Mrs Moynihan wound her long arms round the sobbing, trembling little figure. 'Don't be scared, hinny. I'm here.'

The doctor was packing his bag when Mary finally found her voice. 'Thank you, Doctor,' she said, her body still shaking uncontrollably as she wiped the tears from her face with the back of her hand.

Mrs Moynihan left with the doctor, saying, 'Now, don't cry any more, hinny. I'll just pop down to give the bairns their teas and I'll be right back up. Just knock on the kitchen floor with the broom if you need me in the meantime, hen.'

Chapter Four

Word of Mary's mother's illness spread rapidly from one brown-painted doorway to another. The neighbours' natural warmheartedness overcame their inhibitions and they began to drop in with 'a nice bit o' fish fo' your ma, luv,' or 'just made a big pan o' broth and had some left over . . . thought you an' your ma could do with it, Mary.' But it was Mrs Moynihan who kept Mary and her mother going. She would bound up and down the stairs twenty times a day with 'a little bit o' somethin' tasty' or a snippet of gossip for the invalid. She had an extra juicy bit of gossip today.

'Eey, I just had to come up an' tell you. That tart down the street – you know the one I mean – well, she had it comin' to her, and now she's got it, all right. Well, you know, her hubby come home from work early – laid off, he was. Caught her right in the middle of it wi' the coalman. So he went and kicked him down the stairs. Said he didn't care if they froze to death, he didn't want no more coal, an' he didn't want to see that bugger's black mug anywhere near his house again.' The woman's head rolled back, her raucous laughter filling the tiny flat.

Elizabeth stifled a smile, looking anxiously to see her daughter's reaction. But Mary's face conveyed nothing; she kept her eyes downcast, her inquisitive mind mulling over the amazing facts. What was wrong with the coalman delivering the coal while the husband was at work? She carefully stored Mrs

Moynihan's enigmatic and intriguing stories in her mind for later days. Perhaps when she was grown up she would know the answers.

They had been living in town for over two years now and there was much Mary still had to learn about their new way of life. Sometimes she would try to remember what the old life had been like, especially when she was doing the washing in the damp scullery. But it all seemed worlds away. She knew she must stop thinking about that world; it was over now.

The following day Mrs Moynihan came bounding up the stairs waving a newspaper (she always read the births, marriages and deaths or, as she called them, 'the hatches, matches and dispatches'). 'Hey, what do you know, Elizabeth. That little whore o' your brother's has given birth to a son and heir.'

'Oh, well, I'm glad he's got someone to carry on the family name. The poor little mite is going to have a tough time living up to his father though; I'm glad I'm not there to see it.' She waved her hands, which had now almost resumed their natural whiteness, over the coverlet in a gesture of dismissal. 'I want no more to do with that family.'

'Well, the little maid has certainly made her way up in the world,' Mary said venomously, feeling a surge of pure envy and hatred. Strangely, whenever she thought of Roseanne she remembered the incident of the white boots. She hated her almost as much for that one small negligence as for being the cause of their having to leave their home.

Mary tucked the blankets under the mattress furiously and picked up the water jar to refill it. 'Would you like a cup of tea, Mrs Moynihan? I'm going to make one anyway. I've just got Mother's lunch ready. Why don't you stay and keep her company while she has it?'

'Lunch, eh! Still usin' them fancy words. I'll know

you've really settled in when you start callin' it dinner like everybody else. But whatever you call it, it smells nice. You're turnin' into a right little cook an' house-wife – almost as good as your ma.'

Elizabeth laughed. 'Sometimes better, thanks to your teaching. I had to learn by trial and error . . . mostly by error,' she added. 'I'm sure poor Mary will never forget my first efforts as a housewife, and par-ticularly as a cook.'

'Eey well, luv, I couldn't have learned her nowt if she didn't have it in her to start with, an' I would have helped you if you hadn't been too bloody proud to ask.' Then to Mary: 'No, hen, thanks anyway, but I won't have no tea. I'd better be gettin' back down. I left the bairns on their own – couldn't wait to tell your ma the news.' With that she pulled up her tall, bony frame from the bed and took Elizabeth's hand. 'I'll pop up again later on when Jack gets home.'

The first shock of the illness was over now; day followed day as Mary, with Mrs Moynihan's help, did her best to look after her mother and keep the little flat clean. She scrimped their tiny budget to buy the invalid tasty treats, often dining alone in the kitchen on bread and jam before taking in her mother's tray of carefully prepared fish or rabbit.

As Mrs Moynihan left, Mary ladled a dainty por-tion of rabbit stew on to a warm plate and placed it on the tray with a glass of water. 'Here you are, Mother,' she said, setting the tray carefully on her mother's lap. 'This should warm you up.'

'Thank you, sweetheart. Bring yours in and have it with me.'

'I've already had mine,' she lied. 'I was just going to have a cup of tea now. I'll bring that in.' She left and hurriedly ate a slice of bread and dripping in the kit-chen, returning with her tea.

'How's the money situation this week?' her mother asked.

'Quite good, and I've got some extra washing coming in tomorrow so we should have a shilling or so left over.'

'Oh, I do wish you didn't have to do that. I don't mean to sound ungrateful to the doctor for getting us that allowance from the parish; I don't know where we'd be without it, but I just wish it were enough so you didn't have to take in washing.'

'But I'm only doing two or three loads a week, Mother,' Mary lied again. 'I can manage that, and the extra does help.'

Elizabeth had good and bad days but never complained. But Mary knew the bad days – her mother didn't eat and just lay back on her pillow with closed eyes. Mary had moved her own small bed into her mother's room so that she could more easily keep an eye on her during the night. The sick woman slept little and lightly, and at the slightest sound Mary was at her bedside ministering the interminable glasses of water she craved.

That night was a bad one. Her mother's tossing and turning and heavy breathing kept Mary alert. It was three in the morning and neither of them had closed their eyes.

'Are you all right, Mother? Can I get you anything?' Mary asked, dragging herself up for the umpteenth time to her mother's side.

'No, thank you, dear. You go back to bed and get some sleep. I wish you'd move back to the other room. No sense in both of us staying awake, and you've got a busy day ahead tomorrow.'

'Yes,' Mary yawned, 'I am tired,' and crawled back into bed, pulling the inadequate blankets topped by her overcoat over her head. She closed her eyes and prayed aloud before she fell asleep: 'Please,

God, make Mother better soon.'

It seemed like only minutes later when the unmistakable clatter of the pitmen's clogs on the cobbled street woke her. Oh, Lord, the first pit shift, she thought sleepily, five o'clock already. She'd better get up. She had two loads to finish today and the shopping to do. She glanced at her mother, now finally slumbering. The water jar was empty again. She'd better leave an extra bowl beside her in future. It seemed that no matter how much she left on the wicker nightstand, it was always gone by morning.

She dragged her leaden body out of bed and crept to the kitchen to light the fire. She must let her mother sleep as long as possible.

When Elizabeth finally awoke she asked sleepily, as Mary poked her head through the door on one of her regular checks: 'What time is it?'

'Seven o'clock. I'll just help you down to the privy; I've got the water ready for your wash.' She eased the frail figure out of bed, placed her feet into the warm slippers Mary had saved up to buy for her the previous Christmas, wrapped her in her overcoat and shawl and half led and half carried the light weight down the back stairs to the outside privy.

'Oh, I do wish you didn't have to do this for me. I feel so helpless. Would you ask Mrs Moynihan if she could spare a minute this morning; I'd like to talk to her.'

'Yes, I'll ask her as soon as I get you back upstairs.'

By seven thirty, Mary had helped her mother wash and change into a clean nightgown, and had put the kettle and an egg on the stove to boil. While they were heating, she ran downstairs to Mrs Moynihan's flat and entered without knocking – there were no formalities with Mrs Moynihan. 'My door's always open to you and your ma, hinny,' the woman had insisted from the start.

'Mother said could you spare her a moment this morning, when you can?'

''Course, hinny. What is it?'

'I don't know; she just asked to see you.'

'All right, luv. I can come now. I was just doin' the dishes.' She wiped her hands on her pinafore and trotted briskly up the stairs ahead of Mary, who had long since given up trying to keep up with those long legs.

'Why, you're lookin' a bit peeky today, Elizabeth. Nothin's wrong, is it?'

'No, I'm fine; I just lay awake a lot last night and did some thinking. I've come up with an idea and I'd like you to help me.'

'Anythin' I can do, hinny.'

'Well, I don't want Mary to know about it but I want to sell my gold pin and buy a commode. I know they're expensive and I don't think I'll get much for the pin; it's not worth much . . . just sentimental value really, but it should fetch enough. Could you do it for me? Mary would be upset if she knew I was selling it, but I really can't make the stairs any more and I hate to be such a trouble to her.'

'Eey, what a daft bugger I am! I just never thought. Beattie up the street's got a commode, an' her ma passed away last week. She'll let you have it for as long as you want. She's a good soul.'

'It seems they're all good souls around here. That would be very kind of her.'

'No, we don't think about bein' kind, hinny, just helpin' folks out. You would do the same for her and you know it. When folks haven' got much, they share what they have – it's them that's got that keeps. I'll go right down and ask her now and bring it straight up. What an idiot I am! I should o' thought of it mysel', watchin' you tryin' to manage those stairs in the cold.'

'You're such an angel to us. Thank you.' In her gratitude, Elizabeth was close to tears.

'Angel, you say! Our Jack would call me somethin' different and not so flatterin'. An' that reminds me, I've got the juciest bit o' news about Annie Hardy. I'll save it till I get back and I'll bring up some scones – just made a fresh batch this mornin'. I'll tell Mary to have the tea ready and we'll have a celebration. You're not goin' to believe it,' she added over her shoulder on her way out.

'I wish you wouldn't keep me in suspense,' Elizabeth laughed.

'Aye, well, it'll give you somethin' to think about till I get back. Ta ta, hinny.'

Half an hour later she was back with the commode, the scones, and the story.

'You'd better tell Mary you need to talk to me in private for a minute if it's as bad as it sounds,' Elizabeth warned. 'You know she's too young for your stories.'

'Aye, I keep forgettin' about that. Mary,' she yelled into the kitchen, 'would you mind just washin' down that commode first and then we'll have the tea.'

'Yes, Mrs M.,' Mary answered, grimacing. She knew it was going to be one of those stories she wasn't supposed to hear.

Mrs Moynihan was in great form: 'Well, it seems that yesterday mornin' when Charlie got off his milk round he felt like a bit o' you-know-what, an' his Annie never minds a bit o' the same hersel', any time o' the day or night. Anyhow, she'd just been windin' up the clothes line and still had it in her hand, so he got the idea and tied her to the bed for a lark. Now, our Molly was on her way to school with their Nellie and they heard a lot of commotion comin' from the front room window so they had a peep in to see what was goin' on. Now it's all over the school that he tortures his wife by tyin' her to the bed and bouncin' up an' down on her. Eey, I was mad with our Molly for peekin' in folks' windows an' blabbin' about what she sees, but I had to laugh. I laughed so hard I nearly wet me britches,' she spluttered, doubling up with mirth again.

Elizabeth laughed with her. 'I think it's just as well I haven't got a husband, or my bedroom affairs would be all over the neighbourhood, too. Have you no sense of other people's privacy?' she asked in mock disapproval.

'Eey, no, hinny, not if there's a good laugh in it. Anythin' for a good laugh, that's my motto.'

Mary heard the laughter die down and guessed that she could take the tea in now. It wasn't fair that grown-ups had all the fun.

'Oh, there you are, Mary. Thank you, dear. Mrs Moynihan's just been telling me a story about school, which reminds me. When is the grammar school entrance exam coming up?'

Although Mary had again missed the entrance examination the previous year because of her mother's illness, Elizabeth was determined that she should take it this year.

Mary carefully put the tea tray on the bedside table, keeping her head down. This was the subject she dreaded most.

'Oh, not for a while, yet. Don't worry about that now,' she said, concentrating heavily on pouring the tea.

As she accepted her tea silently, Mrs Moynihan gave Mary a knowing look. Mary hadn't attended school since her mother had been confined to bed, though her mother believed she was going three mornings a week. The truth was that on those mornings Mary and Mrs Moynihan simply exchanged duties: Mary went downstairs to look after the three youngest children, while Mrs M. went up to look after Elizabeth and do some of the washing. The deception was Mrs

Moynihan's idea, for she knew Elizabeth was worrying about her daughter's interrupted schooling. But the conspiracy was becoming more and more difficult to maintain, for the School Board inspectors were calling regularly at the house now. Mrs Moynihan's cunning and Mary's determination combined to keep Elizabeth unaware of the subterfuge. It was Mrs Moynihan's boast that she could 'spot the buggers a mile away', and whenever she saw a likely character approaching the house, or heard an unexpected knock on the door, she would shout up the back stairs to warn Mary: 'Quick, Mary, I need you down here a minute.'

Mary would take the stairs two at a time and hide in the privy, breathless and trembling, until she was given the familiar 'all clear': 'All right, hinny, you can go back up now. I sent him packin'.'

If her mother asked who was at the door, Mary would lie that it was just some man selling brushes, or gypsies, or whatever came into her head.

Handing her mother her tea, she wondered how she would get out of the grammar school situation. But, once again, Mrs Moynihan rescued her, or at least bought her time.

'Aye, don't worry your head about that yet, hinny. I heard it was going to be late this year.' Then, veering from the subject: 'Eey, you know, our Jimmy was bottom of the class last term. Like his father, that one, doesn't like books.' She then expertly changed the subject completely, knowing that one of her juicy bits of gossip would take Elizabeth's mind off school: 'Did I tell you about Rose and her man down the street?' Not waiting for a reply, she went on: 'Well, Arthur went to the tailor's for a new suit for a weddin' an' never paid the poor sod. After a few weeks, the tailor came knockin' on the door an' Rose answered it. She called to her eldest, Jim; he's fourteen. "It's some man about a suit for your poor da." Then Jim came out and looked all woeful: "Me da passed away two weeks ago," he said. Then the poor tailor went all apologetic and said not to worry about it an' that he was very sorry; eey, then they both went into the kitchen to tell Arthur and they all cracked up.' Mrs Moynihan also cracked up as she finished the tale; her bellowing laughter filling the room.

Mary gratefully sipped her tea and smiled. She could always count on Mrs Moynihan.

Six months passed, and it was the day before Mary's thirteenth birthday. Mrs Moynihan was going to make her a cake with thirteen candles and bring the children upstairs for a party. Mary's mother had been sleeping more than usual for the past few days, but her face had taken on a healthier colour and was filling out. As usual, that morning, Mary dived out of her cold bed, put on her overcoat, and groped her way to her mother's bed to look at the sleeping figure before lighting the stove.

She screwed up the old newspapers Mrs Moynihan always collected for her and carefully laid the sticks and coals on top, fanning the puny flames furiously with a rolled up paper until they slowly flared and the small coals began to burn. When they had taken on a healthy red glow and she was satisfied that the fire had taken, she placed the kettle on to boil. She then tiptoed to her mother's bed to remove the cold hot-water bottle and the two flat irons that helped to keep her warm overnight.

Her fingers stealthily crept under the blankets, searching for the cold, hard objects. Oh! That was cold, but not hard. How could her mother's feet be that cold? She felt the one white hand lying on her mother's breast outside the blankets. Oh, God! And the forehead. Cold as ice. 'Mother! Mother!' She shook the still figure in terror. 'Wake up! Wake up!' But the closed eyes didn't open. 'Please, God, wake her up,' Mary screamed. Then she called on her real, living god and thumped on the floor frantically with the broom: 'Mrs M., Mrs M., come up! She won't wake up, she won't wake up.' Mary fell in a crumpled heap on the bed, sobbing into her mother's still bosom. 'Please, God, don't let her be dead! Please, God, don't let her be dead! Let it just be another coma . . . just another coma,' she wailed.

In seconds Mrs Moynihan had catapulted her big frame halfway up the stairs. 'I'm comin', hinny,' she shouted and then turned and yelled at Molly, who was standing with her mouth open in the yard: 'Molly, run quick an' get the doctor.'

The tired looking doctor tried to comfort Mary. 'It's for the best, lass. You wouldn't have wanted her to suffer any longer, would you? God decided it was time to take her into his care.'

'But why did God make her suffer in the first place? And why does He keep on taking people away from me?' Mary sobbed in a fit of anguish, her shaking body cradled in Mrs Moynihan's arms.

'Those are hard questions to answer, lass.' The doctor sighed and then turned to Mrs Moynihan: 'I'll bring the death certificate round tomorrow.'

'Aye, knock downstairs. She'll be down there with me. I'll look after her.' She stroked the damp hair off Mary's white cheeks as she spoke. 'Come on, luv, we're goin' downstairs. Your ma will be right peaceful on her own now.'

The doctor let himself out and Mrs Moynihan half carried and half dragged the still sobbing figure downstairs. She took over and organised everything. 'You're stayin' with us for good, hinny. I'm not havin' them send you to no home for girls. God knows we're pushed for room, but we'll squeeze you in somehow.'

'Thank you, Mrs Moynihan,' Mary said automatically, taking a breath between sobs, and obediently allowing Mrs Moynihan to lay her down on the settee. It would have been all the same to her if they had put her in the coalshed. Was God punishing her for something she'd done? She hadn't been to church since she'd left the convent. Could it be that? Oh, no! She shuddered. She couldn't be responsible for her mother's death. 'It couldn't be *my* fault, could it, Mrs M.?'

'Why, whatever makes you say that, hinny?'

'Well, God's been awfully cruel to us, and at the convent they used to say that we reap what we sow in this life.'

'Why, get that silly nonsense out o' your head. You're a good girl and your ma was a good woman. Take no notice o' what those pious folk tell you. They go to church every Sunday because they're afraid they're goin' to burn in hell for the sins they commit durin' the week. You an' your ma never did nothin' wrong an' she'll be up there in heaven lookin' down on you and feelin' happy, but feelin' sad that you're cryin' and thinkin' these things. You wouldn't want to make her sad in heaven, would you?'

'No, I'll try not to think of that again, but I can't stop crying now.'

'Why, that's all right, hinny. You just have a good cry and get your grievin' out. It'll do you good.' As she spoke she tucked a blanket round the still heaving little body. 'If you keep on cryin' you'll soon drop off to sleep; that's just what you need. I'll be here, don't worry. I've just got to get them bairns dressed; I made them stay in the bedroom out o' the way o' the fire, and now I'm goin' to put them out in the yard to play so they won't bother you.'

During the next few days Mary lived through a blur of tears. How could God be so cruel? Why couldn't

He have taken someone who deserved it? Someone like Roseanne, she thought bitterly. Despite being surrounded by a family, she felt numb and frightened and totally alone.

After Mrs Moynihan had arranged the funeral, she announced that she wanted to talk to Mary: 'I can tell you now, luv. Your ma knew she was goin', so she wrote to her brother, the rotten bugger, and asked if he would have you back. She knew you wouldn't want to, but she couldn't think of nothin' else for you. I told her I'd be happy to have you, but she said she felt she ought to write to that Joseph anyway, him bein' family an' all. That was three months since and not a bloody dicky-bird from him. Mesel', I know what I'd like to do with him, but it's up to you, hinny. Do you want to write again?'

'Oh, no! Please, Mrs Moynihan, I couldn't go back there; I'd much rather stay with you. Please let me stay.' Mary was on the verge of tears again.

'O' course, hinny,' Mrs Moynihan soothed. 'You can stop with us for as long as you have a mind. I just wanted you to know your ma did think o' you, though mesel', I think you're better off without him. You'll fare better here with folk that cares fo' you. And now that's settled, are you up to goin' upstairs with me the night to sort things out a bit? I'd sooner do it mesel', hinny, but I don't know what you want to keep. We'd better get it done with afore the funeral. That bloody landlord's got somebody movin' in afore your ma's cold. Stingy bugger thinks of nothing but his rent.'

But Mary was grateful that things were happening quickly. Her heart had broken when they'd moved the coffin to the funeral home the previous day, but now she was glad that her mother no longer lay in the dingy little bedroom, and Mrs Moynihan had assured her that she'd looked just as though she were asleep. If she had to go back upstairs, she'd rather her mother not be there while she was getting rid of her few precious things. She could hardly see through her tears, and shivered as she entered the flat that held so many unhappy memories, but Mrs Moynihan sat her down and insisted on doing everything anyway.

'Now, I just want you to tell me what you want doin' with the furniture.'

'Oh, whatever you think, Mrs Moynihan. Please take anything you need; you could use the extra bed.'

'Aye, I could, but I've got no room; there's only space for yours. I could really do with the boiler and wringer, though. They'd fit in the scullery under the bench and they'd be a Godsend.'

'Oh, please, don't ask – take them. She would've wanted you to have everything.'

'I haven't got room for everythin'. I'll see if Dollie's man'll take all the other stuff. The stingy bugger won't pay much, but it's better than givin' it all away. It's going to take a fair bit for the funeral costs, but God willin', there should be a few shillin' left for you.'

Mary had stopped crying now but was still shivering. Being back in the flat flooded her confused mind with memories, and her red-rimmed eyes looked glazed and far away.

The woman took her hand. 'Look, hinny, I know this hurts, but somethin's gotta be done with your ma's clothes and things.'

Mary had been dreading this. 'Please, you take them. I can't bear to think of anyone else wearing them.'

'That's right kind o' you, luv, but they wouldn't go nowhere near a great big lump o' scrag-end like me. Our Sally could wear them, though. Her man's just left her wi' the three bairns, and he won't tip up a brass farthin'. Lord knows she could do with somethin' to put on her back – if you don't mind.'

'Of course not. I know Mother would've liked to help her.'

But watching Mrs Moynihan sorting and packing her mother's clothes was more than she could cope with, and she ran to the window to hide the new flood of tears.

'That's all right, luv; it's only natural. There's no shame in tears. The thought o' somebody wearin' my poor ma's clothes would make me blubber an' all.'

When everything was finally organised, Mary reluctantly got down to the chore she dreaded most, but she knew she must do it herself. She opened her mother's little black leather box in which she'd always kept her private papers. There were a few official letters and forms with old dates and, at the bottom in a small red velvet box, the little gold pin. She threw out the old papers and took out the pin, fastening it to her blouse. 'I want to keep this, Mrs Moynihan, but please sell everything else . . . the books, too. Whatever you can get should cover the funeral and if there's anything left it can go towards my keep till I find a job.'

'Keep be blowed! As if a skinny little sparrow like you is going to make a dent in me purse. There should be a bit over; I'll keep it safe fo' when you need it.'

Somehow, Mary got through the funeral. Mrs Moynihan's comforting hand in hers gave her strength and, through her tears, she saw only the varnished wooden box with the spray of yellow roses Mrs Moynihan had helped her to lay on top. It wasn't until afterwards she remembered the hazy figures of the neighbours and realised that the whole street had turned out, some even taking time off work. These people were good friends indeed.

For several weeks she lived in a daze, sleeping in her own small bed in the parlour, while Jimmy, the eldest, was relegated to the hall with his folding cot. The three youngest slept in one bed in the small bedroom and

Molly in her mother's bed, which the father took over while it was still warm on his return from night shift.

Mary was grateful for Mrs Moynihan's and her family's love and support, but she knew she couldn't continue to impose on the good-hearted woman who already had burdens enough. She'd done most of her crying now, although frequently she'd remember something her mother had said, or would see her face, pale and still, as it had been that awful day, and would break down. And not a night passed that she didn't dream about her and wake up to the sick, empty realisation that it was only a dream. Her mother was dead. As soon as she felt able, she announced her intention of leaving school and finding a job.

'Eey! You can't do that, hinny. You know how much your ma wanted you to get into grammar school this year. Better late than never. I promised her before she went that I'd see that you did. You'll just have to wait, an' then you'll be able to get a better job if you have a grammar school certificate.'

'You couldn't possibly afford to keep me through grammar school, Mrs M., and, anyway, I'm too old now to start; I'll have to get a job and it will be better for me to be busy. Mother always said that keeping busy took your mind off your troubles.' She paused and pressed her hand to her forehead. 'Oh, no! I've just realised – my birth certificate, I'll need it to get a job and I haven't seen it. It must have been among the old papers I threw out.'

'Never mind; you don't need it just yet. You can get one when you do. You need more time to get over your mournin', hinny.'

'I shall never stop mourning her, Mrs M.' Mary bit her lip till it hurt, but it stopped the tears. 'It won't make any difference to my mourning whether I get a job now or later.'

She was determined. She cropped her magnificent

hair to a short bob, which gave her an overall appearance of maturity. But it was the face itself, with its air of ineffable sadness and hurt, that lent her a look beyond her years.

Mrs Moynihan gave in. 'All right, if there's no stoppin' you, I'll see if our Lottie can put a good word in for you.'

Finally Mary was granted an interview at the big house overlooking the park, where Mrs Moynihan's cousin Lottie worked as cook and housekeeper, and no one even asked to see her birth certificate. She was given the job after a brief but, for Mary, painful interview. It seemed that the previous girl had 'got herself into trouble' with the butcher's boy and had left in disgrace.

'I hope you won't get up to any monkey business like that,' Lottie said to her as she showed the new recruit round the house and explained her various duties.

Though unsure of what sort of 'monkey business' Lottie meant, Mary quickly assured her: 'Oh, no, I won't cause any kind of trouble, Lottie. Thank you for getting me the job. Full board, one evening a week and every other Sunday off, plus two shillings wages. That's marvellous! I'm very grateful. My mother would have been grateful, too, that you've helped me. She wouldn't have wanted me to impose on Mrs Moynihan for ever.' Her voice quavered and the tears started again. She didn't want to act like a baby in front of Lottie; she wanted to impress her with how grown up she was. 'I'm sorry, Lottie,' she muttered. 'I promise I won't cry when I'm working.'

'Never you mind, hinny. You can cry whenever you like in front o' me. I've done me fair share of it mesel'. Why don't you get yoursel' off to bed now and have an early night. You'll feel better in the mornin'.' Lottie placed her plump hands on Mary's shoulders and gave her a little push towards the stairs. 'An' now mind you go straight to sleep.'

The following morning Mary awoke in her little room at the top of the house, awareness of her new situation slowly permeating her consciousness. She jumped out of bed and, in a fever of nervousness, dressed in the unfamiliar black dress and white cap and apron. She mustn't be late on her first day. She raised her eyes and prayed to her mother: 'Please, Mother, don't let me do anything stupid or break anything on my first day, or ever,' she added hopefully. So far her prayers to God had all gone unanswered, but she knew her mother would listen. On the way downstairs she walked past several pairs of boots and shoes, planted neatly outside bedroom doors. Then realisation dawned. Retracing her steps, she picked up the footwear one by one until her arms were full and made her way, very slowly, down the three flights of stairs to the basement kitchen.

Chapter Five

Although they had the same jovial manner, Lottie and
her cousin were as unlike as a black bullet and a stick
of liquorice. Lottie was short, squat and fat – not fat
like the cook at the old house, though. No rolls of
soggy flesh bulged from under the grey dress and
white apron. Lottie's enormous bulk was as firm as a
punch-ball, even the parts not tightly encased in her
corsets. Her huge sturdy arms looked like hard-baked
loaves beneath the rolled up sleeves, not like soft
dough, and her round, solid face rested on a single,
firm chin. The deep brown eyes and wide mouth
reminded Mary of Mrs Moynihan's, but the broad
turned-up nose was definitely Lottie's own. She was in
a cheerful mood that day and broke Mary in very
gently.

'Now, first thing every mornin', hinny, you're to
light the fire, then clean the shoes and set the table
while I do the breakfast. We eat after them's had
theirs, but we eat the same stuff and you can take it
from me, I make nothing but the best for them.'

'What time do we eat, Lottie?'

'It depends, lass; weekdays they finish around eight,
but weekends they spend longer at it.'

Mary could smell the bacon frying and felt hungry
and nostalgic. The large, immaculately scrubbed
kitchen, with its enormous black iron stove, huge
wooden tables scrubbed almost white, and brilliant
brass pots and pans hanging in every available space

61

on the whitewashed walls reminded her of the kitchen at the old house. She bit on her lip to stem the vision of Roseanne and rubbed polish vigorously into an elegant pair of men's black shoes. The master must be a big man, like Grandpa, she thought, and hoped that he was as pleasant to the servants. Grandpa had always spoken to them in the same way he spoke to everyone, in his soft, deep voice. Her reveries were interrupted by Lottie's homely, sing-song tones.

'You'd better hurry up with them shoes, hinny. Breakfast's just about ready and you've still got the table to set. If you need any help I'll come up, but from what I heard about you already, you probably know all about settin' tables.'

For this and many other things Mary was thankful. Although the domestic skills she'd learned in the flat were basic, she remembered well how things were done in a big house and was even glad that as a child she had trotted around after Roseanne, asking those interminable child's questions: 'Why are you doing that, Roseanne?' and 'What for?' Roseanne's usually irritable answers proved useful now; at least she knew how to set the table and the buffet correctly.

That morning she had her first and unexpected encounter with the master. As she was carrying up to the dining room the silver tray with the last of the breakfast dishes and the teapot, a dark, rounded figure loomed at the top of the stairs, politely moving aside to let her pass.

'You must be the new girl, eh?'

'Yes, sir,' she murmured, giving a little bob as she had seen Roseanne do, her heart bobbing in unison. She tried to hide her agitation and kept her head low. This man had fired the last girl; she must do her best to please him. She couldn't afford to be fired.

'Well, I hope you're made of better stuff than the last one.'

'Oh, yes, sir.' She bobbed again, almost toppling the contents of the heavy tray.

'Indeed, I must say you *look* one hell of a lot better, but not very experienced, eh?'

'No, sir.' Another bob.

'Come, now, that's enough. No need to be so timid with me. Not afraid of me, are you?'

'No, sir.'

'Good! I don't like my girls to be afraid – respectful, yes. You remember that, eh!'

'Yes, sir.'

'That's good! Now that we understand each other we should get on splendidly. What's your name?'

'Mary Maddison, sir.' Her cheeks were pink with confusion and she attempted to hide them by bowing her head.

'All right now, Mary, no more bobbing, if you please. Just tell me what you did with my black shoes.'

'Oh! They're in the kitchen, sir.'

'First thing you must learn, my girl, I wear my black shoes to the office every weekday; they must be outside my door by seven o'clock; the brown ones can be done later.'

'I'll remember, sir. I'll get them as soon as I've taken in this tray.'

'That's right, princess . . . pretty . . . and you speak English, too. You *are* a rare find.'

She stood for a second or two, breathless, until she remembered the tray in her hands and the cooling tea, then she hurriedly made her way to the mercifully still empty dining room.

Back in the kitchen, hastily buffing the black shoes, she thought of the master. Not at all what she had imagined: fat and squat, with dark hair streaked over his thinning, pink scalp, and a stiff waxed moustache, incongruously thin and rigid, spanning his plump, flaccid face. He looked more like a bailiff than a banker, she thought. Still, he seemed nice enough. She hoped he would continue to find her satisfactory. Her hopes for the new job rose. She hadn't noticed that, as she'd neared the dining room, the master had turned, put on his gold-rimmed spectacles, and bestowed on her back view a look as thorough and encompassing as a farmer would give a calf he contemplated buying at the market.

The days passed and Mary became accustomed to her new life. The mistress was a sad-eyed, white-faced woman in her early thirties. She was still pretty, but had an air of withdrawal and a seriousness that made her look old and tired. The children, Emily and James, nine and seven years old, appeared to be her whole life. Mary never saw her laugh except in their company, though often she wondered how even a mother could take pleasure in such ill-behaved children. They were spoiled and rude, especially to the servants. Lottie gave them back as much as she got, but Mary was too aware of her lowly position to show her disapproval. If the brats complained to their mother that she'd scolded them, she wouldn't stand a chance against them.

Unfortunately, as she gained favour in her mistress's eyes, her duties were extended to supervising the children when madam was otherwise engaged. Happily, this wasn't often. Except for occasional official dinners with her husband's business associates and afternoon teas with their wives, the mistress spent most of her time with her children.

On those tea party afternoons when the weather was fine, it was Mary's task to take the children to the park. These times were always a trial, for the children took advantage of her. They would play hide-and-seek, not with each other, but with her, hiding from her until she was almost beside herself with worry lest they not reappear at all. What would the mistress do if she returned home without them? That would certainly be the end of her job. This fear was almost as strong as the fear of the real dangers that lurked in the park and might befall the young ones. Her mother had warned her that sometimes strange men did bad things to children in such places and, because she was still ignorant about what these things were, her fears were boundless.

Toward tea time the two miscreants would always reappear, not because they feared their mother's wrath if they were late but because the thought of tea and buttered scones revived their homing instinct. They knew Mary wouldn't dare tell their mother they had misbehaved; she was only a servant girl, not like Lottie. Lottie was the best cook in the world and she could say what she liked.

Lottie rebuked Mary on her return from one such outing, her huge bosom heaving with indignation and her grey curls bouncing as she shook her head. 'I don't know why you don't tell her what them two little buggers gets up to. It's about time she learned from somebody asides me that they're nobody's angels.'

'I know, Lottie, but she might get angry and fire me and I daren't risk losing my job; if it weren't for that I'd tell her what I think all right.'

'Aye, I know, hinny,' she sighed, her bosom rising almost to her chin. 'It's all right for me to talk; my position's safe here. You're right. They wouldn' stand for any lip from you. I suppose you'd better keep your nose clean, but if them little devils gets too much for you, just tell me and I'll give them a piece o' me tongue.'

'I'd rather you gave them a piece of your hand, Lottie,' Mary laughed. 'What they need is a good old-fashioned spanking.'

'Aye, sometimes I'd like to, but even I'd get kicked out for that, hinny.'

'I'll just have to keep my mouth shut and put up with them, and it's only a small part of the job anyway; I shouldn't complain.' Mary yawned and stretched. It had been a long day. 'Well, I suppose I should have an early night. I've got to clean the silver tomorrow and I'm going to see Mrs M. in the evening. I'm ready for my evening off. If only I don't have to look after the monsters in the afternoon, I should be finished in good time.'

Mary looked forward to those weekly visits to Mrs Moynihan, although Beauchamps Street brought back old, sad memories. Even though her dear mother was rarely far from her thoughts, seeing their old flat upstairs, now occupied by another family, intensified the stabbing pain of her loss. But Mrs Moynihan's chatter and gossip always cheered her up, though she still couldn't understand many of her stories.

That day coincided with one of the private school holidays. It was the day of the entrance examination to the grammar school and those children not sitting the exam had a free day. Mary thought of her mother's desire for her to go to grammar school and polished the silver even harder. It had never shone so bright. But hardly had she finished than the mistress came into the kitchen.

'Mary, I know this is your evening off, but the children are at such a loose end today with no school, would you mind taking them to the park this afternoon before you leave?'

Damn! she thought, but smiled. 'Of course not, ma'am. I'll be ready in just a few minutes.' What a hypocrite I am, she thought, hating herself.

All hopes of an early escape dashed, Mary reluctantly donned her outdoor coat and escorted the two restless, squealing young creatures to their usual spot in the park, seating herself resignedly on her accustomed bench until they deigned to return. By now used to their truancies, she sat quietly, listening for an occasional shout or childish squeal to reassure her they were still playing nearby.

At least she was out in the fresh air, she thought, and felt a delightful sense of release at her impending evening off. Deciding to take advantage of the sunshine, she took off her coat and let the frail warmth of the sun's tentative rays slowly penetrate her thin blouse to the white skin beneath. At first she sensed only the comforting, relaxing warmth on her skin, then her whole body began to submit to the spell and she was transported. Closing her eyes, she felt little flashes of light and dark on her eyelids as the sunlight timidly sought its way through the dusty plane-tree leaves to the patches of grey-green grass below. Not even the park was spared the cumulus of smoke and dust from the factories and coal mines. But still, it was a welcome oasis in that desert of bricks and mortar.

Mary savoured the moment, listening to the trees rustling and the birds chirping, feeling as if her whole being had been taken over by something strange and unseen and unaccountably delightful.

In an instant the spell was broken. She heard the crunch of heavy footsteps on the gravel path, and her skin felt suddenly cold.

The master, sporting unaccustomed casual knickerbockers and a walking stick, appeared as from nowhere. 'Well, then! What's this? All by yourself?'

'Yes, sir, the children usually play by themselves here. They're quite all right . . . I'll call them now.'

'No need, let them enjoy themselves a little longer. Such a nice day, I thought I'd take some time off for a short stroll myself, but you look so lonely here, maybe I'll just sit for a while and keep you company.'

'Oh, please don't worry about me, sir. I'm fine by myself. I always sit here while the children play.'

'Well, today at least, you needn't sit alone. I could

do with a spot of refreshing company. Damned boring, meetings are. Don't you find you need company sometimes, Mary?'

'Not really, sir. I always have Lottie.'

'That's not what I mean,' he said, seating himself next to her on the bench. 'Don't you have a boy friend or someone?'

'No, sir. I mean I have someone, but not a boy friend.'

'Well, a pretty little thing like you ought to have a boy friend. Never had one?'

'No . . . no, sir.'

'Ahah, you really are a quiet one.' He moved closer and laid one plump, pink paw on her knee. She froze. Her freezing he took as non-resistance, which he found encouraging. He moved his hand and placed it across the back of the bench, at first barely touching her shoulders and then gradually increasing the pressure and curving his arm to encompass her slight frame. She began to shake with a mixture of panic and indignation. Being her employer surely didn't give him the right to touch her.

'What's all this shaking for, Mary? Not afraid of me, are you?'

'No, sir,' she almost shouted, trying to inch her body away from his. If only the children would come back now . . .

'Well, that's a good start. I prefer my girls to like me. No reason to be afraid of me, is there? I've noticed you since the first day. Something standoffish about you and yet vulnerable. I like that. You're loyal, too. Wouldn't deny your master a little kiss, would you?' And he held her head in his pink grasp and turned it towards him. The sickly sweet smell of his hair oil and his warm breath on her cheek nauseated her. She averted her face abruptly, but not before his stiff moustache had encountered her by now scarlet cheek, scraping across her skin as she turned, leaving a white weal, like a snail's trail, across the flushed surface. The hand turned her face towards him again, while the other slid over her breast.

At that instant the children came dancing down the path, their stomach clocks telling them it was time for tea. Whether they had seen or heard anything, Mary didn't know, but she had never been so glad to see them.

The master quickly stood up and greeted his children with composure. 'Well, my dears, thought I'd surprise you and pick you up today. So, have you had fun?'

'Yes, Father! We played hide-and-seek and Mary couldn't find us,' James laughed.

'She never can,' retorted Emily, pulling a face at Mary.

'Well, I'm glad to hear you've enjoyed yourselves. Now let's go home for tea.'

As the trio retreated, Mary was left sitting alone, as if she had never existed. How dare he! she thought. If he thinks that my being his servant gives him the right to kiss me, he can think again. She still felt imprisoned by the pink hands and shuddered, jumping to her feet. She must get away from this place, she thought, her heart racing as she ran all the way to Mrs Moynihan's house.

'God help us! What's the matter with you, luv? You're as white as a ghost.' Mrs Moynihan put her arms round the heaving shoulders and fairly marched the little figure down the narrow hallway into the kitchen. 'Now, just sit down and tell me all about it,' she soothed, gently pushing Mary down into the one comfortable chair. 'You bairns go outside and play till I tell you to come in. Me and Mary wants a bit o' peace and quiet,' and she waved the children off as if with a broom. They vanished instantly; they knew when their mother meant business. 'Now, that's got rid o' them. Tell me what's happened, hinny.'

Mary's voice shook as she related the incident in the park.

'The filthy bugger! Interferin' with young lasses. I knowed there was somethin' smelly about that butcher-boy story – butcher boy, my aunt Fannie! I'll bet every penny I have it was him. Probably has a go at all o' them. You're not goin' back there if I have to tie you down to stop you, an' I'm goin' to have it out with both o' them an' all. About time somebody put a stop to his hanky-pankyin'.'

'Oh, no! Please, Mrs Moynihan, don't say anything. I'll lose my job. I'll just have to make sure I'm never alone with him in future.'

'Listen, luv, no job's worth puttin' up with a swine like that. You should o' told him where to get off, master or no master. An' do you mean to say you think you can keep out o' his way livin' in the same house with him? He'll be after you again, I'm tellin' you. I'm goin' to get Jack up now,' she announced, standing up. 'It's about time he was up anyhow; he'll go round to the house an' get your things afore he goes to work. You're not goin' back to that place, an' that's that.'

'My things! Oh, no! I left my coat in the park. I was in such a hurry to get here, I didn't think.'

'Well, don't worry yoursel' about the coat, luv. It'll probably still be there. I'll get Jack to have a look afore he goes to the house. An' even if it's gone, we'll get you another one.'

Mary burst into uncontrollable sobs. 'But the pin's in the lapel, my mother's pin.'

'Oh! Me poor bairn. Jack!' she yelled into the bedroom. 'Get your shiftless carcass in here. You've gotta go to the park, quickstick.'

Jack appeared at the kitchen doorway, heavy-eyed, his burly frame bent, awkwardly pulling on his overalls over his linings, the undergarment he wore day and night. His blond hair was tousled and his bland, good-looking face puffy from sleep.

'What's goin' on? Is the house on fire? Can you not let a poor bugger get his sleep? I'll be on all night, you know.'

But on hearing the news, he put his arm round Mary and the familiar smell of the greasy overalls comforted her.

'I'll be back afore you can say Jack Robinson with your coat an' the pin, an' I'll get the rest o' your stuff from the house, luv. An' he'll be bloody lucky if I don't give him a punch in the nose an' all.' His square jaw thrust forward, he marched out, slamming the door behind him in his indignation and muttering, 'Dirty swine.'

'Jack'll sort things out for you, hinny. An' now I'll mash a cup o' tea – best cheer in the world – an' then I've got bacon and cabbage soup ready for you when you feel like it.'

'I'd love a cup of tea, but no soup, thank you. My stomach feels sort of queasy.'

'Aye, gettin' upset causes that, luv, and to think I had somethin' to do with gettin' you the job. I could kick mesel', an' I'm surprised our Lottie didn' know what he was like with the maids. Well, what's done's done! Here's your tea, love; this'll cheer you up.'

Mary took the cup and, despite herself, a smile started at the corners of her mouth. 'Your remedy for everything, Mrs M.' Then she paused thoughtfully and added, 'It was Mother's as well,' the smile waning and tears threatening again.

Mrs Moynihan sat opposite her. 'Aye, hinny, she liked her cup o' tea an' all. Greatest comforter there is, asides a glass o' whisky o' course.'

Mary stirred her tea absently, before saying, almost pleadingly: 'Do you think things are ever going to go right for me, Mrs M.? My first job and I've lost it in a few months. Not that I liked it much, but at least I was independent.' She grimaced. 'Roseanne would have a good laugh – I'm not even clever enough to keep a maid's job.'

'Now don't let your mind dwell on that bitch an' what she might think. You left o' your own accord because the master was a pig. She *married* her pig – schemin' little bitch. I'm glad you're not clever like that, luv.'

'At least she ended up with money and a rather grand roof over her head.' Mary put her cup down on the hearth, her hands shaking again at the image of Roseanne taking Mother's place in their home. 'You know, Mrs M.,' she paused, and her voice shook as she continued, 'it's strange that it didn't occur to me earlier, but it's been in my mind a lot recently that if it hadn't been for Roseanne, Mother might still be alive today. If she hadn't had to work so hard . . .'

Mrs Moynihan sighed. 'Aye, well, there's no point in torturin' yoursel' about that, hinny. If it was the will o' God she would have gone anyway. You've just got to start thinkin' about yoursel' now, an' your own life. An' you've no need to worry about a roof over your head, hinny. I've kept your bed and this is your roof. So long as I'm here you'll never go without a home and food in your belly. You can always look for another job when you feel like it, but in the meantime, you can just help me out like before.'

'Thank you, Mrs M., but I'm upset about having to lean on you again. And I'm worried about the pin; my mother treasured it so much.'

'Why, Jack'll get that back for you, luv. I know what it means to you.'

Just then Jack returned with Mary's few clothes in her small travelling bag. 'I got all your stuff from the house. They were both out but I'm goin' round the morrow to give him a piece o' me mind.'

'My coat?' Mary inquired, holding her breath.

'I'm sorry, luv. Some bugger's lifted it.'

Chapter Six

Mary gratefully allowed herself to be taken over by Mrs Moynihan a second time. She felt safe in the hustle and bustle of life in the little flat. It seemed that wherever she went there were children under her feet or piercing her eardrums with their incessant, high-pitched shrieks. And she was for ever wiping running noses, washing dirty hands, and settling childish squabbles. But she and Mrs Moynihan and Molly had a couple of quiet hours each evening after Jack had left for work and the young ones were in bed, when Mary would usually scan the evening paper looking for jobs.

'Any luck, Mary?' Molly asked as a matter of form, the answer being evident from Mary's face. Molly put her thin arms round Mary's neck, her large blue eyes caring. 'I don't know why you're worryin' so much about gettin' a job. You know we like havin' you here.'

Although now twelve, Molly still looked like the scrawny little urchin of Mary's early days at Beauchamps Street. She had Jack's blond hair and her mother's wide mouth. Still, there was a promise of beauty behind her spindly, fragile look, and she was just beginning to fill out a little.

Mary addressed Mrs Moynihan, who was sitting cradling a tin mug of cocoa by the fire: 'I can't go on any longer without paying something. I do wish you would use that money; it's not doing any good lying under the mattress.'

'Aye, well, it will some day, hinny. You help enough in the house and with the bairns to earn your keep, such as it is. That money's for if you have an emergency an' I don't see any emergencies around here. There's only nine quid, hinny, an' there might be a day when you'll need it more than you do now. God forbid, though.'

On 4 August 1914, Britain and Germany were at war. The previous day Moltke had secured the dispatch of an ultimatum to France and a note to Belgium demanding free passage of German troops. This allowed Lord Grey to base his demands for intervention upon the protection of Britain's traditional interests, thus fuelling British patriotism. Most of the able-bodied men from the factories, shipyards and pits were volunteering. Jack, of course, was among the first to go.

He arrived home from work late one day just a little bit tipsy, staggering slightly through the kitchen door. 'Well, I done it,' he announced as he sat down heavily in the chair, taking off his boots. 'I hate to leave you all to manage on your own but if I don't go, where will we be?' There was grease on his hair and face and his blue eyes were slightly bloodshot.

'You look a right mess, Jack,' was Mrs Moynihan's only reaction. 'Did you have to get drunk afore you could do it?'

'No, lass, me and the lads just had a couple of pints afterwards. A funny sort o' celebration, eh? We're not going to let them buggers get away with it if we've got anythin' to do with it. So what do you think? I'm now Private Jack Moynihan of His Majesty's Armed Forces, Durham Light Infantry Brigade.'

'Aye, I thought it would be the infantry for you – you'd have to be right up in the front lines wouldn't you?' But there was pride in his wife's voice. 'When do you go?'

'I report for boot camp the morrow mornin'. They just let us home to see our families afore we left.'

'Well,' said Mrs Moynihan, standing up. 'I'd better get you a clean body shirt and press your suit. You're going to report lookin' a bit smarter than you do now – shamin' your missus like that.'

'Don't be bloody daft, lass. I'll be straight into me new uniform and anyhow I'd probably never see me suit again. I can't wait to give that bloody Kaiser some stick. England's a civilised country. The Liberals were just startin' to make things better for us ordinary folk, and now that bloody maniac goes an' starts a flamin' war.' Jack thumped his fist on the table. 'We'll settle their hash – Kitchener and the Durham Light Infantry together. Those buggers'll learn what happens when they threaten Geordies. Just wait till I get over there and get my hands on them.'

The following morning, breakfast was a silent affair, broken only by Mrs Moynihan's even more than usually cheerful voice booming: 'More porridge, Jack? You're going to need some energy for boot camp; they'll be marchin' you off your feet. And our Jimmy, eat that bread an' jam up an' stop playin' with it.' They were all going to miss Jack.

Mary was dismayed about the war, but at least there were more jobs open to women now. There were posters everywhere with a picture of a fine looking woman in an overall, saying, 'On her their lives depend. Women munition workers. Enrol at once!' Mary couldn't wait to find work and help Mrs Moynihan; pitiable though Jack's wages had been, the money from the War Office was even less. Finally, she convinced Mrs Moynihan to break into the little treasure trove under the mattress, and week by week it dwindled to help keep the family adequately fed and clothed.

It took Mary two months to find a job. For the

heavy work such as welding, employers were looking for strong women who could handle heavy machinery, and for the lighter jobs such as testing, they were using older people with more experience. After many disappointments, she found a job at Jack's old factory, Newfield, Black and Company, checking and sorting nuts and bolts as they came off the assembly line. She awaited her first day with some trepidation – she didn't even know the difference between a nut and a bolt.

The day turned out to be just as bad as she'd expected. Although she'd left extra early, she couldn't get on a tram, so crowded were they with factory workers, and she arrived with only five minutes to spare. Wearing the regulation dark blue wrap-round overall she'd bought, she followed a crowd of women to the sorting shop her interviewer had assigned her to. She grimaced as she looked around. It was just like the convent, everyone in uniform.

'Hey, hinny,' a loud female voice boomed over the clatter of the conveyor belt wheels, 'this is *my* spot. Go further down a bit. And while you're at it, you'd better tie up that hair afore the foreman sees you or you'll be in big trouble. They don't want no accidents here, hinny. Not that they care a bugger about us, but accidents cost money, you know.'

'Oh, thank you. I completely forgot.' Mary quickly retrieved from her pocket the scarf she'd bought for the purpose and tied up her shoulder-length hair turban fashion. The short bob had almost grown out but her hair wasn't yet quite long enough to pin up as was the fashion of the day.

It wasn't until tea break that she had time to take a breath and look around her. Her fingers were numb from handling the cold metal objects and her head felt dizzy from the constant movement of the conveyor belt. The interior brick walls and stone floor accentuated the clamour of voices and the clatter of the machinery. Thank God it was only the sorting shop; it was impossible to talk at all in the assembly shop. She got through the first day somehow and flopped into the armchair when she got home.

'How did it go, luv? You look done in.' Mrs Moynihan was unbuttoning Mary's boots as she spoke.

'Oh, thank you.' She sighed with relief as the big woman heaved off the heavy boots and rubbed the circulation back into the numb toes, then tears that she had kept back all day suddenly freed themselves and tumbled down her cheeks.

'It was awful,' she sobbed, 'worse than being a maid. I don't know if I'll be able to stand it.'

'Why then, hinny, don't go back.'

'It's all right saying that, but I've got to earn my living somehow and what else can I do? Besides, I'm lucky they put me in the sorting shop; the assembly shop is even harder work and much noisier.'

'Aw, hinny, you don't have to stick it if you hate it that much.'

'No, I'll give it a fair trial. I might grow to like it more, or at least mind it less, when I'm better at it and when I get to know some of the girls. I was so tired during breaks today that I hid myself away; I didn't want to have to talk to anyone.'

'Why aye, lass! Once you make some friends it'll be more fun. That's the spirit! But remember, you don't have to stay if you don't want to. Now dry those tears and I'll get you your dinner. The kids have all had theirs and they're out in the back lane. It's cabbage soup again, I'm afraid. Things are getting harder to find in the shops; they didn't have no bacon at the grocer's an' he said when it does come in next week it'll be up again by another tuppence a pound. Bloody war! As if things weren't hard enough afore. Come on, luv, have your dinner now and have an early night. You'll need it for the morrow.'

'Yes, I will. Standing sorting and counting all day is boring and tiring. It's not part of the job to count but I want to make sure I fill my daily quota or I'll be out on my neck whether I want to be or not, and my hands are slow; it's so cold in there. And anyway, whenever I stopped counting I started thinking about Mother and how unhappy she would have felt at my working there. She had such grand ambitions for me.'

'Aye, she wanted the best for you, hinny. But she would have done the same without complainin'. Factory work's no picnic for nobody, hinny, but when you meet some nice lasses, a good chin-wag'll help to pass the time, an' you're lucky you get breaks an' half day Saturdays; most o' those places only have one stop for dinner an' work till five on Saturdays. Our Jack never got a tea break in the weldin' shop an' he never got home afore six any night o' the week. O' course he got paid more for the extra hours, but still it was hard on him.'

'I heard we get lighter treatment because a lot of women were fainting from standing still all day; they finally decided there would be less time lost and fewer mistakes made if they gave the women two five-minute tea breaks. It's not long enough for me though,' she sighed.

Again the next morning she just made it in time and sneaked quickly to her place on the belt. By midmorning the monotony caused her mind to wander, thoughts of her mother crowding her consciousness and tears blurring her eyes. She lost count several times and once she put a bolt on the nut belt, hastily running down the line to try to make good her error. The foreman didn't miss the incident.

'Dreamin', eh lass? If you don't want the job, there's plenty would like to take your place.' But he was kindly enough in his gruff way. His middle-aged, leathery, work-lined face had a gentleness about it and his eyes were a soft, deep brown. He seemed to notice that she was tired and nervous and let her go to early tea break. 'Take the weight off your feet a bit, lass; you look as though you could do with a break.'

'Thank you, Mr Cowley,' Mary said, gratefully retiring to one of the benches near the tiny stove in the centre of the shop where two large kettles were boiling. Mrs Moynihan had prepared her sandwiches and put two teaspoons of tea in her canteen, an enamel carrying can. All Mary had to do was add water and two spoons of the condensed milk she carried in her pocket in an old Vaseline jar, and for the afternoon break she simply added more water to the can. She didn't like the sweet, sticky tinned milk, but they were lucky they could afford to eat as well as they did. Her wages were only a few paltry shillings a week, but together with the money from the War Office and the diminishing hoard under the mattress, the family didn't starve, although they had to have at least three meatless days a week now, meat being so scarce and so expensive.

Some of the girls joined her.

'What's your name, luv? Saw you yesterday but you were so busy with your head down an' with the gaffer keepin' his eye on you, we didn't get a chance to introduce you to the welcome committee. Old Cowley always keeps his eyes on the new lasses the first day to see if they're up to scratch. I'm Maggie.'

'I'm Mary Maddison. I saw you yesterday, too,' Mary said, relieved finally to have someone to talk to.

'Why, get a load o' that voice, girls. Where're you from?'

'Well, I used to live near Carlisle but I've lived in Newcastle for four and a half years now.'

'How did you learn to talk like that in Carlisle? They

haven't got plums in their mouths there.' Maggie's tone was mocking.

'Oh, it's a long story, too long to go into during tea break,' Mary said, embarrassed.

'Come down in the world, have you, mixin' with the riff-raff in a factory?' Keeping her gaze riveted on Mary, Maggie addressed her friends: 'Well, what do you know, girls! She's one o' those toffee-nosed volunteers just doin' her bit for the war effort, sacrificin' hersel' to save the country an' doin' folks that needs work out o' jobs.'

'Maggie, get off her,' one of the others said.

Maggie turned her round, rosy face to the group beside her, her blonde curls peeking out untidily from beneath the blue scarf. It was a pretty, full-blown face, which matched her ample, curvaceous form. And the bold blue eyes and commanding voice left no doubt that she was a leader. 'Aye, I'll get off her all right. I don't want nothin' to do with folks that thinks they're better than the rest of us.' With that, she turned her back on Mary and the group departed to the other bench.

Sitting alone, Mary lowered her head and bit her lip. Make friends here? Mrs Moynihan was out of her mind. It was worse than being at school again. Would she always be an outsider? She was glad when the bell rang and she had to return to the bench.

A week went by and the girls, following Maggie's example, continued mainly to ignore her, though occasionally Maggie would throw a remark in Mary's direction, such as, 'Look at poshy workin' fifty to the dozen, there. She's tryin' to make us look slow. Tryin' to impress the gaffer with your free labour, hinny?'

Mary set her face and tried to ignore the remarks, but inside she was boiling up. One day at tea break, Maggie flounced past her, knocking Mary's tea mug out of her hand, the hot tea spilling onto her lap.

'Look out you clumsy idiot,' she screamed.

'Oops, sorry, madam, but I'm sure you can afford another cup o' tea.'

'No, I cannot! I'm working here for my living just the same as you and I'm sick and tired of your attitude just because I sound different. I can't help where I was born. If you think I'm doing this for fun, you're crazy; I'm doing it because I have to eat.'

'Why, listen to that, lasses; she's got a temper an' all. Spunky, eh? Well, nobody talks to little Maggie like that, you know.'

'That's just where you're wrong, little Maggie, *I do*, and stop treating me as though I come from the moon.'

'You mean you're not just doing this work for a noble cause, like them pious Salvation Army lasses, an' them pompous, rich-bitch volunteers that don't need the money?' Maggie's tone was more serious now.

'No, I'm bloody well not. I hate this dump, I hate this job, and I hate stuck up people.'

'Stuck up! You're a fine one to call people stuck up.'

'No! *You're* the stuck up ones. You ignore me because you think I'm different and you can't stand anybody who's different from you in any way. You don't even give people a chance.' Mary's face was pink with indignation.

'Eey, well, maybe we did get you wrong, hinny. We thought you wouldn't want nothin' to do with rabble like us.'

'Well, you thought wrong and—' Just then the bell went and Mary stood up. 'Oh, forget it.' She screwed her mug back on to her canteen and went back to her place on the bench seething. This was just like school all over again, and that Maggie was just as bad as Annie Hattie. She thought of the writing on the school wall episode and felt like making up a rhyme about

Maggie to write all over the factory walls. She grimaced. She was supposed to be grown up now, but then so were Maggie and her gang and they didn't behave much like grown-ups either.

Mr Cowley was around for the rest of the morning and at lunch break Mary secreted herself in her usual place on the bench in the corner, intending to keep herself to herself. She was eating her sardine sandwich when Maggie and the girls approached.

'We've been lookin' for you, hinny. Look, this is hard for me to say, but I just wanted to tell you that we're sorry we made a mistake about you. We really thought you were just puffin' out your chest an' helpin' the war effort; we didn't know you had to work fo' your livin' like us. It really doesn't make no difference that you talk different.'

Mary swallowed her last mouthful of sandwich. 'I'm used to it. I used to get this all the time at school.'

'Which school did you go to then?' Maggie asked, genuinely curious.

'Saint Joseph's.'

'Eey, well I never! I went there, but that was five years ago now. Look, let me introduce you to the girls,' she boomed. 'This here's Lilly,' pointing a chubby finger to her second-in-command, a plain, plump redhead, whose face was covered in freckles.

'Hello, luv, welcome to the sweatshop. Don't worry, the first few years are the worst – if you survive them, like.'

'And these two are Edna and Enid, or Enid and Edna, whichever you like.' Maggie pointed to two identical, dark-haired, pale, thin girls, their four serious brown eyes set on Mary.

'How do you do,' Mary said, wondering how she'd ever be able to tell the twins apart.

'Don't worry, hinny,' one of them reassured her. 'Everybody gets mixed up when they first know us.

I'm Edna; you can tell by my mole.' She pointed to a small brown spot on her left cheek.

'Aye, but sometimes I paint one on and we swap places on the belt – drives the gaffer mad,' said the other. 'We answer to both names, so don't worry if you get us mixed up.'

'So, what brings you to a dump like this?' Maggie sat down beside Mary on the bench and the others joined her.

'Well, the story's too long to bore you with the details, but we lost our home in Carlisle when my grandfather died, and then my mother died,' she bit her lip to stem the inevitable tears whenever she mentioned her mother, 'and now I'm living with a neighbour,' she finished.

'Why, little orphan Annie! That's a shame! I've still got me ma and da, though sometimes I could do without them,' Lilly said. 'Have you got a boy friend, hinny?'

'No.'

'Neither has she,' Maggie interrupted, 'though she never gives up tryin'.'

'You can talk.' Edna gave Maggie a freezing glance and then turned to Mary. 'We're all on the hunt, hinny. A good man is hard to find, especially now with the best ones away in the war.'

'Look out, lasses,' Maggie cut in before Mary could speak. 'Old Cowley's givin' us the eye; we'd better get back to the coal mines. Move your place up nearer us, hinny; it's more fun than down there at the end. We have a good laugh an' a giggle now an' then.'

Mary gladly followed them; she had finally been accepted. Their company was certainly more cheerful than her present neighbours, who all had boy friends or husbands at the front. They talked of little else but the war and spent their tea and lunch breaks knitting scarves and Balaclava helmets, or writing letters, most of which never reached their destinations.

'Won't the foreman mind?' she asked, as she squeezed herself in at the belt beside her new friends.

'No, he won't say nothin' so long as you keep your head down an' your hands busy. He's all right, really,' Maggie assured her.

The rest of that day went fast for Mary as she listened to the girls' bawdy gossip about men, and it helped to keep her mind from dwelling on her mother's death.

Maggie, of course, talked most of the time. 'Well, you know, I could've gone for that old sod at the Bull last night, but I have me limits. Anythin' between fourteen an' forty is all right with me, but that one was pushin' sixty, give a day or two. Oh, for the days when the pubs was crowded with pit lads an' real men.'

'If you weren't interested, why did you egg him on an' let him buy you a drink?' That was either Edna or Enid; Mary couldn't see the mole from where she stood.

'A girl has to survive, hasn't she? I was dyin' for another port and lemon an' I didn't have no money left except fo' me tram fare. An' I paid him well enough by chattin' him up; he probably went back to his wife an' gave her a right good time, all the time with a picture of me in his head. She'd probably have been grateful if she knew.' Maggie chuckled. 'When the old sods get to that age they get their appetites outside but they have to eat at home.'

'Why haven't you got a boy friend, luv?' Mary thought the question came from Lilly but couldn't be sure above the noise. It was difficult talking with your head down.

'I don't know any boys,' she said.

'Ever had one, luv?' That was definitely Maggie's strident tones.

'No.'

'What! Never?' Maggie sounded incredulous.
'Why, you'd better come with us to the Old Ass one
o' these nights, luv, an' learn all about the wicked ways
of men. An' even if there's nobody there worth havin',
it's always good for a belly laugh at least.'

'The Old Ass, what's that?' Mary inquired,
laughing.

'The Old Assembly Rooms, luv. Eey, where've you
been? Everybody knows the Old Ass, the best dance
hall in town. The Army's taken it over as headquarters
now, but they still allow the ballroom to be used for
a dance on Saturdays to make money for the war
effort. Never mind that old bugger Hobson, we can
at least drink and dance an' enjoy ourselves. Folks
won't let him get away with it; they want more, not
less of them things. What does he call them? Oh, yes:
"emollients, sports, and distractions",' she enunciated
carefully.

'Oh, thanks anyway, but I can't dance.' Mary
thought that would be the end of the idea, but she was
wrong.

'Well then, we'll have to learn you. First lesson this
dinner time.' Maggie's voice was adamant. 'And that's
that!'

'I suppose I have no choice,' Mary laughed. 'I'm
outnumbered four to one.'

And so the dancing lessons began and continued to
the end of the week. But Mary was reluctant about the
impending Saturday night dance.

'You're a grown lass, hinny,' Mrs Moynihan told
her. 'You can't sit about the house every night. You're
only young once and you should be havin' a good time
while you can. Why don't you go with the lasses from
work? They sound all right. Mind you, that doesn't
mean I think you should cavort yoursel' the way they
do, but you could go with them and have a dance. But
mind you catch the last tram home. When the war's

over you'll find yoursel' some nice young lad and
you'll have to know how to dance when you go
courtin'.'

'Oh, I'd love to learn to dance properly, but I'd
really rather go to classes. I can't imagine just stepping
on to a dance floor with a total stranger the way I am
now; I've barely learned to waltz and I'm completely
confused by the two-step – I'd be too embarrassed.'

'Well, that's how I learned, hinny, just got on that
dance floor and did it. Nearly wet me knickers with
fright the first time, but I soon learned. That's settled,
then. You're goin' with them on Saturday.'

When Mrs Moynihan said something was settled, it
was settled. That Saturday evening, Mary dressed in
her best blue dress and a new pair of high-heeled dancing pumps. Mrs Moynihan had insisted on the new
shoes. 'You can't go dancin' in them heavy boots. I'll
go to town the morrow and get you a couple o' pairs
to try. They know me at the shop so they'll let me have
them on spec.'

The black leather pumps Mary had chosen were a
little tight and she wobbled on the unaccustomed high
heels. She looked thoughtfully at herself in the
cracked, full-length mirror which had been the reci-
pient of many a childish missile. Mrs Moynihan
glowed. 'Eey, lass, you look a right picture. It's a treat
to see you out o' that overall. You're gettin' a figure
on you just like your ma's.' Mary blushed and dropped
her shoulders, and Mrs Moynihan braced them back.
'Don't do that, hinny. You want to show them bosoms
off; I would if I had a pair like them.'

It was true, Mary was rounding out, and her tiny
waist accentuated the new, curving lines of her body.

'I hope I'm not going to change any more,' she said.
'Men look at me and it's embarrassing.'

'Why, hinny, it's nothing to be embarrassed about;
it's natural. You've got your ma's hourglass figure,

hinny, and she always held hersel' proud. She wasn't ashamed to have curves.'

'That's true,' Mary acknowledged, straightening her shoulders again.

'That's better! Now I'm just going to put a bit o' rouge on them pale cheeks and you'll be the belle o' the ball.'

Mary was nervous but more than a little excited at the thought of the new experience. As arranged, she met the girls outside the Old Assembly Rooms.

'We're not goin' in there yet; it's hardly movin',' Maggie said. 'Let's go to the White Boar and have a port an' lemon till things liven up a bit. I could do with a drink, at any rate. And I expect our Mary here could do with a bit o' Dutch courage. How you feelin', luv? I know I was all goosepimply me first night.'

'Well, I *am* nervous, but I don't drink. And, anyway, I can't go into pubs yet.'

'Eey, listen to that,' Maggie said impatiently. 'With your looks you can go anywhere you want. Nobody's goin' to bother to ask how old you are once they get an eyeful o' that pretty mug o' yours. At any rate, Charlie knows us, so don't worry.'

Charlie welcomed them as they entered the pub: 'Why, hello, me bonnie lasses! What can I do for you tonight? The usual?' His friendly brown eyes under the bushy black brows took in Mary at a glance over the bar.

'Why aye, Charlie, an' one extra,' Maggie grinned.

'Aye, I see you've got a new friend. Bit young to be feedin' her port an' lemons, isn't she?'

'Go on, Charlie, she'll be all right. We're her bodyguards,' Maggie smiled persuasively.

'Now, I wouldn't mind havin' you fo' my bodyguards, but I wouldn't think you'd do her much good. She's a right bonnie lass; you'd better watch out she doesn't steal all the lads away from you.'

'I can look out fo' mesel', Charlie. Never noticed me havin' any trouble afore, did you?' Maggie winked and fluttered her eyelashes.

'All right, me luvs, five port an lemons comin' up. You'll get the coppers on to this establishment yet.'

Mary sipped the illicit beverage. She didn't care for the taste and it made her head feel funny – the noisy chatter in the pub seemed to get louder at each sip. Maggie eyed her with amusement. 'I think our Mary's havin' a job with that port. Here, luv, I'll help you.' She relieved Mary of her glass and downed the contents in one gulp. 'Let's go; things should be hoppin' about now.'

Mary was glad to be out in the night air, but not for long; the dance hall was now very crowded and ten times noisier than the pub. The band was playing a two-step; the saxophone droned while the singer crooned sentimentally about 'the boys over there' and the drums thumped in the background. Mary's head thumped with them and she wished the lights would go down and hide her flushed cheeks. Mercifully, the dance finished, the crowd dispersed, and the lights dimmed; the band was easing into a waltz. Mary sank into a chair by the wall and tried to become invisible. The swaying figures on the floor reminded her of the times she had sat on the landing peeking through the banisters, watching her mother dance at the big parties at the house. Oh, if only she could teach me now, she thought, closing her eyes in despair.

'Hey! Mary, get your arse off that chair and stand here with us.' It was Lilly, looking just as plain and plump in her best pink cotton dress as she did in her overalls. But she was a jolly girl who, according to the girls' stories, had much success with the men, despite her lack of good looks. 'Nobody's goin' to see you if you don't show yoursel',' she added.

The crew were assembled in line at the edge of the

dance floor, big smiles on their faces and invitations in their eyes.

Mary recoiled. 'I think I'll just sit this one out and watch.'

'Suit yoursel', but you'll never get nowhere hidin' over there,' said Maggie.

Almost before the words were out of her mouth, a dark shadow obscured Mary's view. 'Do you want to dance?' the shadow asked.

'Er, no, thank you. I'm sitting this one out.'

'I wouldn't mind a break mesel'. Do you mind if I sit it out with you?' The dark form took possession of the neighbouring chair.

'No, that's all right.' Mary muttered the polite words while her mind said, 'please, God, don't let him talk to me.' But the shadow persisted.

'Do you come here often?'

'No, this is my first time.'

'Thought so. Haven't seen you afore. I noticed you comin' in.'

Maggie and the girls watched the scene. 'Well, would you believe it, our Mary's got off already,' Maggie said, not without a touch of envy in her voice, 'and *we're* supposed to be learnin' *her*.'

Edna, looking as thin and pale and serious as ever, broke in, 'Let the lass alone; she's doin' better than all of us put together, even though it's her first time.'

The dark shape leaned towards Mary. 'Will you have the next one then?'

'Well, to tell the truth, I can't dance.'

'That's nothin'; neither can I, much, but I'll learn you what I know.'

'Well, all right. Thank you,' was all Mary could say. The waltz continued and she fixed her eyes straight ahead on the dance floor, dreading the moment when the dancers would stop and the music change.

'Come on then, it's another waltz.' As the lights

went up, the shadow straightened, and Mary noticed for the first time that it was composed of a dark blue suit and tie, relieved only by a light blue shirt and a glowing red face. She followed obediently. He grasped her round the waist, holding one hand and pushing her back and forth and round and round dizzily.

'What do you do?' he asked.

'Do? Oh, I work at Newfield, Black, checking nuts and bolts.'

'Oh, aye. I had a mate who used to work there once. Got the sack because he never clocked in on time, always gallivantin' every night. I work at Bensons.'

'Bensons?'

'Aye, sausage meat. I chop the meat and put it through the machines so it comes out in the skins.'

Mary closed her eyes. That's what it was! She'd been trying to define the subtle but perceptible odour emanating from him. *He smelled of sausage meat*. She stifled a smile, despite the fact that he was treading on her toes for the umpteenth time and was continuing to push her in circles till she felt dizzy and faint. Her poor feet began to feel like sausage meat themselves, pounded and pumped into mulch inside the tight skins of her new shoes. At last the dance ended.

'Thank you for the dance. I have to go now,' Mary gasped.

'Will you have the next one?'

'I'd like to, but I must go, and I have to say goodbye to my friends first.'

The girls were taking leave of their partners.

'Well, you did all right! At least he was under forty. What was he like?' Maggie asked Mary, again enviously.

'He smelled of sausage meat and he couldn't dance any better than I could, but he was nice enough.'

'Are you goin' to dance with him again? I wouldn't

turn me nose up at sausage meat; I've danced with worse smells than that, I can tell you. Who do you think you are to be so fussy, Mary?' Maggie asked a trifle angrily.

'I'm not being fussy, really; I just have to go home now. I'm tired and my feet hurt.'

'Hey, don't go now, Joe's here. You know, old Cowley's son. I saw him watchin' you on the dance floor. Bet you a pound to a penny he asks you to dance.' Lilly's red curls bobbed with excitement.

'If I was you, I wouldn' throw up a chance like that,' joined in Maggie, her eyes gleaming almost as much as her bright hair, and this time her envious tone was unmistakable. 'But suit yoursel'. When you go, the more chance we've got, eh lasses?'

Mary couldn't bear the thought of another ordeal on the dance floor. 'No, I must go home now, but thank you all for a nice evening.'

She trailed to the tram stop and leaned gratefully against the cool post, her swollen feet feeling as though they were bursting out of her tight shoes. So that's dancing, she thought, in the dim gaslight, looking down ruefully at the bruised and battered leather.

Chapter Seven

Monday morning at the factory began as Mary had expected: the girls teased her. Maggie, in fine form, was enjoying the attention of her audience, grouped outside the shop door where it was easier to talk. 'You should have seen our Mary – the belle o' the ball. But what do you think she goes and does? Afore the stroke o' midnight she does her Cinderella act and, poof! She's off! What's the matter, luv, scared o' success? I would have given me back teeth for a shuffle with sausage skins.'

Mary smiled. 'He really did smell of sausage.'

'What's wrong with that then? It's better than fish,' Lilly piped in her shrill voice, holding her nose between her thumb and forefinger.

They all laughed and Maggie put her arm round Mary's shoulder, saying sadly, 'Why, the poor bairn didn't have a good time with us. What a shame!'

'No, really,' Mary countered, 'I did enjoy myself, but it was so hot, and those lights, and my feet hurt. I'm very grateful you took me, though. I didn't—'

Edna interrupted, grinning. 'Well, hinny, don't worry. At least when you left we had less competition; I ended up with a smelter from Beth Steelworks – he was red-hot all right! We had a great smooching session in the back lane but, just my luck, me gran came out to go to the privy and caught us at it. That put the fire out, I can tell you! I thought she was goin' to tip the bucket over him. He fizzled out like a wet firecracker and scarpered down the lane as if the devil was after him.'

The outburst of laughter dwindled to a few smothered giggles as Mr Cowley came to investigate the uproar. 'Why, I'm right glad to hear you're all happy at your work, but how about gettin' your happy little bodies to your benches? It's Monday mornin' and two minutes past seven. Your weekend's over!'

The girls sobered their expressions and quickly slipped into their places – all, that is, except Maggie. She put her hands on her hips and undulated to her bench, her ample buttocks rising and falling exaggeratedly with each step. As she passed the foreman, who was beginning to look extremely uncomfortable, she winked and tilted her face to one side. 'Mr Cowley, why don't you come with us one o' these weekends? I'm sure you'd enjoy yoursel' no end, an' it would give you somethin' to talk about asides work.'

Mr Cowley composed himself and straightened to his full five feet nine inches. 'That's enough o' your lip, Maggie. Watch out or you might find yoursel' without any work, and you can talk about your weekend all week – in your own time.'

'Just kiddin', boss. Keep your wool on.' Maggie knew when she'd gone far enough.

'Well,' Enid said, 'you almost flummoxed him that time. But I'd be careful o' that one if I was you. You're not goin' to get round him that easy.'

'Didn't do so bad for a first shot, though, did I?' Maggie retorted gaily, nevertheless quickly making her way towards her place on the belt.

'Maggie,' Mary shouted, trying to make herself heard above the noise, her hands already busy sorting an avalanche of nuts and bolts, 'he's a married man with a grown son, he's not for you.'

'Who said anythin' about old Cowley bein' fo' me?' Maggie shrieked back. 'But it doesn't hurt to be on

good terms with the gaffer, does it? I must admit I'd
rather have the son any day, though. He's a fine
lookin' fella, but even snootier than his old man. And
speakin' o' the devil . . .'

Heads rose as the one in question came into view.
Joe Cowley was tall and well-built; with blue eyes and
fair hair parted down the centre, he resembled his
father closely, except for his six-foot frame and the
fact that his good-looking face was still fresh and
alive. He hadn't yet been subjected to years of struggle and hard factory work, inching himself up from
labourer to foreman. The arduous process had griz-
zled his father's features, sallowed his skin, and bent
his back and spirit. Joe blushed under the scrutiny of
the rows of female eyes. 'I . . . I thought I saw my
father come in,' he said lamely.

'You did, right enough, luv,' Maggie said, enjoying
his embarrassment. 'What you obviously didn't see
was that he went out again.'

Joe's face flushed deeper. 'Do you know where he
went?' He was feeling rather foolish and at the mercy
of his female audience.

But Maggie, having a wonderful time teasing him,
was relentless. 'Perhaps he went to the lav, luv. Even
the boss has to do that sometimes, you know. An'
if he isn't there, you might try the office – he spends
enough time in there sippin' tea with the secretary.'

'I've tried the office, smarty,' Joe replied acidly,
asserting himself at last. Mary was delighted; it was
unkind of the girls to embarrass him. She'd noticed
him in passing before but this was the first time she'd
seen him close up. He was even more handsome than
she'd thought. 'It's not urgent, anyway,' Joe added. 'If
he comes back please tell him I'll see him at the canteen
at twelve.'

'Well now,' said Lilly, her face dreamy, 'he looks
like his da but he certainly doesn't talk like him.

Where'd he get that posh voice from? Doesn't sound right on him, with his da workin' in a factory an' his ma in a sweet shop.'

Enid was happy to supply the information. 'I heard they sent him to a posh school somewhere down south – their precious only son. He's come back to work here as an apprentice draughtsman till the war's over and then he's goin' to college.'

'For a quiet one you seem to know a lot,' said Maggie.

'Well, you see, Maggie, it's them that doesn't talk much that listens. If you kept your trap shut a bit more you might learn more yoursel'.'

'I know enough about what's good for little Maggie, an' I don't give a hoot about other people's gossip anyway.'

The sight of the manager, accompanied by two visiting factory inspectors, broke up the discussion, and the girls kept their heads down and worked in silence until the first tea bell sounded. Mary, as usual, took the early break. Glad, for once, to get away from the gang and their chatter, she found a quiet corner of the shop and sat on a wooden box marked 'bolts 3/4" dia., 1 gross'. Her heart was pounding and her head swimming. She'd only seen Joe a few times but, why, she wondered, did he always make her feel this way? It was the way she used to feel when she was summoned to the headmistress's office, or when she couldn't go to sleep on Christmas Eve because of the thought of the following morning's delights. She sipped the hot tea and wondered how feelings of dread and pleasure could be so similar. And why did she feel that palpitating pleasure when she saw *him* in particular? She'd seen many handsome men in her time. Her reveries were interrupted by the second tea bell.

'Hey, luv, are you all right? You've got a funny look about you.' Doreen, who had only started the job the week before, came over and put her hand on Mary's shoulder. 'I seen you hiding away in the corner there looking all washed out.' She had a pale, serious face, soft, brown eyes, and straight brown hair tied up neatly in a bun under her blue cotton scarf. Like Mary, she was an anomaly in the neighbourhood: she came from somewhere near London and didn't sound like the locals. Her father, a railway worker, had been transferred to Tyneside to work on the new branch lines on the main London to Newcastle route when the government had taken over the railways. They needed more lines to get the munitions down south. Although of a friendly, outgoing disposition, she spent most of her time, including her tea breaks, knitting gloves and scarves for her boyfriend at the front and writing numerous letters in the hope that some might reach him.

Mary was touched by her concern. 'No, I'm fine,' she assured her. 'I had a rather tiring weekend, that's all.'

'I don't think Saturday night dances are up your street, Mary. I'm taking my little brother roller-skating this Saturday afternoon. Why don't you come with us and bring one of the kids along? They'll be company for each other. It's good fun and you don't get pestered by dirty old men like at the dance hall.'

'I'd love to learn to skate, Doreen, thanks. I'll bring Jimmy.'

'See you at the rink at two then. We'd better get back now.'

Mary returned to her bench and worked feverishly to stop her questioning mind. She was grateful for Doreen's offer; it would be fun to learn to skate. Remembering her childhood desire to go ice-skating with her friends and her mother's disapproval of anything so dangerous as skating, she felt a pang of guilt. Well, Mother wasn't here to worry any more, she thought sadly. She forced her hands to move more quickly along the belt and started counting. The physical movement felt good and the counting kept her mind occupied.

'Hey! What's up with our Mary? Think you're workin' piece work, hinny? Carry on like that and we'll all be out o' work.' As usual it was Maggie's raucous voice above the din.

'Sorry, Maggie, I didn't realise I was going so fast; from now on I'll count five between each one.'

'Better make it ten,' Edna cut in. 'I'm not feelin' so perky mesel' after me weekend, but roll on the next one.'

The weekend did roll on. Before Mary knew it, the Saturday twelve o'clock siren sounded and the week had worked itself to a standstill. 'See you at two, then,' Doreen shouted as the throng jostled them out of the factory gates, some eager to get home to a hot meal, some eager to spend time with their loved ones, and some simply eager to get out of the factory gates for a day and a half of freedom.

There was a long queue at the tram stop and, just as Mary was about to squeeze on to the platform of the second one, the conductor put out his hand. 'Full up! One behind!' The one behind took almost ten minutes to arrive and there was standing room only. She jumped on and grabbed hold of a strap, determined not to be turned off this one or she'd be late for the rink. A hand touched her arm. 'Here, take my seat.'

Her stomach turned a somersault as she recognised the voice. Joe stood up, smiling. Flustered, she managed a 'Thank you'. He took her strap and loomed over her, endeavouring to keep his place despite the jostling of the boarding passengers. 'You ought to do what I do,' he shouted above the noise. 'I always walk down to the terminus; it takes a bit longer but at least you don't have to wait in the queue and you can always get on.'

Mary was glad she had to shout back; it disguised the tremor in her voice. 'That's a good idea, I'll try it next time.' She folded her arms tightly across her chest to subdue her thumping heart.

'I'm Joe Cowley. I've seen you at work.'

'Yes, I'm Mary Maddison; I've seen you too.'

'What's my father like to work under?' he said, laughing.

'Oh, very nice.'

His reply, if any, was drowned by the tram clanking and the conductor yelling, 'Fares please'. Mary was glad conversation was no longer possible; it was disconcerting enough to have his body swaying so closely over hers as the vehicle lurched and rattled its way through town.

'Green Street,' the conductor bellowed at last. It was her stop. She stood up.

'This is where I get off. Thank you for the seat.'

He took her arm to steady her. 'See you next week then, Mary.'

She squeezed herself on to the platform and jumped off just in time. There was no one waiting to get on and the tram had hardly crunched to a stop before the conductor blew his whistle and the ancient vehicle trundled on with its cargo of swaying bodies.

'I'm home!' Mary greeted Mrs Moynihan.

'Eey, luv, I thought somethin' had happened to you. Jimmy's been a pain in the neck thinkin' you'd changed your mind about skatin' the day.' As she spoke she was bending over the kitchen fire, poking with a wooden spoon the contents of a large white basin bobbing about in a blue enamelled pan, almost as blackened with soot as the trivet it rested on.

'Of course I haven't changed my mind,' Mary

answered, hastily untying her scarf. 'It took me half an hour to get on a tram.'

'Well, here, hinny, just get this into you; it's pease puddin' and saveloys. I've had a terrible time tryin' to keep it hot for you. We've all had ours. I'll just pop out and tell Jimmy you're home.'

Mary didn't need to be told what the meal was. Mrs Moynihan allowed herself one small treat a week: she bought the pre-cooked, steaming hot split peas and spicy sausage from the pork butcher every other Saturday for lunch. On the intervening Fridays, the treat was fish and chips for supper from the fried fish shop, but the real treat for Mrs Moynihan was that for one meal each week she didn't have to cook. However, she had announced that this would be the last week for the treats. 'You'll all just have to tighten your belts; there's a war on, you know, an' I'm not a miracle worker when it comes to makin' the money stretch. We can't afford to pay for cooked food any more.'

As she played with the thick mush, which stuck to the roof of her mouth like glue, Mary thought that the lack of pease pudding was one hardship she could endure, but the spicy sausage was warming and delicious. Remembering 'sausage skins' at the dance, she wondered if he'd made the saveloy and smiled at the thought.

Jimmy came bounding in and she had no more time to think. 'Hurry up, Mary, or we're goin' to be late.' His deep brown eyes were luminous with excitement at the thought of the treat. 'Me ma's given me thruppence for the skates and the tram and a ha'penny for a glass of lemonade.'

'Well, you give that right back to her, Jimmy. I'm treating you today,' she said, swallowing the remnants of the pease pudding.

Mrs Moynihan intervened: 'No, you can't do that, hinny. It's good enough o' you to take him without spendin' your own money as well.' Mrs Moynihan was emphatic, but Mary was learning how to get round her. 'All right, in that case I can take Molly as well,' she said firmly.

'All right, have your own way, but you're far too good to them bairns.'

'Not half so good as you are to me,' Mary said, putting her arms round the gaunt frame. She'd noticed that since Jack had been in the Army Mrs Moynihan was noticeably thinner and her shoulders were more stooped, but her vigour and good humour were unchanged.

The trio finally organised themselves and met Doreen and George at the skating rink. Jimmy and Molly took to the sport as if they'd been born on wheels, but Mary had to rely on Doreen's steadying arm, though after a while she was able to make tentative forays on her own. Hurtling bodies seemed to be charging at her from all directions, laughing as they collided and steadied themselves. Whenever she managed to find a clear path ahead of her she would propel herself gently into it, but it never remained hers for long. Inevitably the gap closed as fast as it had opened. The result was usually a scramble of clinging humanity or a multiple collision involving a mass of tangled arms and legs. Each accident added to her already ample collection of bruises and reinforced her growing conviction that her mother had been right – skating was a dangerous sport. She made her way gingerly, and with only one or two minor encounters, to the nearest exit. Passing Doreen on the way, she managed to convey to her that she was going to take a break for a cup of tea. Her new friend waved acknowledgement.

Mary unstrapped the vagabond wheels from her shoes, relieved to feel solid ground beneath her feet again, and walked unsteadily to the cafeteria, where she bought a cup of tea and sought a table near the window. From there she could see the rink, which from this distance looked like a heaving ant-hill. Happy to be at a safe distance, she settled back in her chair and sighed with relief and exhaustion.

'Mind if I join you?' The voice, above the rattle of the tea cups and resounding chatter, startled her.

'No, of course not,' she mumbled, annoyed that her peace was so shortlived. It wasn't until the voice was seated at her level that she recognised the owner. Oh God, she thought, not him again, not twice in one day!

'I saw you down there on the rink,' Joe said, laughing. 'If you like I'll teach you.'

'Thank you, but I think I've had enough for today.' Already weak and shaking from the physical effort, the thought of going out there again with Joe worsened her condition to a violent trembling. Avoiding his gaze, she hid her hands under the table and gripped her knees tightly.

'It's easy once you get the hang of it. You seemed a bit nervous, but you'll do better next time.'

Anxious to avoid dwelling on her nervousness, Mary thought desperately of something to change the subject. 'Aren't you having any tea?'

'Eh, no, not just now.' He grinned a little awkwardly, then blurted out his confession. 'Actually, I heard you making arrangements with your friend; I came just to see you.'

Not knowing what else to do, Mary looked down at her cup.

'You're not mad at me, are you?' he asked.

'No, why should I be mad?'

'Well, I'm glad you're not. Look, I want to tell you before your friend comes back or I'll never get the chance: I've been wanting to get to know you for a while, but things like that are bloody impossible at work. Then, when I saw you at the dance, I thought you were with that bloke until you left him and joined the girls. I was just coming over to ask you to dance when you disappeared.'

Mary felt she ought to do or say something, so she tentatively unclasped her hands from her knees and attempted to sip her tea casually. Once her trembling hands were above the table, however, she realised her folly and subdued them by putting her elbows on the table and resting her chin in her palms. The tactic worked, but she still couldn't think of anything to say. Uncomfortable with her long silence, Joe was forced into action. 'Look, your friend's coming off the rink. Before she gets here, would you like to go for a walk tomorrow? I'll meet you at twelve o'clock at the Green Street tram stop. Just say yes or no.'

'Yes,' she said, without raising her eyes from the table.

'Good, see you then,' Joe said, departing hastily.

'Did I see who I thought I saw?' Doreen asked, wide-eyed, and collapsed into the chair Joe had just vacated.

Mary looked in amazement at her friend. 'He asked me out.'

'Well, why so surprised? Everybody saw it coming but you. Quite a catch, eh! But I'd watch out for him all the same.'

'What do you mean?'

'He's a clever one, and handsome, and he obviously has a way with the ladies. I'm not saying he's not a nice fellow but I suspect he's used to getting his own way with the girls, so you watch out.'

'We're only going for a walk tomorrow afternoon, Doreen; there's not much he can do to me in the park.'

'I wouldn't count on it, but he probably wouldn't try anything the first time anyway; it's after that you'll have to watch out.'

'Do you think he'll ask me out again then?'

'Mary, you *are* a little innocent. If he asks you out once, he'll probably try again, and most men usually only want one thing and you know what that is.'

'Not really,' Mary blushed. 'Oh, Mrs Moynihan jokes about never letting a man in your knickers until you've got him firmly tied up in wedlock – "first wedlock and then bedlock", she says. And I've heard the girls at school and at work talking. I have an idea what the physical act is; what I'm curious about is why everybody makes such a big thing about it.'

'Well, Mike and I never did it. I wish we had now,' Doreen sighed. 'I'd have more to remember him by, but he was all for saving it up until we were married. We used to play around, though, without going all the way and it was so wonderful that I can't imagine how much better the rest of it could be. Mike confessed that he'd once been with a girl and that it was exquisite pleasure, but it was exquisite pleasure to me even when he just kissed me or held me in his arms.'

'Exquisite pleasure,' echoed Mary. 'That sounds wonderful! I don't know whether I'm more excited or more nervous about tomorrow. I like him so much I shake whenever I see him.'

'Just keep your head about you, luv, and act like yourself; don't let him see you're nervous. Play it a bit cool at first; they respect a woman who keeps her distance.'

'Can you give me any more tips, Doreen?'

'Well, just as I said, luv. Don't let him take any liberties. He could take your arm, the first time out while you're walking, but he shouldn't touch you otherwise, and if he tries anything you just tell him where to get off.'

'How do I do that?'

'Just say you're not that sort of girl and tell him to keep his hands off you. You should have been walking out at least a couple of weeks before he gives you a peck on the cheek when he says goodnight, and another week after that before you should allow him a kiss on the mouth – at least, that's how it was with Mike and me. It was very gradual with us; we'd known each other two months before he got around to putting his hand on my bosom and another week later before he got inside my camisole.'

'Inside your camisole! You let him go that far?'

'That far and a bit further later on, luv. But the thing was, I knew I could trust him. Give some men an inch and they take a mile, but not Mike; he always stopped when I told him to. That's what worries me about that Joe; I don't know if he's the type to take no for an answer.'

'Oh, Doreen, you don't even know him except for seeing him at work occasionally.'

'You're right, luv; I shouldn't label him a lady-killer just because he's handsome. But, anyway, you've got to be firm with all men, handsome or not.'

'I wonder if my mother would have approved of my going out with him, or any young man for that matter. If she were still alive I would have had to ask her permission first.' Mary's face clouded as it always did when she thought of her mother. 'She might not have thought it proper. And I wonder what Mrs Moynihan will think.'

'You daft thing, stop worrying about it and enjoy it. You're old enough and sensible enough, and you've got to start walking out some time or you'll end up an old maid.'

'You're right again, Doreen. Thanks for all the advice. I'll let you know on Monday how I get on. Wish me luck!'

Just then she spied the children heading towards them, 'Here comes the gang; they'd better have their lemonade quickly and then we'll have to leave. Mrs Moynihan will have a fit if I get them back late for tea.'

Chapter Eight

On Sunday Mary was nervous as Mrs Moynihan helped her to dress to meet Joe. 'What shall I say to him, Mrs M.? I'm sure I'll go dumb.'

'No, you won't, hinny; just be your normal self.' She was ironing the blue dress Mary had worn to the dance. It was getting a little frayed around the hem and the cuffs. She'd turned up the cuffs but not the frayed hem; it was only noticeable from ground level.

Mary, in her underwear, was washing her face at the scullery sink. 'I'm even more nervous this time than I was about the dance.'

'You should be excited, luv, not nervous. You've got to have more confidence in yourself; you're a bonnie lass that any man would be proud to walk out with. Here, get this on afore you catch your death o' cold.'

Mary, shivering with apprehension more than the effects of the cold water, pulled the garment over her head and Mrs Moynihan helped to fasten the bodice buttons. 'Now you look pretty as a picture. Come here and sit down while I brush your hair; it's about long enough to put up properly now. I'll do it for you an' you watch an' see what I do.'

'Oh, thank you. I wouldn't know how to start.'

'Well, it's about time you learned. It's much more elegant for a young lady than just pinning it back the way you do.'

Mary winced as Mrs Moynihan brushed and tugged her hair, sweeping it outwards at the sides, then upwards at the back and twisting the curls into an elegant coil halfway up the back of her head. She anchored the coil with two tortoiseshell combs. 'I wore these the first time I went walking out with Jack, and I've kept them for special occasions ever since. I hope they bring you as much luck as they did me, luv.' Stepping back, she surveyed Mary from all angles. 'You know, I think what you need, hinny, is just a few bits o' curls on your forehead. That looks grand but just a little bit severe for your age.' In a flash she'd disappeared into the scullery and returned with a large pair of scissors, delicately pulling out a few wisps from each side of the centre parting and snipping them off just above Mary's eyebrows. 'There now, you look marvellous. Have a look in the mirror, hinny.'

Mary gingerly peeped in the little mirror above the sink that Jack had used for shaving and was pleased with the result. 'Oh, thank you! It does look nice. But won't my hat squash my bun?'

'Not the way I do it. That's why I didn't put it too high,' said Mrs Moynihan, planting the boater on top of Mary's head and tilting it slightly forward, the coil of hair peeking out at the back. 'How about that?' she exclaimed, sticking a long, sharp hatpin through the front of the hat, while Mary winced. 'Now just a bit o' rouge on those cheeks an' a dab on the lips. Rub it in, hinny; it's time you learned how to do these things yoursel'.'

Mary peered again into the mirror. 'Goodness, I feel different,' she said, squaring her shoulders. 'Thank you, Mrs M. You've worked wonders, as usual. I'd better go now. Give me a kiss for luck.'

Mrs Moynihan planted a kiss on her cheek. 'Aye, good luck, luv, but it's a pity you have to put that old black coat on. See he takes you somewhere where you can take it off.'

Mary kissed her goodbye and left, heart thumping,

for the Green Street tram stop. Joe was waiting.

'Hello, Mary, you look wonderful,' he said, smiling approvingly.

'Thank you,' she said primly. Her mother had always said that one should thank a person for a compliment.

Still not taking his eyes off her, he said, 'It's a little chilly but a nice day for a walk in the park. What do you think?'

'Yes, that sounds nice.'

He offered his arm and Mary took it. She felt as if she were floating. By the time they had walked for an hour they had related each other's life stories, discussed life at the factory, and the war, and the fact that even if he believed in killing, which he didn't, they wouldn't accept him because of health problems. Mary didn't think it polite to ask what his problems were. The general gossip at the factory had it that it was something to do with his feet and his eyes, and she knew people laughed about him, but he looked healthy enough. Then he suggested having a cup of tea.

'That would be lovely.' Mary couldn't believe how well it was going and how easily she could talk to him. After the first few minutes of awkwardness they'd just got lost in conversation and she'd never felt so happy.

'Tea for two, please,' he said to the waitress, and then to Mary, 'Would you like a cake or a scone or something?'

'No, thank you,' she said politely, although she was hungry. She knew he didn't earn much money and, since the war, for every cake or scone you bought ready-made these days you could make a batch at home.

Joe's eyes were on her and Mary remembered to take off her coat although it wasn't much warmer in the cafe than outside. He helped her, admiring the dress. 'I've only seen you once before in a dress; that was at the dance. I couldn't take my eyes off you. That was blue, too.'

'It was the same one,' she laughed, pleased that he'd remembered.

'I'd like to see you again, Mary. Would you like to go out on Saturday evening? We could go for a drink or to the dance if you like.'

She wasn't going to let him know she didn't drink and that she was still too young to go into pubs – with her hair up she'd pass. But she'd have to admit she couldn't dance. 'I don't dance, but I'd love to go out for a drink,' she replied, a gleam of triumph in her eyes. She'd been praying he would ask her out again and he hadn't wasted any time.

'Nonsense, I saw you dancing last week. I'll teach you what you don't know, if you like.'

'I'd rather just go for a drink, anyway.'

'Well, we can decide on Saturday.'

After tea they walked back through the park and on to Green Street tram stop. 'I'd rather not leave you here; may I walk you back to your house?'

'Yes, thank you.' He had perfect manners. She hoped Mrs Moynihan would be at the window so she could see him, but she'd probably be in the kitchen.

At the door, he said abruptly, 'Goodnight then. I'll pick you up on Saturday at seven, though I'll probably see you before then at work.'

'Yes, seven would be fine, thank you. Goodnight.' She let herself in and he turned and walked off.

Mary ran down the hall. 'Mrs M., Mrs M., I'm back!'

'Why, hinny, at least he brought you back at a civilised hour. How did it go?'

'Oh, wonderful!' Mary exclaimed, flinging her coat down on the settee and flopping down on top of it. 'He was charming and the perfect gentleman, and we talked non-stop, and now we know each other's life stories and he's asked me out again,' she said in one breath.

'Well, so our little Mary's walkin' out regular now. Is he comin' to collect you next time?'

'Yes, on Saturday.'

'Then you'd better bring him in and introduce him. It's only proper. Your ma would've wanted to see who you were walkin' out with.'

On Monday morning Mary could hardly wait to tell Doreen. She wanted to keep her precious secret from the others as long as possible; she knew they would tease her and take it lightly, whereas Doreen understood that this was a serious matter.

'How did it go?' Doreen asked eagerly, tapping her on the shoulder as she was hanging up her coat.

'Sshh, Doreen. It was splendid! Go to the back corner at break and I'll tell you then.'

At break they both grabbed their canteens and retreated to the back of the shop; the other girls didn't usually go down there.

'Well? Don't keep me in suspense any longer. How was it?'

'We went for a walk and he took my arm and we talked all the time and then we had tea and he took me home . . . and . . . he was a perfect gentleman.'

'That sounds wonderful,' Doreen said, sighing.

'Oh, Doreen! How thoughtless of me! Have you had any news of Mike?'

'No, luv, not yet. I was just thinking of how we used to go for walks and talk.'

'I'm sorry! I pray you'll hear soon.'

'Yes, me too, luv. And now let's hear more about your first walkin' out.'

After break they slipped back to their places on the bench.

'Why, where've you two been?' asked Maggie.

'You missed the story of my weekend. I met a new man at the dance and he's asked me out next Saturday. Would you believe it? He's twenty-five, unmarried and not bad lookin'.'

'Why isn't he in the war then, if he's only twenty-five?' Doreen's eyebrows were raised. Why was it *her* man had to go while others got out of it.

'Well, I asked him and he said he wanted to but they wouldn't have him because he's got a bad chest – bronchitis.'

'That's a pity,' Doreen said ruefully; what she really meant was that it was a pity Mike hadn't had a health problem.

'What about gettin' back to work, down there. Break's over,' yelled Mr Cowley, approaching the bench.

They all put their heads down, but Mary found herself blushing slightly at the sight of Joe's father. Did he know? Would he approve?

On Saturday evening there was a knock on the door promptly at seven o'clock. Mrs Moynihan had put all the children in the parlour and was sitting waiting in the kitchen in her best black dress. Jimmy's bunk bed had been removed from the hallway for the occasion and propped against the wall in the parlour. Mary, wearing her old green dress that she'd patched neatly under the arms, had managed to put up her hair herself and looked very pretty but flustered. This was as bad as the first time. 'Please, Mrs M.,' she begged, 'no embarrassing questions.'

'Why, I'm not goin' to ask what his intentions are at this stage, if that's what you think. Go an' get the door, hinny.'

'Hello,' Joe greeted her as she opened the door nervously.

'Hello, would you like to come in a minute while I get my coat?' She hoped it didn't sound contrived.

She led him into the kitchen where he stood before the quiet, seated figure. 'Mrs M., this is Joe Cowley, and this is Mrs Moynihan, the fairy godmother I told you about.' Had she introduced them in the right order?

Joe, bending and taking Mrs Moynihan's hand, said, 'How do you do?'

'Hello, Joe. Come to whisk our little Mary away, have you?'

Oh dear! Mary had been dreading Mrs Moynihan coming out with some such remark. What now? 'Er . . . would you like to sit down a minute while I get my coat, Joe?' Mary pointed to the chair opposite Mrs Moynihan and disappeared into the hall cupboard to get her coat. How long could she stay there? She counted up to twenty, then drew a deep breath and returned. Mrs Moynihan and Joe were talking affably about the weather; she needn't have worried. 'I'm ready now, Joe.'

Out in the street Joe took her arm. 'I thought we'd go and have a drink first and then decide if we want to do anything else.'

'That's fine,' she replied, grateful that he hadn't actually mentioned dancing.

The pub was warm and crowded and they found a table near the roaring fire.

'What would you like to drink?' Joe helped her off with her coat and removed his.

'I'm not really sure. I tried port and lemon last week but I didn't really like it.'

Joe laughed. 'I didn't like my first drink either, but you soon get used to it. How about trying a sweet sherry?'

'All right.'

She sipped the syrupy liquid and managed to get it down without a fuss while Joe drank his beer. Then he went to get them two more.

'Well, cheers! We forgot to toast last time.' He smiled and raised his glass. 'How about us shaking a leg after this?'

'Shaking a leg?'

'Dancing. Don't worry, I know you're going to say you can't dance, but I can teach you.'

The sherry had made her head feel a little light and the prospect of dancing with Joe didn't seem so daunting now. 'All right, if you promise not to tread on my toes. I had sore feet for days last time, and I'm not wearing my dancing shoes,' she added.

'All the better; it'll hurt less if I do tread on your toes,' he laughed.

On the way Mary prayed the girls wouldn't be there, but she knew they would. At least Maggie might be out somewhere else with her new boy friend. This would be the end of her shortlived secret.

The dance hall was crowded. They sat down for a while and watched the dancers; then Joe asked her for a waltz. He steered her gently around the floor and it was much easier than last time; Mary thought how envious the girls would be if they saw her.

'You did well,' he said as they returned to their seats.

Just then the gang descended, Maggie at the front with her new boy friend. 'Why, hello, Mary, thought you'd given up dancing. Hello, Joe.' Then to her boy friend, 'This is my friend Mary Maddison and this is Joe Cowley, and this here's Jim Blakeman.' Mary was afraid they were going to sit next to them but there weren't enough chairs.

'Well,' said Maggie, 'we've got a table at the other end. See you later.'

The next dance was a tango, followed by a waltz, and Mary was proud as Joe whirled her round the dance floor. Amazingly, she seemed to anticipate almost his every movement and only lost her step a few times. She could imagine the gossip on Monday morning.

She was right.

'Why, Mary, you little dark horse; you never told your friends about your new romance,' Maggie pouted.

'What's he like?' asked Lilly, while Edna and Enid waited eagerly for the news.

'Very nice.'

'Is that all you're going to say?' Maggie asked.

'What else is there to say?'

'Well, how long have you been walkin' out with him an' how far has he got with you an' all that?'

'We've been walking out for a week and he hasn't got anywhere with me. Not that it's any of your business.'

'Why, I've been walkin' out for a week with Jim, but I can't say he hasn't got anywhere yet,' Maggie giggled.

'Mr Cowley's here. We'd better get to work,' Mary announced, ending the discussion, and at break she and Doreen disappeared to the back of the shop again.

'Come on then, let's have it. I've been waiting all morning for this,' Doreen said eagerly.

'First, any news of Mike?'

Doreen shook her head in silence.

'I'm sorry.'

'So am I, luv, but one of these days . . .' Her voice trailed and she sighed. 'Now tell me about Joe.'

'He was such a gentleman, Doreen. After the dance he walked me back to the house, helped me with the key, asked me if he could see me again on Wednesday, and that was it!'

'So he hasn't even tried to kiss your cheek yet; maybe he's not such a lady-killer after all.'

'No, all he's done is take my arm. Doreen, I must tell you: I'm truly in love.'

Chapter Nine

Mary had been walking out with Joe for almost five blissful weeks and when he'd kissed her that first time, softly and then pressing harder on her lips, she knew what Doreen meant by exquisite pleasure. Surely the real thing couldn't be any more wonderful than this? They didn't have the money to do anything very exciting, except for two wonderful visits to the music hall, when he'd held her hand and they'd joined in all the choruses together. And he'd taken her to the Old Assembly Rooms twice, and now she could dance the two-step, the waltz and the 'Gay Gordons' without getting dizzy. It was wonderful to be held in his arms and feel the other girls' envious eyes on her. He was so handsome, and she was proud he had chosen her. Most of the time, though, they simply went for walks in the park or to the pub, or visited each other's homes, but it was more than enough for Mary; she didn't care what they did as long as they were together. He hadn't yet said outright that he loved her, but she knew he did. Why else would he hold her and kiss her the way he did? Once, after he'd kissed her, she'd blurted out, 'Oh, I love you so, Joe,' and he'd answered by kissing her harder. He simply wasn't a man of many words when it came to love, and she loved him just as he was, even when he occasionally had those dark moods.

'Oh aye, our Joe can be a sulky bugger when he likes,' Mrs Cowley had warned her early in their relationship, her chins wobbling as she spoke. 'Watch out for his moods, but don't fret about them; they don't usually last long, hinny. I just ignore them and wait till he comes out o' them, and then he usually comes and puts his arms round me as if nothing had happened. Bein' our only one, I suppose we did spoil him a bit as a bairn, so he's got used to havin' most of his own way.'

Mary liked the plump, motherly woman with tired looking grey hair and tired grey eyes to match. She took her advice and ignored Joe's occasional sulkiness. It wasn't as if he got angry or violent; mostly he just retreated into himself for a short period, and the good times were so wonderful, they more than made up for an occasional bad mood.

But her private joy was shattered when she returned home late from work one Monday to find Mrs Moynihan, sombre faced, nursing the twins in her lap, the older ones solemnly grouped around her. The pot of stew simmering on the hob was beginning to burn. She told Mary quietly and without emotion: 'It's happened, luv. I've had one o' them telegrams from the War Office. I knew it would come one day. Jack was never one to shirk his duty. We're right proud o' him, aren't we, kids?' The little group nodded a non-comprehending response.

'Oh, no!' Mary knelt by Mrs Moynihan and began to sob.

'There now, hinny, don't get all upset. Jack would've been the first one to tell you not to snivel. He went in one piece – gassed in the trenches. An' they're sendin' him back to us for a proper burial, thanks to God! Now you just help yoursel' to some stew afore it burns itsel' to death. I'll put the bairns to bed early the night.'

Molly and Jimmy helped their mother usher the three young ones into the bedroom and Mary was left alone. She couldn't fight the tears. Why was life so cruel and hard? What was God doing up there? Since she'd been seeing Joe she'd forgotten there had ever been anything bad in her life – or in the world. Her only sadness had been that her mother was not there to share her joy; she hadn't given a thought to the war, the ugly factory, the poverty, the shortage of food. Now she was plunged back into reality. How could she have been so selfishly happy when others were suffering so? When Mrs Moynihan returned, she was still sitting staring at the burning stew, the tears meandering down the crevices of her crumpled face.

The woman took her hand. 'Stop your cryin', luv, or the little ones'll hear you. An' eat up this mess afore it turns to cinders,' she added, handing Mary a plate of the congealed fish stew.

'No, I'll have it later.' Mary put the plate on the table and stood up, putting her arms round the stooping figure. 'What are you going to do?' she asked.

'Do! Well, first I'm goin' to give our Jack a good send-off when he gets home, and then I'm goin' to think what I'm goin' to do. Don't you worry, I'll think o' somethin'.'

Molly and Jimmy returned from the children's room. 'They're lookin' at comics, Ma.'

'All right, luvs. You can both stop up a bit the night, an' you needn't go to school the morrow unless you want to.'

Mary, remembering how Mrs Moynihan had supported her when her mother had died, suddenly felt ashamed. 'Why don't you all sit down and I'll make a pot of tea,' she said, relaxing the creases in her face and allowing the last vestiges of tears to fall unimpeded, forming dark spots on her blue overall.

As Mrs Moynihan had promised, Jack's funeral was grand. The entire neighbourhood was there. After the ceremonial spade of earth had been cast on the coffin and the last prayer said, it seemed as if the whole town crammed into the tiny flat.

'Come on in,' she said to each new arrival. 'Mary and me's been bakin' for two days, so you'd better eat this stuff up. The booze is on the sideboard, just help yoursel's.'

The previous evening, Mary had helped Mrs Moynihan make sausage rolls, ham sandwiches, bacon-and-egg pies, scones, and apple tarts. The neighbours had brought two ham shanks for the sandwiches, sausage for the sausage rolls, and bacon and eggs for the pies, saving up and sacrificing their own food for the occasion. And the local pub had provided the sherry and beer at cost price. No one would have known there was a war on.

The drinks soon had everyone chatting jovially, singing Jack's praises and remembering the better days. 'Aye, he was a grand lad, was Jack. Here's to you, Jack!' It was old Mr Pitt, the next door neighbour, offering the toast. 'Aye, to Jack,' the other guests chorused, raising their glasses.

As the alcohol consumption increased, so did the merriment; it was difficult to distinguish the wake from a wedding. Mary was glad it was going so well; Jack deserved a good send-off. Soon she and Mrs Moynihan were able to relinquish their hostess's duties and let the gathering take its course. Mary persuaded the new widow, now on her third glass of sherry, to relax with her friends while she put the children to bed.

Joe followed her into the bedroom. 'Can I help you, Mary?'

'No, it's all right. They'll be off in a minute or two. The amount of food and lemonade they've consumed should knock them out for the night.'

'You handled things pretty well,' he said, putting his hands on her shoulders as she straightened up from the last goodnight kiss. The twins and Michael were head to tail in the bed and Molly and Jimmy were tightly tucked up in the two bunks.

'Oh, I'm used to children.'

'No, I meant the funeral.'

'I suppose I'm getting used to those, too.' She turned her face away as the tears threatened again.

'Let's stay here for a while,' Joe said, sitting down on the cane rocking chair that was the only piece of furniture in the room besides the beds. 'I haven't seen you for days. Come and sit on my knee.'

'All right, but only for a few minutes. Mrs Moynihan's on her third sherry and I'm worried about her.' She sat on his lap like a child and felt the comfort of his big arms round her.

'What's going to happen now?' he asked.

'Sshh! The children!' She glanced at the five little faces in the shadow of the dimmed gaslight. But they were already transported to their own night worlds, confused by the recent events of the grown-up world but warm and secure in their beds.

'What's going to happen to you, Mary? Has Mrs M. decided what she's going to do?'

'Yes, she told me last night. Her brother's a widower with three children; he's a miner at Ford Colliery, and he wants her to move in with him and be his housekeeper. It'll solve both their problems: she won't have to go out to work and all the children will have a mother.'

'Ford Colliery! But that's miles away. How could you get to work? It takes over an hour by train and then you'd have to take the tram from the station.'

'I know. I'll just have to find a room in town. She wants me to go with her, but where could I find work in a pit village? My job is nuts and bolts now,' she added with a half smile. 'But anyway, I couldn't live so far away from you.'

The noise from the parlour grew louder as people began to take their leave and shout farewells. Mary stood up abruptly. 'We'd better go back now. I'll see you at the park tomorrow; we can talk then.'

She left Joe in the bedroom and sought Mrs Moynihan, who was still sitting in the armchair by the fire, her third glass of sherry, untouched, in her hand.

It was a grey, drizzling Sunday when Mary met Joe at their accustomed entrance to the park. The creeping damp permeated her thin, cheap coat, despite the shawl she had thrown over it. Joe put his arms round her hunched shoulders. 'Hello, my beauty; you look frozen.' She nestled into him; it was always comforting and yet exciting to be with Joe. Tilting her chin, he kissed her cold, damp lips, and she had to push him away, breathless. 'Joe, not here,' she laughed.

'So, wench, you spurn my advances. I suppose we'll just have to walk then. I brought yesterday's paper to check the advertisements for rooms. We should go and look at some this afternoon.'

For the moment, Mary wanted only to be with him. 'Not now, let's just go for a walk first and warm up.'

Now and then they passed another pair of lovers, also oblivious of the raw November day. The north wind was blowing the few remaining sooty leaves from the stunted maples and the laden sky enveloped their skeletal branches in a gloomy shroud. Hunched under Joe's protective arm, Mary saw only the ground beneath her feet and felt only the warmth of his body.

'Let's sit down for a while,' he said, leading her to a bench in a small and, to Mary, all too familiar clearing. The bench was normally secluded but now, with the trees bare of foliage, it was open to the pathway and the eyes of passers-by. The last couple of times Joe had kissed her he'd tried to caress her breast, but she couldn't extinguish the memory of the pink paw that had once touched her there.

'No, not here. I don't like this place.' She shuddered, remembering that awful afternoon and putting her hand to her left cheek, which was burning despite the cold.

He shrugged. 'You're such a funny little thing. I see nothing wrong with it.' When they reached the next clearing, he asked, 'Is this suitable, m'lady?'

'Yes, it's fine.' She smiled; she felt like a lady when she was with Joe.

'Looks identical to me,' he said taking off his scarf and laying it on the damp seat.

They sat down and she snuggled into him. Both his arms went round her and his face bent down over hers. He started kissing her gently, and then the pressure grew stronger as his hand reached inside her coat, pulling open one of the buttons. She froze, then melted, until she felt his hand move over her breast, manipulating her dress buttons. 'No, Joe! Please don't!'

Joe sighed and removed his hand. 'There's no one here and there's no harm in it. When are you going to let me touch you? That's all, I promise.'

Trembling, she straightened up and fastened her coat, telling herself: 'That awful day was a lifetime ago, and this is Joe, not that dreadful man.' Yet still she trembled. 'Let's go, Joe, please.'

'All right.' He stood up a little sulkily. 'But I don't know why you're still so prudish. Hell! We've known each other long enough, God knows! And all you'll do is let me kiss you. I'm not going to rape you; I only want to hold you and touch you. I promise.'

'I know, Joe, but please let's walk. I'm cold.'

They walked on in silence. Joe was in one of his moods and Mary felt miserable. 'Let's go to the Tea Rooms,' she suggested. 'I could do with a cup of tea.'

He turned, still silent, in the direction of the Tea Rooms. Giving him an anxious look, she whispered: 'Don't be cross with me, Joe.'

'I'm not cross; it's just that sometimes I wonder if you realise I'm a man and have needs.' He stuffed his hands into his pockets sulkily.

'Of course I do, and I have feelings, too.'

'One of these days you might make me believe it. Of all the girls in this blighted town, why did I have to pick one that's a century behind the times. I'd still respect you, if that's what's worrying you.'

'No, it's not that. Let's change the subject. We always seem to end up like this lately. Why don't we have tea now? I'm frozen.'

Once inside the cafe, Joe cheered up a little. 'Let's have a look in the paper and see if we can find you a room,' he said, rustling through the pages, but while searching for the 'To Let' column, he was diverted by the sports section.

As the waitress approached, Mary inquired over the top of the newspaper, 'Would you like scones?'

'Um, no thanks,' he grunted, absorbed in the Saturday football scores. She ordered a pot of tea for two and waited. The cafe was almost deserted; only fools and lovers left a warm fireside on a day like this, she mused, happy to be grouped among the latter. Just then the proprietor's dog ambled towards her and she called him, stroking his head idly while she waited for Joe to finish reading. When the waitress finally brought the steaming pot, Mary poured the tea into the thick white cups, passing Joe the one without the chip. 'Joe, your tea will get cold.'

'Mm, yes,' he mumbled, laying down the newspaper.

'We were supposed to be looking for rooms, remember?'

'Oh, yes, sorry. I got carried away.' He turned the

pages again. 'Let's see . . . Well, there's one here near Green Street, says ladies only, full board. And here's another, closer to work, bed and breakfast only.'

'I'd rather have full board.'

'Well, no harm in checking both.' He took a pen from his pocket and circled the two.

The bed and breakfast place turned out to be a dreary three-storeyed terrace house, with a dirty front step and grimy lace curtains. Like most of the houses in the area, there was no front garden; the front door opened directly on to the street. A middle-aged woman trying to look twenty answered their knock. Her over-painted mouth and brightly rouged cheeks were smothered in a whitish powder. The powder lodged in the deep lines around her mouth and eyes, serving only to accentuate the ravages of the years it was meant to conceal. Her hair was dyed a bright red – that is, up to the inch of new growth that revealed a contrasting dull grey.

Joe took the initiative. 'We've come to look at the room.'

'It's a single,' the woman replied, wiping her hands on her soiled pinafore.

'That's all right. It's for my lady friend.'

'I'll take you up. It's on the second floor.'

It wasn't a bright day outside, but Mary had difficulty adjusting her eyes to the dark hallway and missed her footing several times on the narrow, unlighted stairway. The room was in total blackness until the woman, who seemed to have an uncanny ability to see in the dark, strode across the void and jerked back a dusty brocade curtain to reveal a small dormer window covered by the ubiquitous grey-tinged lace. The waning afternoon light fought its way through, revealing a bed, a wardrobe, and a wash-stand with three legs, precariously supporting a chipped brown juglet set. In the corner near the fireplace stood a Victorian armchair, its horsehair stuffing oozing from the various tears and cigarette burns inflicted by its many occupants over half a century.

'Breakfast's at six. After that your time's your own. I don't care what you do in your own room. I only have one rule and that's no cookin' on the fire – smells the whole house out. But you can make yoursel' a cup o' tea. And I don't care what time you come in, so long as you lock the front door and don't wake me other lodgers.' She looked keenly at Joe. 'Oh, aye, and visitors is allowed, as long as you don't make no racket.'

'What do you think, Mary?' Joe put his arm round her shoulders.

'I . . . I'd like to think about it first.' She turned to the woman. 'Thank you for showing us. We'll let you know.'

'Suit yoursel', hinny, but it won't be empty long.'

Outside in the cold air, Mary shuddered. 'Oh, Joe, it was horrible.'

'I know it wasn't very grand, but at least you'd have your own key, and "visitors is allowed",' he mimicked. 'Just think, we wouldn't have to go to that damned freezing park to be alone.'

Mary said, hesitantly, 'I'd like to see the other place before I decide.'

That proved to be a terrace house of the same vintage and style, but the step was a familiar yellow and the white lace curtains were clean and starched. One of the curtains moved, and a face withdrew as they knocked. An elderly woman opened the door, her grey hair knotted into a tight bun at the nape of her neck, a clean white apron covering her grey Sunday dress.

'We've come to see the room,' Joe said.

'I only take ladies.' The door was about to be closed in their faces.

'I know,' Mary said quickly. 'It's for me.' The door stayed.

'Well, afore we go up, let me tell you what's what,' the old woman said, eyeing Joe suspiciously. 'You get a full breakfast and high tea or a hot supper during the week and dinner at twelve on Sundays. I don't keep things hot for ever, so if you're late, you get nothin'. I lock the door at half past ten and don't like to be waked up after that – and no visitors,' she added, again eyeing Joe suspiciously.

'I'd like to see the room,' Mary ventured. It was almost identical to the previous one except that it smelt fresh and the armchair had a bright, chintz slip-cover. There were multi-coloured woven rag mats scattered over the linoleum and the bed wore a clean, pink, twill cover. Beside it, on a small table, lay a large black bible, and the juglet set on the marble wash stand was clean, though chipped. Everything was old and shabby, but immaculate, just like the owner.

'I bring hot water up at half past five every mornin' and if you want a bath on Fridays you fill it yoursel', and it's a penny extra for the hot water.'

'How much is the room?' inquired Mary.

'Three and six a week plus baths.'

'That's fine,' Mary said eagerly. 'I'll take it.'

'It's a week's rent in advance if you want me to hold it for you.'

'Yes, of course.' Mary delved into her purse and handed the woman three and sixpence.

Joe said nothing until they were out in the street once more. 'What did you want to do that for? It's like a flippin' convent.'

'I don't mind that. At least it's clean and respec-table. That other place was so dirty, and she was so strange. I know my mother wouldn't have wanted me to live there.'

'Well, your mother isn't here any more, Mary. You've got to stop thinking about her so much.'

Mary winced at his remark about her mother, but

she knew he was just upset about the room. 'Oh, Joe, I know you wanted somewhere where you could come to see me, but we can always go to your house.'

'It's not quite the same with my parents always hanging around; I never get a chance to see you alone. But I suppose now you've paid for it, you'll have to take it.'

When Mary arrived home, Mrs Moynihan was busy packing and weeping. 'You caught me at it this time,' she said, wiping her eyes on the corner of her pinafore.

Mary put her arms round her. 'I've never seen you cry, not even at the funeral.'

'That's 'cause I like to do me cryin' on me own, hinny.'

'I'll make us a nice cup of tea,' was all Mary could say to comfort her.

'Better fill it up. The bairns'll be in soon. Molly took them to the park while I did some packin'. Oh, Lord! That's them now.' She again rubbed her red eyes with her pinafore and darted into the scullery. Then taking a bowl of finely chopped onions from the larder, she tipped them on to the bench and proceeded to chop them further, grinning at Mary. 'I always keep a bowl o' these handy – fools the bairns every time.'

'Onions for *tea*?' Molly inquired incredulously when the gang arrived.

Her mother shook her head. 'Why no, luv, I'm just gettin' these ready for the morrow's dinner.'

Chapter Ten

As the New Year approached, Mary was growing accustomed to life in her lodgings. She'd spent Christmas day with Mrs Moynihan at Ford Colliery and was excited at the prospect of staying with Joe's parents for the New Year; it would be wonderful to be close to Joe for two whole days. He had been a little moody since she had been living in what he jokingly termed the 'Convent of the Urchin Virgins', calling the old lady 'Mother Superior'. Mary wondered what it would be like to live in the same house with him, to have family breakfast together, and not to be forced to part at the end of the street. They were always careful to avoid the ever-watchful eye of the landlady, who appeared to keep constant vigil behind the lace curtains.

Mary always enjoyed visiting Joe's home. His mother took delight in preparing her special Sunday joints to fatten up 'the wee bairn'. Being in the shop trade, she had connections and often bartered for meat. She was convinced the boarding house was a sort of orphanage for over-age girls and that Mary was fed on gruel and weak tea.

On Saturday the factory siren sounded as usual, but this Saturday was different – it was New Year's Eve. Even the war couldn't quell the festive spirit of the northern workers. Living just below the Scottish border, they celebrated Hogmanay with the Scots. Nobody locked his door on New Year's Eve: friends, neighbours, and strangers were all welcome to come in and help themselves to food and drink and merriment, even if the occupants were out celebrating elsewhere. After midnight, visitors always brought with them a piece of coal for the fire, to wish their hosts warmth and prosperity throughout the year, and a bottle of whisky, or whatever they could afford, to provide inner warmth and cheer. War or no war, the Geordies were determined to keep up the tradition of New Year's Eve.

'Mother says you're to bring in the New Year with us,' Joe had informed her. 'Then a mate of mine's having a big party; we'll go there later.'

At the first hoot of the siren on the big day, Mary rushed home in a joyful mood. She soaked in the tub for an hour, careful to sneak in and out of the shed quietly lest the old lady should discover she had monopolised it for so long. Her new plum-coloured dress, a Christmas present from Joe, lay waiting on the bed. She had ironed and re-ironed it several times; she must look her best tonight. It didn't rest on the toes of her buttoned boots like her other clothes, but came almost up to her calves. She felt very daring and fashionable as she held it against herself. Instead of their usual practice of meeting on the street corner in order to avoid the landlady, Joe was coming to collect her at five. She filled the void by manicuring her finger nails, tying up her hair in curling rags, and tentatively experimenting with the new powder and rouge she had bought for the occasion.

At last the doorbell rang and she flew down the stairs, just in time to hear Joe wishing the old lady a Happy New Year. He took Mary's arm and they walked hand in hand in the brisk air. 'Let's go to the pub first,' he said. 'Mother's in such a tizzy getting the food ready and, anyway, we'll have enough of the old folks later; I want you to myself for a while.'

Inside the pub Mary took off her coat, revealing the dress. Gazing at her approvingly, Joe remarked: 'Looks marvellous on you, Mary. I thought it was time you had something that shows off what you're always trying to hide.'

'Oh, I love it, Joe. Thank you again. It's the nicest dress I've ever had; I've been saving it for tonight.'

'Tonight!' he exclaimed, waving his wallet. 'Tonight's the night! I've got half my Christmas bonus left, so we can buy up the bar. How about a large whisky?'

She sank back into the red velvet chair and grimaced. 'Silly, you know I can't stand it, but as it's New Year's Eve, I'll go wild and have a sherry, please.'

'Sherry and a large whisky, Mike,' he yelled to the barman over the mob at the bar. Streamers were flying and balloons popping, and the crowd was already so inebriated it seemed unlikely to Mary that they could last until midnight, let alone until the traditional celebration breakfast. Anyone who went to bed before 8 a.m. was considered an old fogey, and nobody between the ages of fourteen and forty would give in without a struggle.

On the way out they met up with two slightly drunk khaki-clad men. Joe always tried to avoid uniformed men; he'd had some bad experiences.

'Civvies, eh? What's the matter, man? Don't tell us you're in a reserved occupation. Got no stomach for it more likely,' one said, while the other shouted: 'Bloody conchies!'

Joe ignored their remarks and hastily edged Mary through the door. 'I'm glad we're out of there in time. Could turn nasty.'

'Don't take any notice of them, Joe. They don't know about your feet and your eyes.'

Joe grimaced; he'd had a lot of flak to put up with about that from the men at the factory. 'That's not really the point; the point is I don't want to go anyway.

"Pack up your troubles in your old kit bag" – who the hell do they think they're kidding? I just don't believe in killing.'

'Well, *I'm* certainly glad you don't,' she said, gripping his arm tighter.

Joe's parents greeted her warmly. Mrs Cowley had been baking all day, refusing to tell how she'd managed to get all the ingredients. Mr Cowley joked, 'I think she bribed the butcher an' the grocer an' I hate to think what with.' The table was almost invisible under its array of mince pies, home-cooked ham, sausage rolls, and assorted biscuits.

'Come on in, hinny. Give me your coat an' help yoursel' to some o' that grub. It's not up to my usual standard, but the best I could do with a war on. I don't want to see nothin' left by the morrow, even if we starve for the rest of the week.' She hugged Mary to her huge bosom and pushed her away, leaning her grey head to one side to admire the new dress.

'Eey, lass,' the father said, taking his pipe from his mouth. 'It's grand to see you out o' that damned overall. It doesn't look right on you; you haven't got the face to go with it. First time I saw you, I thought: what's that little petunia doin' in this onion patch?'

'Keep your eyes off her, Dad, or Mother'll get jealous,' Joe laughed, putting his arms round Mary's shoulders.

Mr Cowley responded by putting his arms round his wife's ample waist. 'Why, she had her day, you know. She was a grand lookin' lass when I married her.'

'What a cheek, Bill Cowley! I'm still good enough for you. Any woman that's spent half her life lookin' after you two and runnin' a shop is bound to show some wear at the seams.'

'Aye, an' if you get any more paddin' on you, them seams is goin' to split pretty soon,' her husband laughed, giving her plump cheek a playful nip.

They all laughed, and Mr Cowley went to fetch the bottles from the kitchen. It was sherry for the women and stout for the men. He poured the golden, sweet sherry into two small tumblers and then carefully poured the black, viscous liquid into two pint mugs, an inch of heavy, cream-coloured foam forming on the top. It smelled like molasses, and Mary nipped her nostrils in mock disgust.

'Couldn't you get any whisky, Dad?' asked Joe, picking up his glass.

Mr Cowley looked at his son. 'Now, none o' your fancy notions here, lad. I don't care what you do when you're away, but when you're home, you eat an' drink the same as us.' A thick layer of the creamy foam had clung to his black moustache and wobbled as he talked. Mary giggled, breaking the tension, and they all laughed.

Joe and Mary sat holding hands on the sofa in front of the blazing fire. She felt warm and loved, her only wish being that her mother could have been there to share this wonderful hour.

By eleven thirty the older folks had trouble keeping their eyes open. They were unaccustomed to late nights and so much food and drink but were determined to bring in the New Year before Mary and Joe went on to the party. Mary was wondering if she could keep up the pace; the sherry and the fire were making her feel languid, but Joe was in high spirits. On the first stroke of midnight he picked up the half empty bottle of sherry and went outside, on his way taking a piece of coal from the scuttle. On the last stroke, he returned and presented the gifts to his parents. 'Happy New Year to one and all,' he bellowed and they all hugged and kissed and wished one another the same.

Mr Cowley raised his glass. 'Aye, and a bloody unhappy New Year to those Jerry buggers; their time is nearly up. Kitchener can do it if anybody can. Down with the bastards!' he shouted, draining his glass, and they all followed suit. 'If those buggers hadn't managed to save their arses by diggin' trenches when they were fleeing from the British an' couldn't run no more, trench warfare would never have got goin'. An' now look what it's started – a right massacre, thousands o' soldiers dyin', up to their necks in mud and alive with lice, and they're still wantin' to send more out there to die in glory for their country. Bloody propaganda! I see no glory in it for the poor buggers that are givin' up their lives.'

'I know, Bill,' his wife said. 'We all know there's a war on, but why don't you get off your hobby-horse for one night. I hate to think o' them poor lads, some o' them younger than our Joe. It's New Year's Eve, you know; we're supposed to look on the bright side tonight. It'll soon be over.' She yawned and prodded her husband. 'Eey, well, it's past me bedtime an' yours an' all, Bill. Come on, we're gettin' too old for this sort of thing; I can't keep me eyes open.'

'Aye, lass, I'm comin',' he said, rising a little unsteadily from his chair. 'But I still hope Jerry has a bloody awful new year comin'.'

'You've had a skinful the night, Billy-boy. It's a good job it's just once a year.' His wife took his elbow and ushered him to the door. 'Now you kids have a good time at the party. I've left your blankets and pillows on the hall table, Joe; you can make up your bed on the settee when you get back.' She turned to Mary. 'Your bed's in Joe's room, hinny, and I've put a hot iron in it. I hope it's still warm when you get back.'

'Thank you, Mrs Cowley. I don't want to stay out long anyway; I'm tired already.' The sherry and the warmth had conspired with the excitement and Mary was feeling a little tipsy.

''Night, then. Have a good time.' Mrs Cowley

shepherded her husband away and Mary and Joe were left alone on the settee. Joe waited until he heard the bedroom door close and then put his arm round her. 'Let's not go to the party, luv. I'd rather stay here quiet and alone; it's not often we get a chance like this.'

'But, Joe, we must go; they're expecting us.'

Joe pulled her closer. 'Don't worry, they'll all be so bloody drunk by now they won't even miss us.' He leaned over and kissed her ear lightly, travelling slowly to her mouth and increasing the pressure. Her head swam even more. He then gently ran his hands up from her waist and over her breasts, pausing. She started, and then let his hands remain. Her head told her to stop him, but her body paid no heed. She felt herself relaxing under his touch and Joe, encouraged, gently manoeuvred her dress buttons. She stiffened, but only for a moment, as he slipped his hand gently inside her camisole. More feverishly now, he undid the buttons completely and pulled both garments down her shoulders to her waist. She shivered, but not from the cold. His hands stroked her bare flesh and a warm, tingling sensation travelled over her entire body. Her head was still saying no, but she was immobilised. He was laying her down on the sofa, bending over her, brushing her face with his lips as he gently raised her feet. Her head took over. 'No, Joe! Not like that,' and she sat up.

'What's wrong? It's just more comfortable; I'm getting a crick in my back.' It didn't sound like Joe's voice; he was breathing strangely.

He eased her down again and leaned over her; then she felt the full weight of his body on hers and she moaned, 'No, Joe.' But she couldn't cry out. Her head and her body were parting company; she was aware only of a throbbing sensation all over and of his lips crushing hers. Her head fell silent.

* * *

'Mary, it's just struck five. They'll be getting up soon – you'd better go to bed.' She opened her eyes and the memory of the past hours flashed before her. 'Oh, God! Joe, we shouldn't have.' Dear God! Mother! Why didn't you stop me? she cried out silently.

'What do you mean, we shouldn't have? It was bloody marvellous and you know it.' She sat up in the dark, shivering, and he pulled the blanket round her.

'Yes, it was, but now it seems so wrong.' She huddled under the blanket and forced her eyes to see in the gloom. He was kneeling over her, naked, amidst the disarray of blankets and pillows on the floor. Slowly, her head aching from the sherry, she got up and groped for her scattered garments.

Chapter Eleven

Taking her place at the belt on Monday morning, Mary felt different and hoped the girls wouldn't notice the change. She was a woman now and it made her feel worldly and grown up; now she could understand all those stories Maggie and the girls told – but how could they make jokes about such a thing? Making love was the most wonderful experience in life – at least in her life so far. Her earlier guilt had vanished. How could anything so wonderful be wrong? She wondered if she should tell Doreen at break but decided against it. Doreen was a virgin and might be shocked.

'Dreamin', Mary?' Edna's voice interrupted her thoughts.

'Yes, I suppose I was.'

'How was the New Year's Eve party, luv?' Maggie shouted over the clatter.

'Party? Oh, we didn't go; we stayed at home with Joe's parents.'

'Some excitin' New Year's Eve! We all went to the bash at the Old Ass. I've still got a hangover but it was worth it. We picked up some Army lads on leave and went back to Lilly's house. Her folks were away at her Auntie Moll's. Didn't we have a good time, girls?'

'Aye, you all had a good time all right,' said Lilly in an angry voice, 'canoodling with them soldiers an' drinkin' beer an' them lads bein' sick all over the place. *I* was the one who had to clean up the mess. An' I don't

139

know how I'm goin' to explain to me ma how three o' her best glasses got broken.'

'Eey, that was funny,' said Maggie. 'Ed, that's the one I was with, bet us all a tanner he could balance three glasses on his head at once and walk across the room. He was so drunk he couldn't even stand up straight.' She burst into laughter. 'We would've all won a fortune but he didn't have no money left to pay up; he'd spent it all on beer.'

'Aye, it was a good night, but it's a lousy day the day. I don't know why you're all laughin' so much,' Enid moaned. 'For the first time in me life I really fell for someone an' he bloody well had to go back last night. An' he told me some things they don't tell us in the papers; he said his letters to his folks from the front were a far cry from the truth o' the war. They were all ordered to be cheerful and their letters is edited anyway. He said it's bloody awful an' they're stuck in their trenches most o' the time and they've hardly taken any territory an' there are thousands o' lads dyin'. He said dear old Blighty listenin' to them politicians' lies has no idea what's goin' on.'

'Is he goin' to write to you, luv?' Even Maggie's voice was quieter now.

'No. He says he doesn't want to send me a pack o' lies an' that he most likely wouldn't get my letters anyway, but he took me address an' said he'll come an' see me on his next leave.'

'I'm sorry, Enid,' Mary said feelingly. She knew how she would feel if Joe were over there. 'But it can't go on much longer judging from the news.'

'Aye, but that's just what Ed said – don't believe all you hear over here about the happy, victorious Tommy wallowing in the excitement o' war; all they ever wallow in is mud. He says they're singin' "The Bells o' Hell" out there now instead o' "Tipperary".'

Mary bent her head over the bench and sorted and

counted feverishly. She was seeing Joe this evening and she felt guilty in her happiness.

She met him at seven on the corner and he was in one of his moods. 'Are you feeling all right, Joe?' she asked tentatively, recognising the familiar expression.

'I'm all right; I just need a drink that's all. Met some of those blasted Tommies on the way and they all but roughed me up. I'm getting sick and tired of them. That's their business if they choose to go and get their heads blown off, they shouldn't expect everybody else to be as bloody stupid as they are.'

She took his arm soothingly and they made their way to the pub. It was crowded, even on a Monday evening.

'A beer and a sherry, Jack,' Joe said to the barman.

'Aye, Joe, how are you doin'?'

'Not so good, Jack. How are you?'

'Aye, not so good either. Bloody income tax has gone up from one and tuppence before the war to three shillings in the pound an' still goin' up more, they say. Still, can't complain. Business is still good an' Newcastle's playin' Glasgow next week. At least they haven't taken away our beer an' sports.'

'Yes, but no thanks to that Hobson bloke. If he had his way, we'd have no fun left in life, just when we need it more than ever.'

Joe rejoined Mary at the table and put down their glasses. 'What happened? You were a long time, Joe.'

'What's the matter? Can't I have a chat with old Jack when I feel like it?'

'Oh, Joe, you are crusty tonight. There's no need to take it out on me because of those soldiers.' She was near to tears, but at least she'd said what she'd felt. She was usually intimidated by Joe when he was in a bad mood.

'Sorry, luv. Cheers!' he said, raising his glass. 'This will raise my spirits.'

That was the first time he'd apologised to her for anything. So, she was finally learning to stand her ground with him. She sipped her drink and happily embarked on Enid's tale about her new boy friend and the war. She should have known better.

'Damn and blast the war! Can't you think of anything more cheerful to talk about?'

'I'm sorry, Joe. That was stupid of me, but please don't shout. You've no reason to shout at me.'

'Sorry, luv. Don't take any notice of me tonight. Maybe another beer will help.' He returned to the bar.

Mary sat thinking. He was difficult when he was in these moods, but it seemed she was learning how to deal with them. That was twice tonight she'd stood up for herself and twice he'd apologised. Perhaps his mother's advice about ignoring his moods had been wrong.

He returned with his beer, looking more cheerful. 'Mum and Dad are going out to the neighbours' to play cards at eight o'clock. We can go home after this and have some time alone together. Can't miss a chance like that.'

'Oh, Joe! That would be wonderful, but what if they come back?'

'We'll worry about that if it happens,' he said, looking at his watch. 'By the time we get there they'll be gone and we should have a couple of hours, till ten o'clock at least.'

'But I have to be back by then.'

'Then we'll have till nine thirty at least. Let's make haste, my sweet.'

At exactly five minutes past eight they arrived at the darkened house. Joe unlocked the door and led Mary through the flat to his bedroom. 'This time we'll have a comfortable bed and I shall have the delicious pleasure of seeing you naked with the light on,' he said, putting a match to the gas mantle.

Mary sat on the bed, feeling a little nervous and yet full of exquisite expectation. Joe took her coat from her and threw it on a chair with his own; then, bending over her, he kissed her as he had done on New Year's Eve, travelling from her lips all over her face: 'Oh, Mary, Mary,' he whispered hoarsely as he eased her gently up from the bed and started undoing her dress buttons.

When they were both naked he held her at arm's length and drew in a deep breath. 'My God, Mary, you're lovely,' he said stroking his hands over every curve of her body.

All she could do was whisper his name as he lifted her and carried her to the bed, covering her breasts in kisses. He lay down beside her and she felt the full force of his body on hers. 'Oh, Joe! Joe! Don't stop, don't ever stop,' was all she could say.

It was wonderful, even better than the first time. She had no idea it could be any more wonderful than that.

Just then they heard a sound outside. 'Sshh! It must be my parents,' Joe said. 'Don't move!'

Mary couldn't have moved if she'd wanted to. Oh! What disgrace to be found with Joe like this, and by his parents who had been so kind to her.

'There's our Joe's bedroom light on, Bill. Is that you, Joe?' They heard his mother's voice outside the door.

'Yes, it's me. I came back for an early night, just reading a bit first. Goodnight, Mum, goodnight, Dad. I'll put the light out when I'm finished.'

'Your dad was feelin' a bit tired so we came back early. Have a good sleep then, luv.'

'You too.'

The lovers lay rigid in each other's arms for what seemed hours until they finally heard the bedroom door close. Joe heaved a sigh of relief. 'Afraid we'll have to get out through the window. Thank God it's a ground floor flat.'

Mary was breathing heavily and her face, which had been aglow a few minutes earlier, was now pale. 'Oh, Joe! How awful of us, deceiving your parents like this.'

'This is no time for remorse, luv. Get dressed as quietly as you can.'

They slipped stealthily out of bed and sorted out their mixed clothing from the heap on the floor. Once dressed, Joe soundlessly eased up the lower sash window an eighth of an inch at a time. He stepped out and helped Mary over the sill. It wasn't till they were two houses down the street that Mary got her voice back, and then she giggled. 'I never thought I'd be doing a moonlight flit from a man's bedroom window.'

'Well, now you've experienced everything, luv.'

'Yes, Joe, I really think I have.'

Chapter Twelve

It was the end of July 1916 when Joe broke the news. 'I'm going, Mary,' he said.

'Going? Going where?' She put down her glass of lemonade, the force causing the bubbly liquid to spill over the rim, forming a frothy pool on the sticky bar-room table.

'I've got my papers.'

In early summer of that year, conscription for single men had begun. Kitchener's appeals, which had attracted over two million volunteers, had not been enough. Mary had been dreading this moment. She stared at the froth, making its way in rivulets to the table edge, where it dripped on to the stained red carpet. 'But I thought they wouldn't have you.' She still couldn't accept the news.

He lowered his eyes, looking embarrassed as usual on this subject. 'Let's go outside. It's too noisy to talk in here.' He gulped down the remains of his beer and she stood in a trance while he helped her with her coat and then ushered her out through the Friday night throng.

Outside, the air was dank, but it helped to clear her head after the smoky atmosphere in the bar. 'But you always said they wouldn't take you anyway,' she persisted.

'They can't afford to be so fussy now. Getting desperate, I suppose. Fallen arches and a lazy eye don't seem to be such a handicap after all, and the worst is, I'll still get ridiculed about them. I suppose I'll end up peeling spuds and dishing out bully beef hash; it's a damned nuisance. The only consolation is that it can't go on much longer. But they don't need more *men* to end it quickly; what they really need is more motorised vehicles and fewer bloody horses and carts . . . and more machine guns, and fewer rifles and bayonets. But men are a cheaper commodity than machines. Let's hope things will start to move faster when the new air force gets its arse off the ground.'

'But what if it does go on, Joe? And what if they send you to the front?' Mary clung to his arm desperately.

'I doubt I'll ever make it to Flanders and, don't worry, I told you, even if I do, I'll be put in some sort of office filling in forms, or in the cookhouses, or maybe if I'm really lucky I'll get latrine duty. The worst I can come back with is housemaid's hands or writer's cramp,' he said, laughing nervously. 'Maybe they'll even pay for me to go to college when I get out . . . or send me to cookery school or something.'

Mary disappeared into the collar of her coat. 'Oh God, Joe, I'll miss you! When do you go?' Her heart felt as though it had slipped down to the soles of her feet and each step she took trampled it.

'Nine o'clock Monday morning,' he answered gloomily.

'You mean I shan't even be able to see you off?'

'It's just as well; I hate goodbyes anyway. You know, the worst part is being a recruit. They treated us like shit at the conscription place. Those bastards think if you didn't sign up voluntarily you're a bloody coward and all I can say is they're bloody idiots. I don't see anything noble about this damned war. Killing's killing and can't be justified. Wherever I go I'll probably get it in the neck for being a conchie.' They were passing another pub and he took her arm and guided her to the door. 'Let's go in here.' The smell of stale beer outside made Mary feel sick but at least it was quiet inside – only a few locals playing darts and sipping their pints in silence. Joe ordered two whiskies, while Mary slumped into a seat by the door.

'Here, this'll warm your cockles,' he said, handing her a glass and sitting beside her, knocking down his own drink in one gulp. Mechanically, she took a sip, her hands clenched round the glass; the liquid burned her throat and she coughed violently.

'Hey, don't choke to death before I leave; I'd like you to be here when I get back,' he said jocularly, thumping her back.

She took another sip and said nothing, her thoughts too many and too devastating to be voiced. She tried to concentrate on the minor ones: 'I shall miss him,' and 'What shall I do without him?' But the major one overpowered the others: 'What if he doesn't come back?' She shuddered and he put his arm round her shoulders.

'Are you cold, luv?'

'No, I'm fine.' She knew she had to pull herself together. After all, he was the one going to the war, she would be safe at home. She sought his hand and squeezed it. 'I was just being selfish and thinking about how I'd miss you rather than what you'd be going through.'

'Well, they say the Army makes a man out of a boy; perhaps peeling spuds and writing memos will be good for my character. Let's have another one,' he said picking up his glass.

'No more for me, thank you,' she said, placing her hand over her still half-full glass.

'Let's go then,' he said miserably, draining his glass, his blue eyes a little glazed. They walked back to her lodgings, he a little unsteadily and she deep in thought. He stopped abruptly and put his arm round her. 'Mary, come home with me. By the time we get there they'll be in bed.'

'Joe, be sensible! You know I can't. I couldn't possibly get back by ten thirty and I'd be locked out.'

'Let's go to the park, then. I need you, Mary.'

The thought that on Monday morning he'd be away in the war dominated her mind. She always felt guilty and nervous making love furtively in the park shelter, but it was the only place they had to go. They walked silently towards the park and made their way to the wooden open-fronted shed but, as they approached, muffled voices and giggles emerged from the dark interior.

Joe grunted. 'Occupied – rotten luck! We'll just have to find a spot somewhere else.'

He guided her towards the nearest shrubbery and took off his jacket to cover the damp grass, pulling her down beside him. He then kissed her roughly, the pressure of his lips bruising hers painfully, but she was barely aware of it. She could think only 'one more day', and she didn't even notice the cool night air and the damp grass as he began feverishly unbuttoning her coat and then her dress. She clung to him, returning his kisses and embraces frantically. Oh God! Don't let this be the last time he'll make love to me.

They were spent, huddled together, shivering and silent, when the light suddenly shone on them.

'Move on, now. This is a respectable park, better do your canoodlin' somewhere else.'

'We're just going, constable,' Joe said, straightening up.

Mary pulled her coat close to cover her dishevelled clothing, dismayed by their demeaning situation.

Joe helped her up. 'Come on, luv. It's time we were moving anyway.' He walked with her back to her lodgings and, though it was twenty minutes after curfew, the door was, mercifully, still unlocked. She clung to him for a second and then let herself in and crept quietly up the stairs.

'You're late, Mary. I left the door open 'cause it's not like you, but next time it'll be locked.' The old woman was standing on the darkened landing in her dressing gown.

'I'm sorry, it won't happen again,' Mary whispered.

'I hope it doesn't neither,' was the reply. 'I don't want you settin' no bad examples here.'

Mary trailed up to her room, undressed, washed in the cold water from the jug and climbed into bed, but she couldn't sleep. One thought took over her mind relentlessly: only one more day.

By Monday morning at the factory, word had spread. The girls, who had been following her love affair with Joe with their usual curiosity, were sympathetic and concerned. Doreen put her arms round her. 'You'll just have to take up knitting, like me, luv. It helps the time pass.' Doreen still hadn't heard from Mike, but every day she expected there would be a big bundle of back letters lying on the hall floor. There never was, but there was always the next day to hope.

'You'll have to teach me, Doreen. I'm about as good with a pair of knitting needles as I am with a pair of skates.'

'Well, at least you can't fall off them. The worst you can do is drop a stitch.'

Mary sighed. 'I'll learn. I'll need something else to do besides writing letters.'

Maggie tried to be comforting: 'You can always come dancin' with us again, hinny. You can't bury yoursel' at home just because your man's away.'

'Thanks, Maggie, but I don't want to dance without Joe. How are things going with Jim, by the way? I hope they don't get him too.'

'It's all the same to me if they do. I found out this weekend he's been double-crossin' me anyway, with

Annie Slater of all people. He's not gettin' nowhere near me once he's been inside *her* knickers.'

'Oh, I'm sorry, Maggie.'

'Well, I'm not really, luv; I was gettin' a bit bored with him anyway. Roll on the next one, an' I hope he'll be a bit more excitin'. In the meantime, we'd better be gettin' to our places afore old Cowley bellows at us.'

At tea break Mary raised her eyebrows at Doreen, who knew the signal, and they both disappeared to the back of the shop. Mary just didn't feel up to the well-intentioned banter of the other girls; she'd always had more in common with Doreen anyway.

'I know how you're feeling, luv. I felt like that when Mike went. Just be glad you know for sure he's still alive.'

'Yes, I'm grateful for that. We made love for the last time this weekend, Doreen. You've no idea how I'm going to miss him in every way.'

'You mean, you've gone all the way?' Doreen's eyes popped.

'Yes, but I couldn't bring myself to tell you. I thought you'd be shocked.'

'There was a time I would have been, luv, but not any more. I'm glad you did before he went away; I just hope you were careful.'

'Oh, I leave that to Joe. He knows a lot more than I do about such things.'

Doreen was still trying to take in the news. 'Wow! So you've actually done it! I don't mean to be personal, luv, but is it as marvellous as Mike said it was?'

'Oh, yes, and more so. It's heavenly, Doreen; it's the most wonderful experience in life. I love Joe so much, though; maybe it isn't so wonderful if you don't love the man.'

'Aw, Lord! There's the bell and just when it was getting interesting. We'd better get back. For God's sake don't let the others know what you've been up to; it's none of their business and, you know Maggie, she'll just turn it into something dirty.'

The first week without Joe was unendurable, although Doreen spent two evenings with her to keep her company. Mary decided to visit Mrs Moynihan on Sunday; she needed the comfort she knew her good friend would give her. Since she'd been walking out with Joe, she'd rarely had a Sunday free to visit her friend, though she'd kept in touch by letter.

Mrs Moynihan was delighted when Mary arrived unexpectedly. 'Why, me little chicken! What a lovely surprise!' she hooted, as Mary poked her head through the kitchen door before throwing herself into Mrs Moynihan's arms. After a moment, the woman pushed her away. 'Well, let's have a look at you, hinny. You're a bit pale, but that's nothin' new. Come on in and tell me how you're doin'. Nothing wrong, is there?'

'Oh, Mrs M., Joe's been called up.' Mary burst into tears.

'Dear God! So that bloody Kitchener's got him at last. As if his blasted posters and pointin' finger wasn't enough, now he's forcin' them to go that doesn't want to. Sit yoursel' down, hinny, an' I'll make a pot o' tea. The kids are all at church. I've been sendin' them every week lately, not that I'm gettin' religious in me old age, but it's nice to have an hour's peace of a Sunday mornin' an' it doesn't do them any harm neither to do a bit o' prayin' these days. Have a sit down, hen; I've just had a cup o' tea but I'll have another one with you,' she said over her shoulder, getting a cup from the dresser.

Mary sat by the fire, her eyes still brimming. 'I just had to come and see you, Mrs M. You're the first person I need when things go wrong; I don't know what I'd do without you.'

'Why, I'm glad o' that, luv. Now here's your tea and dry those eyes. Cryin's not goin' to do Joe any good. Where's he goin'?'

'I don't know; he's still at boot camp. He seems to think they won't be sending him to the front because of his handicaps but I'm not so sure. If he was good enough to conscript, then I suppose they'll consider him good enough to send over there. I had a letter yesterday and he says they've got some of the boys digging trenches at the camp, and he's been assigned to the cookhouse.'

'What the hell are they diggin' trenches for up here? The Jerries aren't goin' to pay us a visit, are they?'

'He said the sergeant said we'd better be prepared, just in case, and we need some coastal defences.'

'Well, bugger me! I didn't think of it endin' up right on our own doorstep.'

'Joe says he's sure it won't; they just want to keep the recruits busy till they can send them to the front. There's a shortage of rifles and ammunition at the moment.'

'Aye, shortage! Shortage of everythin'. I've got sausage an' mash for dinner and we're lucky to have that. Gone are the days when you could get a roast for Sundays. Even if you had the money, you've practically got to sleep with the bloody butcher to get meat. How are they feedin' you at that house, then? You look as skinny as ever.'

'Oh, the food's enough. We get fish on Fridays and meat on Sundays, and in between it's the usual sardines, pilchards, or sausages, or whatever she can find. But the landlady's clever at making simple things tasty.'

'Why don't you come to see us every Sunday now that Joe's away, luv?'

'I'd love to, but it's the fare.'

'Aye, I know it's a bit steep, but still you'll be able to come more often now, won't you? Now you haven't got Joe at weekends?'

'I'll come as often as I can afford to.'

'That's my lass. And now I'd better get those sausages on afore the mob gets back from church.'

Chapter Thirteen

During the weeks following Joe's departure, Mary went through life in a daze. She worked mechanically and spent her evenings and weekends writing to Joe and knitting him warm gloves and socks. He'd need them when winter arrived. She had received two letters from him, the first saying that he was still assigned to cookhouse duty, and the second that they were going to move him, but he didn't know where.

The day after she received the letter, her mind was on Joe when her hand slipped between the rotating belt and its supporting wheels. 'Hey, look out! Stop the belt!' she heard a faraway voice shout as she slipped into blackness.

A white-robed nurse was bending over her when she regained consciousness on a couch in the factory ambulance room.

'Well, the sleeping beauty's awake! How are you feelin', pet?'

Mary opened her eyes and remembered. 'My hand! Is it all right? God! How stupid of me. I wasn't looking.'

'Hey, don't let nobody hear you say that, luv, and I didn't hear it neither. It was an accident – *not* your fault. Do you hear? Negligence means no compensation and no compensation means no money. Listen to them that's older and wiser.'

Now that Mary was more fully awake, she felt her left hand throbbing. 'How bad is it?'

'Not bad, hinny, just a couple o' little broken bones and a lot o' bruisin'. Only a small flesh wound. Your little finger might heal a bit crooked if you don't exercise it proper but, apart from that, you'll be as good as new.'

Mary stared at the mummified hand. 'Then why am I bandaged up to my wrist, and why does it hurt all over?'

'The bandages is just for the swellin', luv, and to hold the splint in place and keep the wound clean. You'll never know it happened in a few weeks.'

'You mean I can't work all that time?'

'What are you complainin' about – a few weeks on the sick? Don't be daft and shut up now, doctor's comin'. An' remember, you *were* mindin' what you were doin'. Sick pay isn't much but it's better than nothin', and that's just what you'll get if you admit carelessness.'

The days dragged for Mary. She spent her time between her room and the park, and visited Mrs Moynihan every other Sunday. The train ride was her only extravagance, and it relieved her loneliness and boredom. She couldn't knit, but she could still write letters. She had received only one from Joe since the accident, three weeks ago, saying that he was moving the following day but still didn't know where. 'At least I'm versatile,' he'd said. 'My spud bashing and hash throwing talents are useful anywhere but, as the song goes, "I don't know where I'm going until I'm there".'

She had to report to the ambulance room twice a week to have her dressing changed and to sign on for sickness benefit. But she was glad to have something to do. On her next visit she went to see Mr Cowley to ask if he'd received any further news of Joe.

'Just the same as you, lass. I suppose he'll let us know when he gets there. The old lady's worried sick about him an' all.'

'But where can I write to him now?'

'You can still try the old place and they might send it on, but I wouldn' bank on it if I was you. I'm sorry, Mary, I wish I had somethin' more to tell you, but you know our Joe. He probably wrote you a letter an' forgot to post it.'

She appreciated Mr Cowley's optimism, but it didn't lift the cloud hanging over her.

Finally, the big day arrived: the bandages were to be removed and within a week she would be back at work. This was good news, for her tiny savings were by now depleted, having been dipped into every week to make up the rent, even though she'd been skipping lunch to make ends meet. The landlady was strict but not unkind and had offered her a job doing the light dusting and window cleaning in return for a rent reduction, yet still there was no money left for lunch. Her daily letters to Joe cost money to send, and she'd received no further word from him. Her thoughts were obsessed with him. Where was he? How was he?

Eager to be rid of the final dressing, she arrived at the ambulance room ten minutes early and found a different nurse on duty.

'Sit down and just hold your hand still.'

Mary obeyed. The nurse pulled and tugged at the bandages until she got down to the splints. As she tore off the tape, Mary winced. Not daring to look, she averted her eyes, but she had to see. As the splints came off, the little finger, thin and bluish, was lifeless. 'I can't move it! I can't move it!' she cried.

'Nonsense, you're not even tryin'.' The nurse grasped the limp finger and began to move it, and Mary felt a sharp, searing pain. Feeling the contents of her stomach rising, she asked feebly for a bowl, and then her head began to slip away from her.

Later, on opening her eyes, a strange doctor was bending over her.

'How is it? Will it ever be normal?' Her voice was a whisper and her head felt far away.

'Yes, it will, in time. In the meantime, you ought to be more concerned about your general health; you've been out cold for two hours.'

Her throbbing head couldn't take it in. 'Two hours! Why? What happened?'

'We can't be sure at this stage; we'll need to know your medical history.'

She closed her eyes, remembering her mother's blackouts.

'Do you feel like telling me now, or would you rather wait until morning? We're keeping you here overnight. You should be able to leave by then.'

Mary whispered, 'My mother died of diabetes.'

'Of what?' the doctor's voice boomed.

She tried to shout, but her voice was still barely audible. She fixed her eyes on the white-coated figure hastily scribbling notes on the chart he'd removed from the foot of the bed. 'Diabetes,' she whispered again.

After a pause, he said, 'I see. Well, that gives us something to go on. Try to get some rest.'

Mary closed her eyes gratefully and, during fitful bouts of sleep, she dreamed of Joe and her mother.

The next morning the nurse took her pulse and brought her breakfast tray. 'Doctor's written a report for you to take to your own doctor for a physical check-up. We only deal with accidents here. Get your doctor to send a report to us; you'll need it to qualify if you need more sick pay – time's runnin' out on your hand now.'

Mary looked at the hand, trying to move the little finger. But she had no power over it. 'Will it ever . . .?' she began.

'O' course it will. You just keep exercisin' it, and

make sure you make an early appointment with your doctor. I'm off duty now. Good luck, luv!'

Joe was sitting on his bunk writing a letter while the other boys were dressing for a night on the town.

'Hey, Joe, are you comin'? This is our last night before God knows where.' The voice came from a slight seventeen-year-old from Durham, who had attached himself to Joe, admiring his good looks and worldliness.

'Er, yes, I'll meet you later. I'll just finish this first.'

'Must be some smasher if you'd rather write to her than handle the real thing, mate.'

Joe laughed. 'Well, you lads would say she's a smasher all right, but I suppose you're right, she is a long way off. A bird in the hand and all that, and this is our last night.' He tucked the letter under his pillow. 'I'll finish it some other time.' He put on his jacket and set his cap at a jaunty angle. 'Let's hit the high spots, then. This could be our last chance.'

'Dead right, mate! And we're goin' to make the most of it.' It was Bill – tall, blond, handsome Bill, to whom everyone listened. His success with the girls and disdain for his superiors had earned him the respect and admiration of his fellow privates. 'Let's start at the Bull,' he said. 'A couple of draughts there and whatever we can pick up; then the Red Dragon and a look at whatever's there. And after that, me lads, the town's the limit. Onward march!'

Joe joined the troop as they filed out, singing, 'We don't know where we're going until we're there.'

After an hour's wait in the doctor's surgery, Mary was summoned by the receptionist. She had gone to her mother's old doctor but he had left and a new name was on the door.

'Doctor'll see you now, miss,' the girl finally announced.

He was an old, bald man, with a gruff, impatient manner. 'Well, what can I do for you?' he almost barked. She handed him the factory doctor's sealed note nervously. 'Diabetes in the family, eh?'

'Yes, my mother.'

'And your father died of consumption?'

'Yes, before I was born.'

'Age?' he asked, scribbling notes on a yellow pad. 'Sixteen.'

'Well, if you'll just go behind that screen and get undressed to the waist; then lie on the couch and I'll take a look at you.'

He poked and probed all over her, paying a lot of attention to her breasts. His hands were cold and rough. The examination over, Mary gratefully retreated behind the screen and dressed. When she emerged he was seated behind his desk and looked over His horn-rimmed glasses at her.

'Sit down,' he said curtly, pointing to the chair opposite his desk. 'How long have you known you were pregnant?'

Mechanically, she sat down in the chair indicated. 'Pregnant!'

'You didn't know?'

'No.' She gripped the wooden chair arm with her good right hand.

'But you must have known your periods had stopped.'

'Yes, of course, but that often happens when I get upset.'

'Well, I'd say you've got a great deal to be upset about this time. How long since your last period?'

'Three months.' Not since Joe left, she thought miserably.

'Well, that sounds about right. You seem to be at

least three months on. You'd better start making plans. Do you have family?'

'No.'

'Friends?'

'Some.'

'Then I'd suggest you confide in them, and I'd also suggest you decide what you're going to do. If you haven't got money, I can give you a card for St Michael's; they only take cases like yours. Catholic, aren't you?'

'Yes,' she whispered. She knew of St Michael's. Women who went to St Michael's were not only poor, they were also in disgrace, all having babies out of wedlock. She heard his voice faintly over the humming noise in her head.

'Come back and see me if you have any problems. My receptionist will give you a card for St Michael's on your way out.'

Chapter Fourteen

Outside, the fresh air slapped Mary's burning face and jolted her out of her torpor. Was God still wreaking vengeance on her? Now He'd taken Joe from her and she was pregnant and unwed – a fallen woman. But she was going to have a child, Joe's child, a part of both of them. Her emotions were seesawing so much she couldn't keep her mind straight. She must let him know. He would want to marry her. He would want the baby. She loved him and he loved her. Although he'd never actually said the words, she knew he did; the way he made love to her told her as much as any words could, and his mother had always told her he was no good at expressing his feelings.

She reached her door and went up to her room, falling on the bed, sobbing. She didn't know how much time had passed when the sobs finally ceased, but when they did she stroked her belly tenderly. A new life was growing in there, their very own baby, hers and Joe's. God! She must pull herself together – she felt so confused. And she had to go to work on Monday. She would get there early and speak to Mr Cowley then; he might have a new address by now. She'd get up and write the letter immediately. But the sobs had exhausted her and she slept intermittently until the next morning.

Her face was a greyish white and her eyes swollen as she approached Joe's father on Monday morning:

'Have you had any word from Joe? Do you know where he is yet?'

'No, lass, we're still writin' to the old place and hopin' they'll forward them. But don't worry, it was just the same when he was down south; the only time we got a letter was when he needed money. He never was a letter writer. So long as we don't get one o' those War Office letters, he's all right. Our Joe knows how to take care o' himsel'. You tell him off next time you write, and tell him it's time to put pen to paper – to us an' all. His mam's complainin' all the time; she'd love to hear from him, even if all he says is that he got at least one o' her parcels or letters. It's not as if he was actually in the trenches, you know; he's a lot safer wieldin' a screwdriver than a gun.'

His last letter to his parents had informed them that because of his engineering background at college and his apprenticeship at Newfield, Black, he'd been transferred to maintenance, and that he was now a mechanic, repairing and maintaining the precious few vehicles and guns they had. Nevertheless, he was out where all the action was, and Mary knew that his parents were as worried as she was.

'Yes, you're right,' she replied, but her voice didn't sound convincing as she placed a comforting hand on his arm. 'We should be grateful he's not in the fighting, but I desperately need to get in touch with him.'

'Hinny, you're worryin' too much; you're lookin' right peaky this mornin'. How's your hand? Are you up to workin' yet?'

'Oh, it's fine, thank you,' she said, turning to go to the belt. She would write as soon as she got home . . . if only she knew where he was. Damn the war! Why did it have to take Joe away from her just when she needed him most? He would certainly reply to *this* news in a hurry.

Just then Doreen entered and waved as she hung up her coat.

'Doreen, I need to talk to you at break,' Mary whispered as her friend passed her.

'What's up, luv?'

'I can't tell you now; I'll see you later.'

At break they both escaped to the back of the shop. 'I've been worrying about you all morning. What is it? You look terrible.' Doreen sat beside Mary and took her hand. 'You haven't had bad news about Joe, have you?'

'No, Joe's all right. It's me . . . I'm pregnant, Doreen.'

'Dear God! Are you sure?'

'Yes, the doctor says about three months.'

'Oh, you poor kid! What are you going to do?'

'I was so confused when I first got the news, I thought only about the disgrace of being pregnant and unwed, but then I started to think of the baby. I still feel stunned, but I'm going to write to Joe tonight. I know he loves me, Doreen, and I'm sure he'll want the baby and want to marry me. They might even give him compassionate leave.'

Doreen frowned. 'I'm not so sure about compassionate leave, luv; I think they only give that if there's a death in the family.'

'The doctor wants me to have it at St Michael's but I couldn't possibly go there, and I know Joe wouldn't want me to either.'

'You'd best get the news off to him as soon as possible; at least he ought to reply to this letter in a hurry. Let me know if there's anything I can do, luv.'

'Thank you, Doreen. You're a good friend.' She squeezed Doreen's hand.

'You'd better keep it quiet as long as possible. You know what a blabbermouth Maggie is, and we don't want the management knowing until they have to. It's a miracle you're not showing yet. Oh, blow, that bloody bell. We'd better get back.'

It was five miserable weeks before Mary received Joe's reply, forwarded from London. Trembling with excitement, she ripped it open:

Dear Mary,

I'm very sorry to hear you're in trouble – damned rotten luck. I'm also sorry that I'm in no position to help you. Have you told my folks? Perhaps they would lend you some money to help you through, and I'm sure they'd be able to help you have it adopted. I know you'll understand that marriage is out of the question.

Things are getting hotter out here and there's no guarantee that I'll get back in one piece, if at all. And, anyway, Mary, we're both too young to tie ourselves down.

I can understand your point of view; having just found out, you must have been in a very emotional state when you wrote. However, I'm sure that you can be more rational now and see that the best solution for the baby would be to find it some good parents. I certainly don't feel capable of being a good father yet – if ever. Even if I survive this blasted war, there are so many things in life that I still need to do before I'll be ready to settle down. You know I want to finish my education and travel and see the world from a better vantage point than this bloody situation I'm in now, and you're much too young to be bogged down with a family and responsibilities.

I'm sure you'll see my point and do the sensible thing and, again, please don't hesitate to ask my folks for help. I know they'll want to do everything they can to get you out of this mess.

> Look after yourself and let me know how
> you're getting on.
>
> > Yours,
> > Joe

Mary sat staring at the letter long after she had read
its contents. It was several minutes before the tears
came – tears of hurt, anger, and despair. How could
Joe treat her like this? How could he be so cold and
uncaring? This was *his* child. *He* had given it to her,
yet he talked as if it were just an inconvenience and left
it to her to sort out the mess. Her body racked with
sobs. He couldn't get away with this; he would *have*
to share the responsibility. She meant to keep the
child, no matter what. She loved it even now – it was
hers. Even if he didn't want it, she did. Perhaps it was
the war making him so cold and unfeeling. Perhaps his
parents could talk some sense into him . . . Yes, she
would go to them now and tell them everything.

Mrs Cowley was preparing supper when Mary
arrived at six o'clock. 'Why, luv, what's the matter
with you? You look as if you've lost a pound and
found a penny. I'll put the kettle on. Sit yoursel' down
an' I'll be back in a minute.'

Mary sat on the edge of the couch, her hand clutching the letter in the pocket of her voluminous black
skirt. She'd bought some larger clothing at the second-
hand stall and, so far, had managed to escape prying
eyes. 'I don't want any tea, thank you.'

'Come on, luv. What's up? Have you heard from
our Joe? It's not him, is it? My God! He's all right,
isn't he?'

'Yes, he's all right. I mean he's not hurt or anything.
I should have told you before . . . I'm going to have
Joe's child. I was waiting to tell you that we were going
to be married, but he doesn't want to marry me,' she
wailed into the chintz couch arm.

'You're havin' a bairn – Joe's bairn!' Mrs Cowley

exclaimed incredulously, dropping on to the sofa beside Mary. And then, after a pause, while she collected herself: 'How far gone are you?' She looked searchingly at Mary's concealed form.

'Just over four months, I think.'

'God help us! Are you sure? You're not showin'.'

'Yes, I am; it's only these clothes.'

'Dear God! I need some tea even if you don't.' Mrs Cowley got up and retreated, waving her hands in despair.

While she was brewing the tea, Mr Cowley arrived. 'Hello, stranger!' he greeted her warmly. 'You've neglected us since our Joe left.' Then, noticing her red eyes, his face paled. 'He's all right, isn't he?'

'Aye, he's all right,' Mrs Cowley interrupted, bringing in the tea. 'It's her that's not. She's havin' Joe's bairn and he won't marry her. She's had a letter from him. Let's see it, luv.' She put down the tea tray and sat beside Mary, placing a comforting arm round her shoulder.

Mary withdrew her clenched hand from her skirt pocket and passed Mrs Cowley the damp, crumpled letter.

There was pain on the woman's face as she read it aloud, and she sighed as she passed it back to Mary. 'Eey, we're sorry, luv. His granny always said there was a bad streak in him, but I never thought he could do a thing like this.'

Mr Cowley thumped his fist on the table. 'I'll tell you what *I* think: I think we've spoiled that lad rotten and I think it's time we stopped treatin' him like a bairn. He's not gettin' another penny from me. It's high time he learned to stand on his own feet.' He turned to Mary, putting his calloused hand over her clenched knuckles. 'Eey, lass, he's our lad; we'll do what we can, but things aren't too rosy for us neither. Me blood pressure's bad and the doctor wants me to finish work now.' But, glancing at his wife's anxious face, he addressed her: 'Don't worry, hinny; I'll be around to torment the life out o' you a bit longer yet.' And then he turned to Mary: 'She'd have me tucked up in bed already if she had her way. Didn't she tell you, luv? We're movin' to Wales to live with her sister. Couldn't afford to keep this place on. An' anyway, it's time *she* had a break an' all. The sweet shop's doin' next to no business because o' the shortage o' sugar, so there's really nothing left to keep us here.'

'I'm sorry you're not well,' Mary commiserated politely while her mind raced. What else could go wrong? Who else could help her? Mrs Moynihan's brother's flat was already full to bursting point. Anyway, she couldn't travel all that way to work every day, and she'd have to continue working.

Mr Cowley interrupted her thoughts. 'O' course, we'll do what we can. I've got a bit put by, so I can let you have somethin' to help out. Won't be no more than about twenty quid, but that should keep you goin' the time you're not fit to work. After that, lass, I really don't know. Have you thought what you're goin' to do after?'

'Yes, I've thought, and I'm not having it adopted,' she said adamantly.

'Eey, lass,' Mrs Cowley cut in, 'it was our Joe said that, not us. God knows, I couldn't give a bairn o' mine away. But who's goin' to take care of it when you're at work?'

'I'll just have to think of something, don't worry. And thank you for the money; that'll be a big help.'

'I wish we could do more, lass,' Mr Cowley sighed. 'You will write to us and let us know how you're goin' on? As if we all didn't have enough troubles with the war, without our Joe makin' more. I'll write to him and give him a piece o' me tongue.'

'Do you think you could make him change his

mind?' Mary asked hopefully, remembering the main reason for her visit.

'Our Joe? Make him change his mind? Eey, luv, God in heaven couldn't make 'im do that once he's made it up. An', from the sound of his letter, he certainly has. I'll try it, o' course, but I can tell you now, it won't do no good unless he wants to anyhow.'

Mary's mouth tightened into a grim line. 'No, I don't suppose it will, but I'd appreciate it if you'd try.'

It was grey and cold on Sunday when Mary took the train to Mrs Moynihan's. Nevertheless, the train journey was relaxing, the motion calming. A toddler wriggling on his mother's lap eyed Mary intently. She smiled, inadvertently cradling her belly. She would be a mother soon. She wondered how Mrs Moynihan would take the news. As with Joe's parents, she'd waited to tell her until she could soften the blow by including the good news that Joe was going to marry her.

As expected, Mrs Moynihan took the news calmly, giving away her surprise only after Mary had finished her story, with a slight intake of breath and a whispered 'God help you, me poor bairn . . . So the waster's got you into trouble and gone and left you in the lurch. It's always the good ones that catch it. Aye, you and your ma alike – like mother, like daughter, as they say.'

'My mother? She had hard times but at least she wasn't ja fallen woman, like me.'

'Aye, you're right, luv,' Mrs Moynihan quickly corrected herself. 'I don't know what I'm sayin', I'm that upset. When's your time?'

'Around May, I think.'

'You're that far gone, eh?' She sat down heavily. 'You're not showin' yet.'

At this point Molly arrived back from church with

the entire flock, which, including her uncle's children, made eight. Molly hugged her, and Jimmy showed his pleasure by giving her shoulders a rough shake and bellowing, 'Why, it's our Mary. Come for Sunday dinner?'

The little ones scrambled around her and Molly and Mrs Moynihan had to forcibly pick them off. Drawing in a hearty breath, Mrs M. bellowed, 'All o' you! Go on! Get out an' play, and give us some Sunday peace. Dinner won't be for another hour, not till your Uncle Jim gets back from the pub.' She shut the door with a sigh. 'Them kids'll be the death of me yet.' Then, looking at Molly, who was now almost fifteen, 'It's all right, luv, you can stay. The joint's in the oven. I managed to get a scrag end o' mutton and *scrag*'s the word, but the bone will make good soup the morrow. The potatoes and cabbage is on the stove. It's too soon for the Yorkshire puddin', so let's just sit down a bit. It won't hurt you to hear Mary's troubles, Molly. Be a good lesson for you.'

'What's the matter, Mary?' Molly's large, green eyes were concerned. Her blonde hair, now pinned up under her Sunday boater, gave her a ladylike air. The thin, scraggy little schoolgirl was now definitely a part of the past; she was filling out and blooming, and the boys were finally paying her attention. Mrs Moynihan was right to be worried.

'She's fallen, luv, that's what's the matter, and the bugger won't do the right thing.'

'Oh, Mary! Is it Joe?'

Her mother cut in, 'O' course it's Joe, you daft thing. Who else do you think?' Then, turning to Mary, 'What are you goin' to do, hen?'

'I'm going to keep it. I'm not having it adopted.'

'Why, nobody said you was, luv, but you've got to think sensible about where you're goin' to live and how you're goin' to look after it. You can't take it to work with you. War or no war, they wouldn't stand for that.'

'I'm going to try to find another job, with shorter hours, and leave the baby with someone during the day. Then I can look after it during the evenings and weekends.'

'Shorter hours! Weekends! You'll be lucky, luv. They're makin' the workin' week longer, not shorter. There's a war on, you know. An' what about a place to live? As soon as that landlady sees your belly growin', you'll be out on your neck. She'd have a fit if she knew one o' her ladies was in trouble.'

'I've thought of that; I'm going to look for another room and tell them my husband's in the war.'

'You know you're always welcome here, pet; we can always make another bulge in the wall for you – and the bairn. But what you'd do for work around here, I don't know. Molly's job on the farm isn't worth spit; it's heavy work an' the pay's not worth havin', although we do get a bonus of potatoes and vegetables now an' then. I don't want to send her back to town if I can help it, but the way things is goin' it looks like she might have to go back to find a real job that pays.'

'No,' said Mary, 'I know I'll be better staying in town, and I'll move somewhere where no one knows me.'

'Aye, I suppose that's sensible. But they're goin' to know at work; have you thought o' that?'

'Yes, I have, and I'm worried about it, but since I've been back, no one's noticed anything except that I look pale. It's lucky I'm so late in showing. I've just told them my hand's still hurting. It's much better really but I still can't move my little finger much.'

'Aye, it doesn't look right, hinny, but I'm not talkin' about your little finger. What about your belly? You can't hide it in that skirt for ever.'

'I know, Mrs M., my overall is beginning to get tight. I've told Doreen, but not the others yet. I'll have to tell the girls soon, of course, but the rest can just keep their noses out of my business. I don't think they'll sack me. I'm quite good now, and they need all the experienced hands they can get. Ironical, isn't it, the war being lucky for me. I'll just have to keep going and keep on looking for another job. Mr Cowley's money's going to be a Godsend.'

'Aye, a right Godsend, that, but it's not goin' to last for ever. You'll need stuff for the baby. Eey, an' I just gave the bairns' pram away to me neighbour last week.'

Molly, who had been sitting open-mouthed during the conversation, suddenly came alive. 'Me friend Annie's ma might want to sell hers. She just had an operation an' Annie overheard her talkin' to her granny. Somethin' went wrong and now she won't be able to have any more bairns. I've seen it; it's seen a bit o' wear but it's good for one more.'

Mrs Moynihan stood up, rubbing her back. 'It'd have to be really cheap, luv; have you thought o' the cost o' sendin' it to town?' She sighed, 'Well, I suppose I'd better get me lazy bones movin' and put that Yorkshire puddin' in. You know if our Jim comes back from the pub with a skinful and there's no dinner ready, there'll be hell to pay.'

'I'll set the table,' Mary said, standing up.

'Aye, hinny, an' we can talk some more afore the gang comes in. Molly, you go outside and keep them busy another five minutes and then mind that they all wash their hands first. The basin's beside the rain butt, an' I don't want none o' them puttin' their soapy hands in me rainwater.'

Mrs Moynihan tipped some hot fat and juices from the meat tray into a large baking tin and poured in the thin pudding batter, all the while keeping her eye on

Mary, who was moving deftly round the table, setting places.' 'Our Mary, you always was a skinny little whelk. How long since you had a square meal? You've got two to feed now, you know; you can't scrimp on your dinners now.'

'I have been eating, but I feel a bit queasy in the mornings.'

'Aye, I thought so. An' you'll be feelin' even queasier if you don't get some good square meals down yoursel'. Why don't you come over here at weekends, luv? You could come straight from work on Saturday and stay over until Sunday night. At least I can see to it that you get some nourishin' food into you.'

'I'd love to, but I can't manage it every week. The train fare's just gone up again.' Mary was finishing mixing the mustard, the yellow powder forming sticky lumps as it mingled with the water. The sight made her stomach turn over, as did the smell of cabbage. But she knew there would be no escaping lunch under Mrs Moynihan's watchful eye.

'God help us! Here comes our Jim, pickled, as usual, on a Sunday afternoon. I wish I had half the money he spends at the boozer every weekend. Takes after his da with that. At least he doesn't get nasty with it, like his da, though. He'll just fill his belly full o' dinner and conk out for the rest o' the afternoon till openin' time the night.' She flung open the scullery door, yelling, 'Molly, bring them kids in now. Dinner's ready.'

Chapter Fifteen

When Mary arrived at work early the following day, Doreen was the first to greet her. 'Have you heard anything, luv?'

'Yes, and he doesn't want to marry me.' Mary busied herself tying up her hair in the regulation blue scarf, the tears starting at the sound of the concern in her friend's voice.

'The bastard! He actually said he won't?'

'Oh, yes! Joe doesn't mince words. He wants me to have it adopted, but I don't care what happens, I'm not going to. And would you believe it, Doreen, he actually signed the letter "Yours, Joe". You'd think it was a business letter.'

Doreen's jaw dropped. 'Oh, you poor thing. If there's anything I can do to help . . .'

'Maybe you could come over this evening and help me sort out in my mind what I'm going to do. I felt confused before, but now I'm confused *and* desolate.'

'Of course, luv, I'll be at your place at seven.'

'Any word yet from Mike?' Mary asked, trying to take her mind off her own worries, but knowing that if Doreen had heard anything she would have assailed her with the news.

'No, still no word, but missing doesn't mean dead, and I'm not giving up hope till I hear definitely. Look, luv, here's Maggie and the rest. Try not to let them see there's anything wrong. If I don't manage to see you at break, I'll see you at dinner time.'

'Not here. I'll go to the gate.'

'All right, luv. Try to keep your pecker up. Here comes the avalanche.'

The girls arrived in a cluster after their customary make-up session in the washroom, Maggie at the head, as usual. 'Why Mary, hinny, you're lookin' a bit peaky this mornin'. Feelin' all right?' Her piercing voice alerted the entire shop floor.

'Oh, I'm fine, just tired.'

'You certainly don't look fine, luv. How's that lad o' yours – still in the land o' the livin'?'

'Yes, he's fine.' Mary averted her face as she answered, angry at herself for blushing. If anyone else asked her how Joe was she'd scream. She'd like to tell them just how Joe really was – a dirty, rotten, unfeeling bastard. No! He wasn't really; it was just the war distorting his perceptions. He'd feel different by the time he got her next letter; he'd have had more time to think.

'Oh, sorry I asked. Got out o' the wrong side of the bed this mornin'?'

Maggie peered curiously at Mary as she spoke and Mary, in no mood to put up with the banter, turned slowly to face her. 'How's *your* "man" situation, Maggie? Still hunting for one?' Her voice had an unusual, biting tone.

'Eey, why listen to that, girls. Our Mary's gettin' a sharp tongue in her old age. Aye, I'm still huntin', regular as clockwork at the Old Ass, but there's not much there, you know. You got the pick o' the bunch just in the nick o' time afore he left, Mary. There's nothing there now but old men lookin' to find out if they can still do it, or school lads lookin' to find out if they can learn to do it. Either way, I'm willin' to oblige. Half a loaf's better than no bread, as they say.' She wiggled her round buttocks. 'And you can all see that I'm not goin' short.'

Lilly, as plump and plain and jolly as ever, cut in, 'Hey, Mag, are you still gettin' on at our little Mary? Let up, now. You know she's doin' a damn sight better fo' hersel' than you are.' She then delivered Mary a hearty slap on the back that left her with a hollow reverberating sensation in her chest.

'You've been very quiet since you got back, luv,' Enid remarked. 'We'll have to catch up on your news at dinner time. Aw, God help us, here comes the new foreman. I wish old Cowley was back. This one's a real pain in the backside. See that you keep your eyes down and your hands movin'; it doesn't matter if they're doin' anything useful or not, just so long as he sees them fingers dancin'. Ta ta for now! Into battle, lasses.' The gang marched to their places, Maggie winking at the foreman on the way.

Mary couldn't handle the nuts and bolts at her usual speed; her left hand was still stiff and painful. Today her mind was on Joe's letter and she was slower than ever. This didn't escape the new foreman's notice; she saw him looking in her direction several times, until she became so nervous she could barely move her hands at all. She was also nauseated, and the constantly moving belt made her feel dizzy. Everything was late with this pregnancy; she hadn't felt sick the first three months, why now? Several times she had to disappear into the lavatory, and lunch time was a welcome break. Although still feeling queasy, she forced herself to eat her sandwich; she'd need the energy to get through the afternoon.

Doreen came bounding over and sat down beside her on the kerb outside the gate. Mary usually ate her lunch here when weather permitted; just getting outside the factory gates helped to break up the day.

'You look as white as a sheet, luv. I could kill that bastard.' Doreen's genuine concern fired Mary's growing self-pity, and she burst into tears.

'Here's the letter, read for yourself.'

'Blimey, what a hard, unfeeling bugger,' Doreen said as she folded the letter. 'You're right, luv. He seems very definite; I can't see much hope he'll change his mind.'

'No, neither can I. Now I'm really in disgrace – pregnant and not even a fiancé.'

'It's rotten news, luv. I suppose you've really got to start to think now what you're going to do.'

'I've got a sentence for life as a marked woman, Doreen.' Mary gave way to tears again.

'Holy Moses! Stop worrying about what other people think; just you think of the baby and yourself.'

Mary's voice was bitter: 'How dare that bastard say he's not ready to raise a family when he was ready enough to start one!'

'Hey, that doesn't sound like you, Mary. Have you gone off Joe? I mean your feelings for him?'

'Well, it's hard to be "on" someone who gets you into trouble and then leaves you holding the baby – literally in this case,' she said wryly. 'I wrote him a very strong letter last night; I told him it's his duty to do the right thing by his child *and me*.' She sighed. 'But his parents know him better than I do and they said he's not likely to change his mind.'

'I know what they mean. Oh, I know you loved him and all that, Mary, but he always was, well, a bit selfish and irresponsible. Frankly, it doesn't really surprise me.'

'You mean you never liked him all the time I was going out with him, and you never said so?'

'I didn't say I didn't like him, luv. Crikey, he was very handsome and charming, and I could see why you fell for him. But there's more to folk than good looks and charm. I never thought he was a *bad* sort; I just didn't think he was very mature for his age. Oh, anyway, what's the point of talking like this now?'

'No point, but it's interesting to hear you say that. I suppose I should have seen it. But it may not be too late; he might change his mind. This might make him grow up, after he's had more time to think about it.'

The siren went. 'Good God! Already!' Doreen gasped. 'We'd better run. I'll come over and talk to you at tea break, if I can get a private word in with those nosy parkers swarming all over the place.'

The next couple of weeks dragged and Mary was finding it more and more difficult to conceal her shape. Maggie was, of course, the first to catch on. As Mary took advantage of tea break to embark on one of her frequent trips to the lavatory, Maggie's big blue eyes scanned her thoughtfully. 'You know, if I didn't know our little Mary better, I'd say she's got something up her sleeve – or rather up her skirt. Are you in the family way, luv? You can tell your auntie Mag.'

Mary turned crimson. 'What's it got to do with you, Maggie? At least I know who the father is, which is more than you could say. One of these days your luck will run out.'

'Gettin' gutsy in more ways than one, eh? Motherhood's helpin' you to find the sharp edge o' your tongue at last. But it's not *luck* with me, luv, it's takin' care, pure and simple. If you don't know how to handle a situation, you shouldn' get yoursel' into it.'

'Shut up, Maggie. You're not funny,' cut in Lilly, while all eyes turned in Mary's direction.

'Eey, we're sorry, kid. You of all people.' Edna's kind remark was followed by a brief, stunned silence while they all tried to take in the amazing news. Maggie, penitant, broke the silence as the girls gathered round Mary.

'You know I didn't mean it, luv. Sometimes me tongue runs away with me. I'm sorry. If you'd told

179

me sooner, maybe I could've helped you do somethin' about it.'

'Maybe she didn't want to, Mag,' said Lilly. 'What are you goin' to do, Mary? Does Joe know?'

'I should be hearing from him soon,' Mary said, still clinging to the faint hope that he might change his mind when he got her second letter.

'When are you due, then?' Maggie asked, dropping her usual flippant manner.

'I'm not exactly sure, but the doctor thinks around May.'

'Golly, you're that far on,' exclaimed Maggie. 'You're not showin' much yet, but you will soon. Eey, we'll do what we can to cover for you, but once old beady-eyes over there catches on, he'll give you the push. First thing you've got to do is get a bigger overall. I've got a spare I'll bring in the morrer for you; you can have it till your time's up. Never thought I'd see your little bum in my great big finery,' she giggled. 'Eey, I'm not laughin' at you, Mary, honest.' She sobered her voice again. 'It's just hard for me to keep me face straight for long. Don't take any notice of me in future if I get on your nellie.'

Mary had seen at least ten rooms, but none of them suitable. Either the rent was too high or the landladies didn't want children around or, even worse, they guessed she wasn't married and made transparent excuses. She'd have to find somewhere quickly, before she was thrown out of her present room. She'd been wearing her shawl wrapped loosely round her shoulders and pinned over her belly, but she knew she couldn't fool the old woman much longer.

At last she found a place she could afford, and the landlady didn't seem to mind babies if they were kept quiet. It was a very small attic and she could see light through the ceiling. No doubt it would leak when it rained, but it faced south and was sunny and cheerful; maybe she could stuff up the cracks. It was cheap at three and six a week.

It was sparsely furnished with the usual iron bedstead, juglet stand, chest of drawers, wardrobe, and small bedside table and chair. But the fireplace had two trivets, which caught Mary's eye; at least she could heat up food over the fire and make tea when she didn't feel like going down to the kitchen. She decided not to voice her thoughts to the landlady lest there was a rule about cooking in the rooms. There was space for a cot, but she couldn't possibly get a pram up three flights of stairs. 'I'd like to take it if it would be all right to leave my pram in the hall,' she said to the weary looking, fragile old woman. Her mobcap and apron looked too large for her emaciated body, and her eyes too large for her thin face. She clutched a crumpled white handkerchief into which she coughed periodically. But the voice was surprisingly strong. 'Aye, that'd be all right, but I can't hold the room for you without a week's rent.'

Quickly Mary delved into her purse and withdrew her last half-crown. 'Will this do till Saturday when I'll bring my things?'

'Aye, hinny. That'll do. Just come round any time Saturday and I'll have your key ready.'

Thank God for that, Mary thought as she walked home. She wished she had taken more money with her; now she had no change for the tram fare, and her feet were swollen and tired. But thank heaven for Mr Cowley's money, now safely stashed in a brown envelope under her mattress.

She would let the old woman know she was leaving as soon as she got home. At the thought of getting home, her pace quickened. The post would have arrived by now. Maybe there'd be a reply from Joe to her second letter. She opened the door hurriedly and whisked through the pile of letters on the hall table with excited fingers. Nothing for her.

When Mary finally broke the news to the landlady, the old woman's face didn't change. 'Aye, I've been expectin' it. I didn't say nothin' 'cause I thought you'd have enough sense yoursel' to get movin'. I'm surprised at you! I would have thought you'd have more decency. You can't tell about people nowadays,' she added, shaking her head.

Mary felt ashamed. This was the first overt disapproval she'd received. She knew there'd be a lot more to come, and she wasn't looking forward to it. She'd always cared a lot about what people thought of her and had been proud of her good reputation. Her mother had been proud, too, she mused, remembering the lace curtains at the window of the empty parlour. What was it Mrs Moynihan had said? 'Like mother, like daughter.' Maybe that's what she meant.

Mary went up to her room and sobbed tears of humiliation and self-pity. Why did this have to happen to her? Why could the Maggies of this world do the same thing and get away with it? Yes, she admitted, she had enjoyed making love – more even than she'd allowed Joe to know. She'd thought he might lose respect for her if he knew she wasn't doing it just for him; she'd always been afraid that he'd think her unladylike, and *now* look at her, a woman of shame. Her big mistake was in not being clever about it, like Maggie. She stroked her belly. Yet despite everything, she loved this baby.

The next day, the letter arrived. She tore open the envelope in a frenzy of excitement, her eyes barely able to focus on the scrawled note it contained:

Dear Mary,
    I received your letter and I'm sorry you're taking it so badly. I know it's a rotten situation

to be in and I'm very sorry things have turned out like this, but I'm just not able to do anything about it. I've thought about things some more, but just keep coming up with the same answer – I'd be no good for either you or the baby. I'd make a lousy husband and an even worse father. I'm just not ready for that sort of life yet, Mary, and I couldn't deal with it. You're good with children, and I know you'd give the baby enough love for two parents, if you're determined to keep it, that is. However, I'm still convinced that the best solution would be to have it adopted. Think about it some more, Mary. I'm sure you'll see sense in the end.

I hope you're feeling well and are coping with everything all right, and I hope also the money from Dad will help you out with expenses.

Again, I'm very sorry about this mess and hope everything goes well for you.

Take care of yourself,

Joe

Mary stared at the words. Her heart had sunk to the pit of her stomach, which thumped inside, but she felt too dead to notice the baby kicking. And then she came alive. How dared he treat her like this? She wasn't just some trollop to have a fling with and then throw away like spoiled merchandise. She wouldn't let him get away with it. If he wouldn't marry her, he'd have to pay, and pay through the nose. If he refused to be a father to his own child, the least he could do would be to support it, and its mother. Anger overwhelmed her. She had never felt this angry. She remembered her mother's fits of anger, and how, as a child, she used to hide from her until they had subsided. Like mother, like daughter, she thought again, as she pulled out her dresser drawer and grabbed her pad and pen. Her hands, shaking as she started to write, calmed as she set her anger on paper:

Dear Joe,

I've just received your letter and I find it hard to believe that you could be so selfish and thoughtless about me. It took both of us to get me into this mess and it's going to take both of us to get me out of it. If you won't do the right thing by me morally, the least you can do is pay for your fun and do the right thing financially to help keep your child and its mother out of the poorhouse. And to think I thought you loved me! How could I have been so blind and stupid?

How long do you think your father's money is going to last? I intend to keep this baby, and I don't expect you to leave me in disgrace *and* poverty. The least you can do is send me money every week. For now, you could send me half your Army allowance. I know you don't get much, but what else can you spend it on over there except beer and women when you have the chance? When you come back and get a job, we'll discuss it again.

By the time you get this letter and I get a reply, it might almost be my time, so please send the first week's money with your letter.

I hope God keeps you safe out there, if only so that you can make amends for your sins over here.

Mary

Chapter Sixteen

It was mid-April and still no letter from Joe. Mary had handed in her notice at the factory. She could no longer stand at the belt all day long; her blood pressure was high and she had been warned by her doctor to rest until the baby was born.

Time dragged and her money dwindled. The doctor's visits were a heavy drain on her resources and she had already delved into Mr Cowley's money, which she had sworn to keep until the baby came. Reluctantly, she had agreed to have the baby at St Michael's; she simply couldn't afford hospital bills. A charity organisation for unwed mothers – would she ever be able to hold up her head again? The next step down would be the poorhouse, and she'd rather kill herself than sink that low.

Lying on her bed all day gave her much time to think, and the more she thought, the more bitter she felt. She would have sunk completely had it not been for Doreen's regular visits; evening could never come soon enough. The doorbell finally rang and she heard her friend talking to the landlady. 'I'll just put it here; is that all right?'

'Aye, I told her she could leave it there. I didn't know it was goin' to be such a big one, though. I suppose me other lodgers'll just have to squeeze past it. It's goin' to damage the wall an' all,' she added in a surly tone.

'Oh, don't worry, Mrs Foster,' Doreen reassured

her, 'I'm sure she'll look out for the wall. I was lucky to find one at all, never mind pick and choose the size.'

The ancient door creaked and Doreen's head poked into Mary's tiny room. 'Hello, luvvy. How are you feeling?'

'Pretty rotten, but I'm glad to see you; I'd go out of my mind up here if it weren't for you.' Mary's voice was thin and her face grey. The window was closed but a heavy wind blew through the cracks and the chimney, carrying with it the smell of decaying fruit and vegetables from the greengrocer's next door, which mingled with the omnipresent factory smoke and filled the air. 'The stench is nauseating in here. Thank goodness it's not a fish shop down there,' Mary complained to her friend.

'Well, it could be worse. My house is only a few doors from the knacker's yard. You wouldn't believe the stench! If it comes to rotting carcasses or rotting vegetables, I know which I'd choose any day. But never mind, luv, I've got something downstairs to cheer you up.' Doreen's usually soft voice was deliberately loud and forced; she was concerned about her friend. 'I got that pram I saw advertised. It's in nice condition and it's a big one.'

'Thanks, Doreen; I'll go down and see it later. How much do I owe you?'

'Nothing, luv. That's a present for the baby. We passed the hat round at work and it's from all the girls. Even Maggie chipped in. Can you believe it? Our stingy, mingy Maggie actually put her hand in her pocket.'

'That was nice of them. Funny, isn't it? People will sometimes give money more freely than their time; not one of them's been to see me. Not that I blame them, I'm not much fun to be with at the moment. I feel as though my dancing days are over for ever,' she added, her hands resting on her swollen belly.

'I know, luv, but it's not that they don't care about you. You know how the girls are; every free minute they're out of that sweatshop they want to be enjoying themselves, dancing or drinking or both.' Doreen yawned and lay back in the lumpy chair.

'How about *you* enjoying yourself, Doreen? Have you had any word?' Mary still went through the formality of asking.

'No, not yet. But you know me, I'm not giving up hope till I know for sure.' Doreen changed the subject. 'I picked up a couple of fresh eggs on the way. Let's have some toast and a boiled egg. I'm starving. Mum's doing liver and onions tonight – anything to get out of that.'

'Sounds good. I've got a bottle of lemonade up here. Let's have some first and then I'll waddle down with you to the kitchen. It's a busy time now with everyone getting home from work; I usually go later to avoid the crowd – and the looks,' she added bitterly.

Doreen looked anxiously at her. 'I take it you haven't had any good news recently. That swine still ignoring you?'

'Yes, but not for much longer.' Mary's tone was determined.

'What do you mean?' Doreen leaned forward curiously.

'I mean I intend to do something about it. I've had a lot of time to think since I've been stuck up here, and I've decided if he doesn't do his duty by the time the baby's born, I'm going to take him to court.'

Doreen's brown eyes widened. 'You! Take Joe to court! Golly me, I'd never have believed it. Becoming a mother has certainly brought out the fighting spirit in you.'

'I have another life to think of now; I can't afford to be soft any longer, and I'm fed up with men messing up my life, Doreen. I've had enough, first my uncle and now Joe. I'm just not going to take it any more. I'm also going to write to my dearest, long lost Uncle Joseph and my honorary Aunt Roseanne – the bitch! She's living a lady's life in what should have been *my* home and spending *my* money.'

'Golly me!' Doreen repeated. 'You *are* pulling out all the stops. Well, I can't blame you for trying with your uncle. After all these years, Roseanne's novelty must've worn off; maybe he's not so much under her thumb now. I don't know about Joe, though. As I see it, if you haven't heard from him by now, it means you're not going to. But taking him to court, that's a bit drastic, and it's a nasty business. Maybe when he gets back and sees the baby he'll change his mind. The war does funny things to people, you know.'

'I know taking him to court is drastic, but so is the trouble he's got me into.'

Doreen's eyes grew even wider at the bitterness in Mary's voice. 'Mary, be careful! I know he's being a waster, but he couldn't have got you into trouble if you hadn't let him. I hate to say it, but it's true, luv. You could have said no if you'd wanted to, and the court will go into all that. It's not as if he forced you. And believe me, Joe would make mincemeat out of you if you tried to say he did.'

'I see! So you're telling me I'm a loose woman and it's my own fault.' Mary's voice was trembling and she was near to tears. 'You think just the way everybody else does.'

'No, I don't, Mary,' Doreen placated. 'All I mean is that you made a mistake; you *are* half responsible, you know. It takes two to polka, and when the dance is over it's always the woman that pays for the music; it's just the way things are. I think if you still want Joe – and I know you do – you'll squash any chances there are that he might come back to you. Why don't you hold off a bit till the baby's here and the war's

over? You'll not get much out of him while he's on
Army pay anyhow, even if you can take him to court
while he's fighting for his country. And that would
go against you, too; you know how soppy people
are about the war. Any bloody spud-bashing, beer-
swilling rookie is a hero if he's "over there". If you wait
and do it friendly-like when he's back, you'll get more
money or, better still, maybe you'll even get him.'

'I suppose you're right as usual, Doreen,' Mary
sighed. 'But I thought if he got a court order to pay,
he might decide he'd be better off marrying me. At
least he'd have a free housekeeper and bed partner for
his money,' she added sourly.

'Phweeoo! You don't sound like you at all, Mary.
It must be your nerves affecting you.' Doreen looked
with concern at her friend. 'Are you sure you're feeling all right?'

'No, I'm not! And it's *not* my nerves; I'm just seeing
sense for once in my life. I want fair play.'

'It sounds a bit like revenge to me, luv. Are you
sure you won't wait till you're feeling yourself again
before you decide about Joe? Why not just write to
your uncle first? If you get money from him, you
wouldn't win a court case anyhow; you'd have to go
through a means test, you know.'

Mary looked surprised. 'I never thought of that.
You're always so practical, Doreen. You're right, I
mustn't let my anger take me over; I'll just write to
Uncle Joseph and see what happens. I was dreading
the idea of a court case anyway.'

'Well, I'm glad that's settled.' Doreen sighed with
relief and stood up. 'My stomach's rattling so I can't
hear myself think. Let's get those eggs on and make
some toast; I think malnutrition's affecting your
brain. You can see the pram on the way down – that'll
cheer you up.'

*   *   *

Two weeks later Mary admitted herself to St Michael's. As soon as her labour pains started, she grabbed her two nightdresses, and three she had made for the baby from one of her old ones. Mrs Moynihan had knitted her a white wool shawl and some tiny vests and booties. She wanted to get there early, while she could still walk. Spending money on a taxi was extravagant and the tram was out of the question – people would stare at her. She thanked God that the grim, red-brick building was only five streets away.

A granite-faced nun in a black habit answered her frantic pulling on the doorbell. The face was old, yet solid and unlined; it was as if the skin had petrified while still young, before it had had time to form any signs of laughter or sadness. 'No need to make such a rumpus.' The stone face didn't seem to move when it talked; the words simply issued from the thin, barely parted lips. 'You'll wake the whole place up. I can see why you're here. Name?'

'Mary Maddison,' Mary gasped to the face, which was all she could see, as the black habit blended with the blackness of the hallway. The pains were getting stronger now and she had to hold on to the doorpost for support.

'Follow me. You'll have to wait until a bed's made up for you. We're short of beds.'

When the face turned away, Mary had to follow the voice until her eyes became accustomed to the gloom. The last rays of daylight were struggling to reach the hall and staircase from a dust-laden skylight. Thank God it was only one flight to climb. The face flung open a door, revealing a small cubicle containing a bed with a bare, horsehair-filled mattress, and a wooden kitchen chair. 'Sit down till I get the bed made.'

Mary eased herself on to the hard chair gratefully and watched the black figure retreat and return, arms laden with a grey rubber sheet, which she arranged carefully over the blue and white striped mattress. 'You might as well start taking your things off. I see you've got a bag. Got a nightdress and baby clothes?'

'Yes,' Mary whispered feebly. She couldn't sit on the wooden chair much longer.

'Well, get your nightdress on.' The face was bent over the bed. 'You can lie down now. When did the pains start?'

Mary eased herself gratefully on to the rigid bed; even the cold rubber sheet was blissful comfort to her aching back after the wooden chair. 'About an hour,' she whispered.

'First one?' The face glowered, throwing a red wool blanket over Mary's prostrate form. Mary nodded her answer, too embarrassed to say anything. This was worse than going to confession; she didn't have to confess – her sin was visible to the world. But her baby was coming. How could she possibly consider her baby a sin?

'I'd say you have a while to go yet; just pull the cord above the bed if you need anything. Father Malone will be up soon to hear your confession. It's enough that children have to come into this world bearing their own original sin, without the burden of their mothers' transgressions as well.' With that the black silhouette whisked up Mary's clothes and the door banged shut.

Mary lay there, panting and gripping the iron bed rails above her head, frantically pulling on the cord whenever she felt a severe pain coming on, only to receive a rebuke from the nun for being such a baby. 'You've a while to go yet and I've got other things to do than keep on running up and down on wild goose chases. You'll know all right when it's coming. Keep your eye on the clock on the wall and I don't want to hear another peep out of you until the pains are at least three minutes apart. Oh, and Father Malone's been called to a deathbed, so he may not be able to get to you before tomorrow.'

Thank God for that reprieve, Mary thought. She had blisters on her hands from gripping the rails so hard, and the perspiration running into her eyes blurred her vision so that she had trouble seeing the clock. She'd never dreamed it would be this bad; would this night never end?

It was two o'clock before the pains came every three minutes and she dared to pull the cord again. The nun arrived, this time with a white-robed novice, whom she immediately sent away to get hot water. Donning a rubber apron, she whisked off the red blanket, saying, 'All right now, bend your knees and do as I tell you. You're lucky for your first time; it could have gone on much longer.'

Mary had no idea how long she had slept, but the moment she dragged her consciousness up from the depths of night to dawn, she remembered: she had a baby boy! And he was perfect! The mumble of voices in the background grew louder as she surfaced into reality. She opened her eyes to find herself in a long, green-painted room, with at least a dozen beds, all occupied by young girls and women. The occupant of the next bed, a girl about her own age, with bright red curly hair and striking emerald eyes set in a round, pretty face, exclaimed, 'I thought you'd never wake up! How are you feelin'?'

Mary moved her aching body underneath the red blanket and sighed, 'I hurt all over; I feel like one big bruise.'

'Aye, I know what you mean. What did you have then?'

'A boy,' Mary said dreamily. 'What about you?'

'Aye, I had a little lad as well. Makes you feel funny, doesn't it? Being a ma, I mean. What do they call you? I'm Doris Leeming.'

'Mary Maddison,' she whispered; somehow, giving her name seemed to advertise her shame. 'What time is it, and when will I see my baby?'

'It's six o'clock and they'll be bringin' them in any time now fo' feedin'. They keep them in the nursery, except fo' feedin' time, until we can get up and look after our own. And then we have to look after the new ones as well until their mothers can get up.'

'When did you have yours?' Mary asked. It was nice to be talking to someone in the same situation – at least she felt like an equal.

'Yesterday mornin',' Doris replied. 'Thank God that's over. Never again, not even when I'm married – that's supposin' some bloke'll ever ask me now. I never want to go through that caboodle again.'

'Me neither,' Mary agreed, straining her eyes towards the door as she heard the thumping of heavy-soled boots outside. Oh God, she thought, as in marched the face from the night before, carrying a tightly wrapped white bundle. Behind her came more black silhouettes and some women in nightdresses and shawls, all carrying similar bundles.

The face handed her the bundle. 'He's been crying a bit but he's had a good sleep. He's very hungry now. He'll let you know when he's had enough. And don't hold him after he's finished; just lay him beside you till we come for him. Too much holding and they cry when they're left alone, and we haven't got time to hold them whenever they want it.'

Mary took the baby in her arms as if he were made of tissue paper. She'd had plenty of experience with Mrs Moynihan's children, but a new-born baby was different, and he was hers . . . her David. She'd decided to call him David, as the name Joseph had too many unpleasant associations. Strange that the two men in her life who had made her most unhappy

193

shared the same name. She had still not received a reply from her uncle. But at this moment she could think only of the little warm body in her arms. She examined every feature again: the shock of fair hair, the blue eyes, and the little turned-up nose. It was difficult to say if he resembled his father at this stage; she didn't mind if he had inherited Joe's good looks, but she hoped he didn't have the same disposition. He was beautiful, and he was hers.

He sucked so eagerly at her breast that she was worried lest he choke; she kept easing him away so that he might take a breath, and so that she might take another look at him. When he started to slow down, she carefully unwrapped the shawl and undid the ribbons of his gown, just to make sure he was as perfect as she remembered him from the night before. He was wearing a rough cotton nappy, peeping out from an outer covering of the same grey rubber as the bedsheet in the labour room. Oh God! She'd forgotten to bring his soft white nappies. She must ask Doreen to bring them when she came to visit.

He was sleeping peacefully now and she cradled him to her as tightly as she dared lest she smother him, covering his face in kisses.

A dark figure approached the bed. 'That's enough now! Leave him be when he's quiet, or he'll turn into a spoilt brat, wanting attention all the time.' The sound issued from the petrified lips as the black shadow bent over her and removed the baby.

As soon as the nun was at a safe distance, Mary whispered to Doris, 'That one gives me the creeps. Who is she?'

Doris pulled a face. 'Aye, me as well. She's the sister-in-charge of layin'-in; she always looks after the new ones the first day. I had her yesterday; you're welcome to her. Sister Monica's her name. Some o' the others is better, especially the ones with the white head-dresses; they're the novices. They haven't had time to get so frostbitten. If you need anythin' special, ask Sister Veronica; she actually smiles sometimes. That's the one comin' down the aisle now with the breakfast trolley. Thank the Lord! Me stomach thinks me throat's been cut.'

The one in question approached Mary. The face, shrouded in white, was round and generous, the brown eyes bright, and the full lips even sensuous. Mary wondered how long it would be before the young, pretty face petrified like Sister Monica's. 'You're Mary Maddison, aren't you?' The voice was kind.

'Yes.' Mary reached out gratefully for the proffered tray.

The nun put her hand in her pocket and propped an envelope against the mug of tea. 'Your friend came this morning. On her way to work she went to see how you were and was told you'd gone, so she picked up your post and kindly brought it for you. You're not supposed to have visitors on your first day, but I don't suppose a letter will hurt.'

Mary forgot the tea and bread and butter. She grabbed her knife and slit open the envelope, unsuccessfully trying to read the blurred postmark. It wasn't Joe's writing; it was from Uncle Joseph:

Dear Mary,
    I received your letter and was sorry about your news, although not surprised. I'm very sorry that I can't be of much help to you. The war hasn't been kind to the business, and it's hard to get good help. I'm having to work in the allotments myself, as well as at all my other duties. Roseanne has had to take over the financial side, as I'm just too tied up with other things. We now have two children and a third on the way, and

I'm afraid our funds barely stretch to keep us fed and clothed and to prevent the estate from going bankrupt. Surely, the father should be responsible for his own child?

I'm sending you a gift of five pounds, which Roseanne doesn't know about. She'd quite rightly be distressed to think that money that should be feeding our little ones is going to someone else. I hope it helps out until you can resume your job. I hope also that God continues to watch over you.

Your uncle,

Joseph

Chapter Seventeen

Leaving St Michael's and carrying her precious bundle home, Mary could hardly wait to take care of him herself without having to take orders from the nuns, though how she was going to survive without help from her uncle or from Joe was a nagging problem.

She bought the paper on the way; she couldn't afford to waste any time finding a job and finding someone to look after David during the day. Back in her room she put David in his new cot and lit the fire. She needed something hot to eat but she had nothing but a tin of pilchards, which she opened and ate from the can, screwing up her nose in distaste. There was half a tin of milk on the dresser; she sniffed it and it was still all right. At least she could have some hot tea if she went down for water. She glanced at David in the cot; he was sleeping.

Returning with the water, she sat beside the now cheerful fire and put the kettle on to boil. She opened the paper and scanned the jobs columns. They wanted women to work on the land but she'd have to travel out of town and that was out of the question. And then something caught her eye: Newfield, Black were looking for workers again. No, she couldn't go back there, even if they would have her; she needed something with shorter hours now. A grocer wanted a part-time assistant, three mornings a week. No. That wouldn't pay enough to live on. Just then there were footsteps on the stairs and a loud rap on her door.

Not expecting anyone, she opened it curiously and there stood Doris with her little white bundle in her arms.

'Hello, Mary, I thought I'd drop in an' give you a welcome home. Thought you might be feelin' a bit lonely an' strange like, bein' home for the first time. I know I did yesterday.'

'Doris! Lovely to see you. Come on in. I was just about to make a cup of tea.'

'Oh, thanks, I could do with one, luv. Bloody freezin' spring we're havin'.' Doris placed her bundle carefully on the bed and sat down on the floor in front of the fire. Seeing the open newspaper, she exclaimed: 'Don't tell me you're lookin' for a job already? You'll need a bit of time to recover and spend quietly with the bairn.'

'I wish I could, Doris, but it's out of the question. I'll have to find something straight away.'

'Aye, I suppose you've got no choice. I'm lucky havin' me da an' his pension, an' Harry's agreed to pay two bob a week for the bairn – not that that'll go far.'

'My old company is advertising for more workers. I never thought I could go back there, but at least I know I can live on the wages. So much for my dreams of shorter hours!'

'Well, you know, you can always leave the bairn with me during the day, luv. I'm stuck with one, might as well be stuck with two.'

'Oh, thank you, Doris; I might take you up on that but only if I pay you.'

'You can pay for the bairn's bottles an' his food later on, but nothing else, luv. It won't cost me nothin'; why should I charge you?'

'Well, we'll argue about that later, but thanks; it would certainly help me to get started.'

'Well, you know my address, an' I'm home most of

the time except when I'm doin' the shoppin'.'

'Talking of shopping, I have nothing in the house.'

'Well, after tea let's go out an' see what we can find, luv. I've got the pram downstairs.'

'And mine's in the hall; we can take them out for their first proper outing. I don't know what I'd have done if I hadn't met you in that place.'

'Me neither! That is, once I got used to that posh voice o' yours and found out you weren't no different from anybody else. I must say I thought you were a bit snooty that first mornin' though.'

'Well, I thought you were wonderful and I was delighted to have someone to talk to. Still am. Come on, let's give the prams their first outings.'

On arriving back from the shopping trip, Mary went down to the empty kitchen; it was wonderful to have it to herself until the other lodgers got home from work. She left David in his pram in the hall where she could keep an eye on him and started to make a stew. She'd managed to get some ox tail and vegetables, even potatoes, which were in short supply. If she added plenty of stock, the stew would last several days. The pot simmering, she prepared David's first bottle. She hated to do this but she had to start weaning him now for when she began work again.

By five forty-five the stew was sitting on the hob in her fireplace (she didn't like to leave it in the kitchen because hungry lodgers had been known to help themselves) and David had finally taken his bottle, although periodically he'd dropped the rubber teat from his mouth and had clutched at her breast.

Just then the door burst open and Doreen invaded the room.

'Hello, luv! The old girl let me in. I thought I'd give you a welcome home. Bet you're glad to be out of that place; it gave me the willies just visiting you there.

Here's a present for David,' she added, waving a large rattle and dropping it into the cot.

'Oh, thank you, Doreen, you're so thoughtful. It seems to be my day for visitors; Doris came earlier. Come and sit by the fire; I've just made some stew.'

'Oh, thanks, luv. I'm both starving and freezing to death. Not exactly spring-like today, is it?' She took off her coat and hat and wrapped her outer shawl round her shoulders over her overall, sitting by the fire. 'Actually, I came round for two reasons; the other one is that the old woman they got to replace you was fired this morning. She was at least sixty-five, poor old soul, and had bad arthritis, especially in her hands. She had a bad do when the weather got so freezing and damp. The poor thing could hardly move her swollen joints and kept dropping things, so that was the end of her. They fired her without notice this morning, so I thought you might be interested in getting your old job back.'

'I noticed in the paper they were advertising for women.'

'Not for this job, luv. They want more women in the assembly shop; there's a rumour about them making parts for tanks and aeroplanes. Can you believe it, having our own air force? But that's bloody heavy work, Mary. You'd be better off at the belt and I'm sure they'd take you back; you were always a good worker.'

'You might be right, Doreen. The foreman never really liked me but I have got experience; they just might take me back, and at least I'll be able to manage on the wages. I'll go to the office first thing in the morning and apply. Anyway, I'd already given up hope of finding anything with shorter hours.'

The next morning, dressed in her overalls underneath her overcoat and shawl, she took David and his full day's supply of milk to Doris's address at 7 a.m. If the factory wanted her back, she would be prepared to start immediately.

Doris answered her knock with surprise. 'Why, Mary! What are you doin' at this hour?'

'I might have a chance of getting my old job back, so I've brought David. If they take me I could start today, if you don't mind?'

'Course not, luv. Come on in. It's goin' to be tight but I think we can get the pram into the kitchen where it's warm.'

They manoeuvred the large vehicle down the narrow passage and edged it into the kitchen, where Mary was startled to see an old man lying on the sofa covered in blankets.

'Oh, this is me da an' this is me friend, Mary.'

The man wheezed and coughed into a handkerchief before saying, 'How do,' and Mary was horrified to see blood on his lip and on the white handkerchief.

'How do you do,' she said, afraid to proffer her hand.

'Me da's not doin' so well this cold weather so he's sleepin' in the kitchen where it's warm.'

Good God! She had forgotten! Doris had told her at St Michael's that her father had consumption. She panicked. She couldn't leave David here day after day among all these germs – it was a fatal disease.

'I'll take good care o' him,' Doris said, unloading the pram's cargo of nappies and bottles and milk. 'An' if you're not back in an hour I'll take it you've got the job. Good luck, luv!'

'Thanks, Doris. I'd better be going then.' She gave David's cold cheek one last kiss and started out for the factory. There was no choice for the moment, but she'd have to find another place for David, kind though Doris's offer was. Doris didn't seem to worry about bringing up children in that unhealthy environment. Maybe she didn't know how serious it was. Well, Mary couldn't hurt her feelings; she'd just have to get out of the arrangement tactfully.

At the factory they were glad to sign her on again because of her experience – the foreman, thank goodness, had nothing to do with the hiring. The girls were delighted to see her back.

'Why, welcome back to the sweatshop, luv,' cried Maggie, as Mary took her old place at the belt.

'How are you feelin'?' chorused Enid and Edna. 'We hear the bairn's a smasher; we'll be around to see him one o' these days.'

'Aye, glad to see you back,' said Lilly. 'I knew that poor old woman's days were numbered from the start.'

'I never thought I'd be so happy to be back,' said Mary, automatically falling back into the sorting and checking routine. 'It's thanks to Doreen, or I'd never have known the job was open again.'

'I'm thrilled you got it, luv. See you at break,' shouted Doreen from across the belt.

By the following week Mary had found a baby minder for David. It had been difficult lying to Doris that she simply couldn't impose on her any more, and that the baby minder only charged two shillings a week anyway when, in fact, she charged two and sixpence and extra for Saturdays.

'Well, you know, luv, I'm happy to have him any time you need me,' Doris had said goodnaturedly.

'I know, and I'm happy to have Jimmy whenever you need a break and I'm at home, but dumping David on you all week is just too much to ask, even of a good friend like you.'

'Have it your own way, luv,' she'd said. But she'd looked at Mary strangely. Did she suspect her motive? Well, if she did, much as Mary hated to hurt her friend's feelings, she couldn't afford to expose David to any risks. It was bad enough that she had to go to work and leave him every day; the least she could do was make sure she left him in a healthy environment.

Chapter Eighteen

It was the summer of 1918 and Mary had settled into her new routine, day following day and month following month. Blond, blue-eyed David, at one year and three months, was a bundle of energy, toddling all over the tiny room. Mary felt tired most of the time, and the war was getting everyone down.

The Germans had stopped using Zeppelins against the British but were now launching aeroplane attacks in the south-east, though Britain was finally retaliating with its own air force. Soon the news from the front would be a little more hopeful, or so everyone said.

On 8 August, Mary, pushing David's pram home after picking him up from the baby minder's, noticed a shouting crowd at the newspaper stand. What was happening? There was so much noise she couldn't hear. Parking the pram, she elbowed her way through the mob and bought a newspaper. Balancing it on the pram handle, she read as she walked. The British had attacked the Hindenburg line and, according to the paper, this would ensure Allied victory. Since June, America had been pouring men into France by the hundred thousand and in July the British had opened a great and successful campaign. But, if today's report were true, this was the brightest day yet for the British Army.

Mary sighed, even at the hopeful news; in war, good news always meant more men dead. The only truly good news would be the end, whenever that might come, and she wouldn't raise her hopes until then.

But it came. Three months later, on 11 November at 11 a.m., the armistice was signed. The war was over! The smash at the end had been amazingly swift, and the Kaiser and the Crown Prince had made an undignified retreat into Holland. As soon as the news reached the factory, the workers left their posts and poured out into the streets to join the shouting, cheering crowds, disregarding the fact that it wasn't even lunch break yet. Everyone kissed and hugged everyone else, even the foreman, who grabbed every girl within reach, including Mary. Clerks rushed out of offices; shop assistants deserted their counters; bus, tram, and military lorry drivers embarked on illicit joy rides, picking up loads of astonished and cheering passengers, no one knowing or caring where they were going. It was peacetime once more.

That evening, tucking up David in bed, Mary listened to the noisy revellers below and rejoiced in her heart. The boys would be coming home – Joe would be coming home soon. She'd received a letter from his parents saying he would be returning to Newcastle. He would see his son.

The outside doorbell shrilled and then she heard a knock on her door. Doreen darted in. 'Hello, luv. I know it's late but I just thought I'd pop in for a chat on my way home. The girls talked me into joining the rowdies in the streets but I've had enough noise for one night and I don't feel like going to bed just yet.'

Mary hugged her friend solemnly. 'No letter again,' she stated rather than asked.

'No, not yet, but there's still a chance. When all this mess is sorted out they could find him in a hospital over there. Lots of men are shell-shocked and don't know who they are. Still no news from Joe, I suppose?'

'Not directly,' Mary said, avoiding her friend's eyes. 'But there was a letter from his parents waiting for me when I got home. He told them that when it was all over he was going to pay them a visit, then have a short holiday in London and after that he'd be coming back to finish his apprenticeship.' She couldn't help the rising excitement in her voice.

'That's good news, luv. I'm glad for you,' Doreen said, rising from the chair she'd sunk into and hugging her friend. Mary hugged her back, both ignoring the fact that Joe himself still hadn't written to Mary.

Disengaging herself and dancing over to the cot, Mary exclaimed, 'Daddy's coming home to see you.' She gazed down fondly at the chubby, chuckling child, kicking his legs in the air and chortling a victory song of his own. 'He thinks he's joining in the celebrations tonight,' Mary laughed. 'Nine o'clock and he just won't go off.' As she spoke she tried vainly to tuck the little legs under the blanket and to stroke the soft, flailing arms to soothe him to sleep. 'Time to go bye-byes, sweetheart; close those little eyes,' she exhorted vainly and, giving up, sank down on the bed. 'Oh, I wish I didn't have to get up at five to take him to the baby minder's.'

'Well, just think yourself lucky it's Saturday half day,' Doreen reminded her with her usual cheerfulness. 'You can have a rest in the afternoon.'

'Oh, yes?' Mary laughed. 'Rest! I have to pick him up after work, go to the washhouse, go to the market, come back and do the ironing – that is, if the weather's all right to hang the washing in the lane – make dinner for both of us, bathe him and get him to bed. Call that rest?'

'I know it's hard for you, luv. But thank God you've got work. Jobs are going to be really tight from now on with all the lads coming back.'

'I know you're right,' Mary sighed, 'and I'm grateful,

but I still have that old dream of getting a part-time job with a living wage.'

'What are you doing Sunday then?' Doreen asked, hugging her knees to her chin.

'Well, weather permitting, I'm just meeting Doris and going for a walk in the park as usual.' She shrugged. 'Not very exciting, but the babies need the fresh air. Why don't you come with us? Doris is a laugh a minute and you need cheering up.'

'Thanks, luv, but we're giving our Johnny and some of the neighbours' kids a little tea party to celebrate and I promised to help.' She yawned. 'I think I'd better be going and let you get some sleep as well, if his lordship lets you, that is.' She gave David a goodnight kiss. ''Bye then, see you tomorrow.'

'As ever,' said Mary, grimacing. 'Thanks for coming, Doreen. I enjoyed the chat. Goodnight then.'

On Sunday morning she pulled David's tiny, blue knitted bonnet over his curls. This Sunday would be extra special – their first walk in peacetime. She tied a new red ribbon round her faded boater; it cheered it up and made it look almost new again, she thought, as she glanced in the dusty mirror on the brown-painted landing wall. Heaving David's weight down the stairs, she was out of breath but happy when she reached the hallway.

As she pushed the pram slowly towards the park gates, she felt the cobblestones penetrating her thin soles and mentally calculated whether she could afford to take her shoes to the cobbler this week. The grey November sky glowered but the lighthearted crowd laughed and cheered. At last she spotted Doris, approaching from the opposite direction, jumping up and down and waving across the throng. Mary waved and shouted, 'Can you make it over here?' But it was futile to try to make herself heard above the crowd, bent on enjoying themselves on this first Sunday of peace. Trying to push the cumbersome pram with its large wheels and oversized body towards the gates was like manoeuvring a ship through pounding seas.

She'd become accustomed to seeing wounded soldiers in the streets, but never so many at one time, and the sight of all the maimed bodies with missing limbs or scarred faces saddened her. Her face must have shown it, for two men in uniform, one pushing the other in a wheelchair, shouted to her, 'Hey, lass, cheer up! It's over, you know!'

She forced a smile. 'Thanks to you. Welcome home!'

'Aye, it's good to be home. Here, hinny, that's for the bairn,' the one in the wheelchair said as they moved on, thrusting a paper Union Jack into her hand.

'Thank you,' she said, moved to tears. How is it their spirits weren't as maimed and scarred as their bodies? she thought. How could the poor creatures have much to celebrate? Yet she watched men and women alike surrounding the uniformed men, kissing them and hoisting over their heads in triumphal march those strong enough to bear it. Heroes for a day! Thank God Joe would be returning in one piece, she thought, and forced herself to join in as the people nearby began singing to the strains of the brass band coming from the park: 'Rule Britannia, Britannia rules the waves. Britons never, never, never shall be slaves.'

Finally, the two girls met, breathless, at the gates. 'What do you think, Mary? Isn't it marvellous?' Doris's red curls fluttered in the breeze and her sparkling grin lit up her happy face.

'I can still hardly believe it's over, after all these years,' Mary answered.

'Aye, it's wonderful that the lads'll all be comin' back. I can't wait to see me cousin again. Haven't clamped me eyes on him for over three years. He was only seventeen when he left and now he's gettin' married to his childhood sweetheart when he gets back. Romantic, isn't it?'

'Yes, it's nice to hear at least one happy ending to the war. Poor Doreen won't give up; she's still hoping he's in a hospital over there, but she'll have to face reality soon. It's just as well her family's moving back to London; it'll do her good to start a new life down there. I shall miss her, though.'

'Aye, I'm lucky. I only had me cousin out there. Went off a snotty-nosed kid an' comin' back a man.'

'Yes, he should certainly be grown up by now,' Mary said thoughtfully. 'I'm hoping Joe will be more mature, too. He'll be coming back after he's seen his parents.'

'Good God! Have you had a letter at long last?' Doris inquired eagerly.

'Not exactly,' Mary lowered her eyes, 'but his parents wrote and told me.'

'Why, the bugger could've wrote to you himsel'. Doesn't sound to me like he's changed much.'

'I know, but I'm hoping that when he sees his son, he'll change his mind.'

'I wouldn't count on it. From what you've told me, he's got a mind of his own an' he's already made it up.'

'How's Harry behaving?' Mary quickly turned the subject back to Doris.

'He came to see the bairn same as usual last night, afore he went to the boozer, an' he's regular about givin' me two shillin' a week, but he still hasn't told his wife. I'm glad for her sake though. She's got her hands full with three bairns an' him. It's a full-time job just tryin' to keep his eyes at home, if you ask me. I'm sorry for her, and I don't want to make things any worse between them, so I'm just keepin' me trap shut. He still has a go at me every time he comes, an' I have to admit

I gave in last night. I've been missin' it.'

'Oh, Doris, you didn't!' Mary exclaimed in horror. 'After all you've said! Isn't one mistake enough?'

'Aye, luv, you're right. So I made sure there was no mistake this time. Once you get caught you have to get clever. I know you're shocked, but honest, luv, I just couldn't help mesel' even if I'd wanted to. Everybody else was out enjoyin' themselves an' celebratin' an' there was me stuck with the kid an' me da on a Saturday night. A girl has to have a bit o' fun.' She noticed her friend's dismayed expression. 'Aw, don't look so shocked, Mary; you might find yoursel' in the same boat one o' these days. Come on, laugh and be happy like everybody else.'

'I'm sorry. I'd just hate you to get yourself into trouble again, especially as he's already married.'

'I know,' Doris sighed. 'I wish to God he wasn't. I don't know what it is about that man, but he just does somethin' to me. Maybe I'll find a young lad that's single now they're all comin' back, but I don't think I'll ever feel the same about anybody else as I do about Harry.'

'I know what you mean, but you won't know till you meet someone else,' Mary tried to cheer up her friend. 'Maybe you'll feel different about him, but that doesn't mean it won't be just as good.'

They were having to shout above the bustle and noise in the park. Left-over streamers and burst balloons from the earlier festivities littered the grass, and an old man with bloodshot eyes, still drunk from the night before, tottered towards them and kissed both the babies. 'Look after them bonny bairns, me bonny lasses; the country's future's in them prams.' And he wobbled on his way.

It was a raw January Saturday seven weeks later and Mary arrived at her place on the belt late and dishevelled. David had had one of his active nights and she'd overslept. She rubbed her hands together to get the circulation moving before putting on her working gloves, an old pair that Mrs Moynihan had knitted for her two Christmases earlier. She had carefully cut out the fingers and stitched round the resulting holes, leaving her fingers free to handle the small, cold fasteners. She started to work feverishly, worried lest the foreman had noticed her lateness again. That damned clock-in-card! There was no hiding her record. She wondered when her time would come. Jobs were needed for the old soldiers now and, of course, the women were the first to be paid off.

It was tea break before she even paused for breath. She sat down on the bench, her stiff hands gratefully cradling her warm tea mug.

Maggie was, naturally, the one to break the news. 'Well, Mary luv, how do you feel about lover boy comin' back? I heard the foreman say he'll be back to work on Monday. You're a dark horse! Why didn't you tell us?'

Mary's stiff fingers lost their grip on the metal cup and it bounced on the concrete floor, her startled face and wide eyes giving her away.

'Why, do you mean to say you didn' know, hinny?' Maggie, as always, was surrounded by the girls, and Mary tried to hide her confusion.

'It's none of your business what I know, Maggie, and I'd be glad if you'd stop shouting out my private business for the whole world to hear.' In order to gain time to collect herself, she bent to pick up the fallen cup that had rolled under the bench.

'Eey, luv, I'm sorry,' Maggie repented. 'I thought you knew – honest.'

Doreen attacked Maggie: 'When are you going to learn to think before you open your big mouth, Maggie? Whether she knows or not, or tells you or not, is her own business.' She sat beside Mary and put her arm round the thin shoulders. 'Are you feeling all right, luvvy? You've gone a funny colour.'

'I'm all right,' Mary announced to the group, 'and of course I knew. I just got my dates mixed up. I thought it was the following Monday,' she lied, realising too late that the lie was all too obvious.

Fortunately the end-of-break bell rescued her, and she returned thankfully to the bench, her head swimming with conflicting thoughts. The rotter! Why hadn't he written to let her know? She'd sent him dozens of letters – some to his parents' address to make sure he'd receive them. And then dizzily her thoughts turned to Monday. She would be seeing him on Monday. Despite herself, her heart thumped with excitement.

When the siren sounded at twelve thirty indicating the end of the working week, Mary rushed to the terminus to catch the first tram. She walked to the baby minder's to pick up David and hurried home to feed him and to change out of her work clothes. No time to do the washing today; she must get something decent to wear and take her shoes to the cobbler. It wouldn't do to let Joe see her looking as if she'd let herself go. She must win him back.

Saturday afternoon was the cobbler's busy time, and her voice was pleading as she asked, 'Could you do these while I wait?'

'No, hinny,' he shook his head, 'I can't have them ready till Monday mornin' at the earliest. You'll just have to leave them.'

She looked forlornly at the leathery face and lowered her eyes to the tough old hands on the counter, blackened with leather dye. 'I haven't got another pair,' she confessed.

'All right, hinny,' he sighed, his face softening. 'Take them off.'

As she sat on the waiting bench, rubbing her cold feet against her calves, a pair of black gaiters on the unclaimed articles shelf caught her eye. She needed some new ones. 'And I'll take those gaiters, too,' she said as she gratefully forced her frozen feet back into the newly mended shoes. She tried the gaiters on, her numb hands struggling with the tiny buttons. Yes, they were in much better condition than her old ones. 'How much are they and would you take these?' she asked, holding up her limp, cracked, leather offerings.

'Why, there's not much wear left in them, lass.' The old man shook his head. 'But tell you what, I could use some o' the leather for patchin' and the buttons are still good. I'll take thruppence off the soles and the gaiters. That'll be a bob altogether.'

Another shilling gone, she thought as she handed over her money; that didn't leave much to spare for the market.

She pushed the pram to the market, which resounded with the raucous shouts of the stall holders selling their wares and haggling with potential customers. Usually Mary went first to the greengrocery and fish stalls, but today she headed towards the racks of clothes. Daringly, she ventured first to one of the racks of new goods. A row of black wool skirts caught her eye. The stall holder had temptingly hung one at the front of the rack, topping it with a white silk blouse with a high frill round the neck, a black velvet ribbon crossed demurely at the throat adding a further touch of elegance. 'How much for the blouse and skirt?' Her bold question surprised her.

'Ten bob to you, me bonny lass. It'll look a right treat on you.' The stall holder pumped his hands together and stamped his feet as he talked, his breath forming little clouds of vapour as it encountered the cold air. 'That's best lamb's wool and Chinese silk from China, lass. Can't do better than that anywhere. Go over the road to Binn's and have a look there. They're askin' more than double the price fo' the very same articles.'

'No, thanks, that's too much. I'll give you six shillings the two,' she ventured daringly. Ten shillings was a fair price for such a quality outfit but it was far above her range. She was getting even bolder.

'No, hinny. You know as well as I do that's top quality merchandise. But, tell you what, I'll take eight bob from you because you're such a bonny lass.'

He was already looking for her size on the rack and she panicked. 'No, thanks, I need to look around some more anyway.'

She turned away, embarrassed, and set off for one of the second-hand stalls. She hated bartering, but it was expected here. She knew she could have got him down to seven shillings if she'd persevered, but that was still more than she could afford.

She'd almost given up hope when on the last stall she spied a black twill skirt of similar cut to the first one. That will do, she thought. One side seam was split, but she would have to alter it to narrow the waist anyway. For the rest, it was in good condition. She then scanned the blouse rack and saw a white taffeta blouse with a plain, high, round neckline; she could always dress it up with black velvet ribbon to look like the other one.

She eyed the stall holder, an old man with a mottled purple face and eyes to match. He's a drinker, she thought, remembering her mother's warnings about the dangers of alcohol: 'You can spot them by the colour' of their skins and eyes,' she used to say. 'Always beware of a man who drinks.' And then Mary remembered Mrs Moynihan's advice about bartering. She'd been stupid to ask for the price of the entire outfit first at the new clothes stall. She pointed to the skirt and asked, 'How much for that one?' The purple eyes darted from the garment to her. 'Two bob to you, lassy. That's real quality.'

'It's split down the side,' Mary countered.

'Why, then, one and ninepence, luv. You can't beat that for a bargain.'

'How much the two?' Mary ventured, sliding the blouse off its hanger and holding it against the skirt.

'Aye, that's a lovely blouse with that skirt. For you, luv, half a crown the lot.'

'I'll take them,' Mary said quickly, delving into her purse. She'd done enough bargaining for one day and, anyway, she knew she'd got a sensible price.

David was getting restless in his pram, and he was hungry. But she still had to go to the food stalls; she would get that over with and then have a cup of hot tea before going home. It was a long walk back to Dorset Street. After buying some vegetables and fish, she picked up a loaf of bread and two iced cakes from the bakery stall, giving one to David as she pushed the pram to the Tea Shop. The sugar rationing was limited in scope; it was still possible to buy an occasional cake and cheaper than buying one in the cafe. But she must have a cup of tea before walking home; she felt exhausted.

Parking the pram outside the cafe she lifted David out; he was still clutching half the sticky delight in both hands, his face and coat now covered in pink icing. Oh, well, she thought, I'll clean him up when I get home. 'One cup of tea, please,' she said to the waitress as she approached an empty table at the back.

'That one's taken,' the waitress said. 'The one at the window's free.'

Mary didn't care where she sat, as long as she sat. She sank down on to the cane chair, arranging David more comfortably on her lap, and stacking her purchases on the empty chair beside her. They were too precious to risk leaving outside in the pram. By now her black coat was also covered in pink icing and cake crumbs. Serves me right for giving him food in the pram, she scolded herself as she tried vainly to clean herself up with her handkerchief and endeavoured to keep the icing from straying any further than David's face.

While waiting for her tea, she entertained herself by gazing at the passers-by through the frosty window. The Saturday afternoon shoppers, huddled up against the cold in inadequate greatcoats or jackets and shawls, looked as grey and gloomy and undernourished as before the armistice. She wondered how much longer it would be before life would improve. The cost of food was prohibitive and jobs were even scarcer than before the war, not to mention that income tax was now five shillings in the pound. Eight hundred and fifty thousand soldiers killed and all for what? When were they going to see the prosperity that Lloyd George promised?

Her reveries were interrupted by the sight of a tall, blond figure stopping in front of the window to greet a passer-by. Oh, my God! she realised with dismay. It's Joe! Please don't let him see me looking like this. Panicking, she tried to avert her head, but too late. Their eyes met. His immediate surprise turned to embarrassment as he waved tentatively through the window, looking first at her and then at the large, blue and pink bundle in her lap. He said a few words to his friend, whom Mary recognised as one of his drinking companions, and then his bulk loomed in the doorway and edged slowly round the tables towards hers.

Her eyes were glued to his handsome, rugged face. The war hadn't changed him. Her heart was pounding, but her lips didn't smile.

'Hello, Mary,' he said, clearing his throat and pushing a lock of hair from his forehead. 'How are you?'

All her pent-up anger welled up in her and she replied in a voice louder than she'd intended: 'I'm well, thank you, and so is your son. Let me introduce you.' People nearby turned their heads, and Joe looked even more embarrassed.

'May I sit down?' he said, lowering his head to conceal his confusion. 'He's a handsome boy,' he muttered, taking one of David's sticky fingers in his big hand.

'Yes! Like his father, wouldn't you say?' Again her voice was loud and more heads turned in their direction.

'Look, Mary, I'm sorry about the mess, you know that. But let's not talk here. I can't stay anyway . . . I . . . I've got a friend waiting outside.'

'I thought keeping people waiting was your speciality.' Mary's voice was bitter and she was surprised by her own reaction. She didn't even care that people were staring at them.

'Look, can I see you tonight? I'll come over at six. I've got your address. We can talk better then.'

'Oh, so you've got my address. Got my letters too, then? I assume you saved them all up to reply to in person.'

Joe stood up, anger now overtaking his embarrassment. This was clearly not the Mary he remembered. 'I'll see you at six then,' he said in a cold, controlled voice, turning and edging his way out of the room.

Chapter Nineteen

Mary pushed the pram home blinded by tears. Were they tears of self-pity, frustration, anger or what? She didn't know. She knew only that the sight of Joe had provoked in her a strange reaction. If she still loved him as she thought, how could she have felt nothing but pain on seeing him? And how could she have made such a public scene in the cafe? She had deliberately humiliated both of them in public. No, not deliberately, she had simply lost control of her emotions. But that again raised the question: what *were* her emotions?

Back in her room, she quickly changed David into a clean nightgown and put him in his cot, where he immediately fell asleep. 'Yes,' she said wryly, tucking him in more tightly, 'and now you'll be awake half the night.' But she was glad of the time his nap afforded her. She looked at the clock. She had only an hour and a half to clean herself up, alter the new skirt, iron the blouse and give David his dinner before Joe arrived.

As she moved quickly at her chores, her mind raced. She couldn't deny that she felt excited at the prospect of his visit; she knew she still loved him. But she must keep calm and act rationally – no more tantrums like the one in the cafe. If she wanted him back, she must act with guile and care and handle the situation more gently. Even though she had a right to be angry at the way he had abandoned her and their son, no man responded well to a complaining woman, and she must keep David's best interests in mind.

The clock said six thirty when the front doorbell rang. Almost beside herself with worry lest he had changed his mind, her stomach lurched with relief. Quickly smoothing down the new black skirt and neatening the blouse round her waist, she rushed down the stairs to answer the door herself. On her way she glanced swiftly into the hall mirror, tucking a loose strand of shining hair back into its neat coil and, in complete control of herself, she opened the door, determined that she wouldn't remark on his being late.

'Hello, Mary,' he said sheepishly. 'Sorry I'm late. I got waylaid . . . met someone I knew.'

I know what waylaid him, she thought, the smell of whisky on his breath invading her senses, but she heard her voice saying, 'That's all right. I had some things to do anyway. Come in.'

'I see you're at the top again,' he remarked as he followed her up the steep flights.

'Yes, of course. It's either the attic or the basement on *my* wages.' Oh dear! She hoped her voice didn't sound accusing and added more lightly, 'But I've got a nice view of the chimney pots and rooftops.'

He stood, hesitant, as she held the room door open.

'Please go in. This is our little nest – David's and mine.'

He took a few steps over the torn linoleum and looked at the cot where David was now contentedly sucking on his bottle. 'He's a beautiful baby, Mary. You did well,' he said as he ventured closer to the cot.

She was about to remind him that they had *both* done well when she remembered her resolve. Instead, she said pleasantly, 'He's got his father's eyes and colouring, don't you think?'

'Yes, I suppose he has.' He touched the blond curls awkwardly and David's blue eyes smiled, while he continued to clutch his bottle of milk and suck vigorously.

'Would you like to hold him?' Mary inquired.

'Well, er, yes . . . when he's finished his bottle. He seems occupied.'

'Yes, he enjoys his bottle just like his father, too.' It just slipped out, and she quickly smiled and added, 'And his food.' She plumped the cushion on the old armchair, making sure no broken springs were visible, and invited him to sit down.

Dipping into his pocket and pulling out a bottle of sherry, Joe made an obvious attempt to relieve the strained atmosphere. 'I brought you a present. I know how much you like sherry.'

She wondered if that last remark was to get back at her for her comment about his drinking but smiled to hide her thoughts. 'Thank you. I'll get some glasses.' She brought back two small tumblers and, filling them, gave one to him, seating herself on the bed and holding the other.

'Well, cheers,' he said, taking a large gulp.

'Cheers,' she responded, sipping the sweet liquid. Thank God! Maybe the sherry would loosen the tension for both of them. 'Why don't you take off your coat and I'll stoke up the fire a bit.'

Again he looked uncomfortable and took another gulp. 'Thanks, but I can't stay very long. I'm meeting a mate in town.'

Her stomach lurched once more, this time in disappointment. He didn't even intend to spend the evening with her! But her face was impassive as she said, 'Well, while you're here you might as well make yourself comfortable.'

He obeyed and took off his coat, draping it over the back of the chair and sitting on the edge of the seat. She knew she would have to be the one to broach the subject and, taking another sip of sherry, went straight to the point. 'What are you going to do about us, Joe?'

'Us?'

'Yes! Me, David and you; we're a family now.'

'Now look, Mary, we've been through all that before. It was your decision to keep the child, not mine. You knew how I felt about it then and I haven't changed my mind. It was your choice and now it's your responsibility.'

'How can you say that about your own flesh and blood? If you'd had to carry him around in your body for nine months and put up with all the stares and whispers and embarrassment, and if the only person you loved had left you all alone to go through it, wouldn't you want to keep the child? He's all I have, and shameful though my situation is, I need him and I love him.' Her voice quavered. 'If you have no feelings for him, don't you have any left for me?'

'You know I was fond of you, Mary.' Joe's eyes were riveted to a small stain on the linoleum in front of his right foot.

'Was!' Her voice was beginning to rise hysterically now. She could hear it and was afraid of it.

'Well . . . no . . . I still am, I suppose,' he said, flushing, 'but things have changed since then, Mary. We're not the same people; we've each decided on different courses in our lives. You want to get married and settle down, and I want to do things with my life. I want to finish my studies and get somewhere. I want to travel. I want some interest and excitement in my life, not to mention comfort. I don't want to end up like Dad, squeezing out a bare existence in his old age. Just taking care of Mum and me and giving me some sort of an education drained him financially and physically, working every day of his life at that bloody factory just to keep a roof over our heads and put food in our mouths. That's what's putting him into an early grave. I used to watch the two of them, Dad coming home at night exhausted, and Mum with his dinner waiting on the table, all washed out after an exciting day's cleaning, shopping and cooking and working at the shop, all just to stay alive. She never even took her bloody pinafore off, except after Sunday dinner and Christmas dinner. I want to do more than just stay alive. I want to live!' He drained the last of his sherry and got up for the bottle, refilling both their glasses.

She was losing ground, she knew, and it upset her resolution to remain calm. 'You tricked me into thinking you loved me,' she said accusingly. 'And all you wanted was one thing.'

'Now, Mary, if you didn't want it, you didn't put up much of a fight, did you?'

'What are you insinuating? I did it for you because I loved you and I thought you loved me. How much more stupid could I have been?' Her voice was beginning to break and she didn't care. Maybe if she stopped trying to be strong and he saw how upset she really was he would soften. Her face crumpled and her body shook, as she sobbed hysterically, the sherry in her full glass spilling over her new skirt.

'Here, Mary, don't get so upset.' He relieved her of the now half-empty glass and took out his white handkerchief, dabbing at her skirt with it before handing it to her. She covered her face with it and her sobbing subsided until there was only a faint tremor in her shoulders.

He held the remaining sherry up to her lips. 'Take a sip; it'll make you feel better.'

'Thank you,' she said, obediently swallowing the calming drink, her body feeling as drained as the empty glass.

'Look, Mary,' Joe muttered, visibly uncomfortable. 'If you won't change your mind and find David a good home, we can come to some sort of understanding for a while. As long as I can, I'll help out with money. After I've paid my rent and night classes, I shan't have much left, but I could let you have about half a crown a week.'

Half a crown a week, when what she wanted was Joe and a home for David! But she decided not to push matters too far at the moment – at least he was acknowledging some responsibility. Maybe he would change his mind later when he got to know and love David, and maybe he would begin to feel something for her again. She would try to make him love her again. 'All right,' she agreed. 'That's a start.'

'I can't start till I get my first wage packet next week,' he said gloomily. 'I've used up all my army pay.'

'I've waited this long, I can wait another week,' she replied bitterly, and immediately forced a smile to cover up her tone. It wouldn't do to antagonise him now, just when she'd won her first small victory.

'Well, I'll be going then.' He jumped up hastily and put on his overcoat.

'But it's only just after seven. I made some sandwiches.' Her disappointment was evident.

'I told you I couldn't stay, Mary. I have to meet a mate in town and I'm late now. I'll see you at work on Monday, anyway.'

'Oh, yes, work. What do we say to them at work?'

'Why nothing, of course. It's none of their damned business.'

'But what are people going to think? They're going to talk!'

'They can think and talk as much as they like as far as I'm concerned. It's none of their bloody business,' he repeated. 'You always were too worried about what people might think, Mary. In some ways you haven't changed.'

'You mean that in others I have, then?'

'Well, yes, you have.'

'In what ways?'

'Oh, never mind, Mary. This sort of talk won't get us anywhere.' He shrugged, picking up his coat and heading for the door.

'Aren't you even going to say goodbye to your son?' She could feel her anger rising again.

'He's fast asleep, Mary. What do you want me to do, wake him up?'

Mary glanced at the sleeping form in the cot, the bottle abandoned, realising she'd completely forgotten his presence during the past half-hour. It was unusual for him to sleep so much in the evening, but at least he hadn't interrupted their talk.

'Goodnight, Mary. See you at work.'

'Goodnight, Joe,' was all she could say as he let himself out, in his haste leaving the door swinging open behind him.

She stood, feeling drained and dejected. So much for her preparations for the evening. The draught from the outside door closing had slammed the room door and wakened David. Ignoring the whimpers that came from the cot, she poured herself another glass of sherry and curled up on the bed to think. David was always fretful when he first woke up. But this time the whimpers didn't stop; they grew louder and developed into loud, distressed, choking cries. She murmured soothing sounds as she lifted him out of his cot. His forehead was hot, very hot. So that was why he'd been so obligingly sleepy all evening: he was feverish and damp with perspiration. 'Oh, God!' she said aloud. 'Please let it be only a little cold.'

She laid him on the bed and sponged him down, while heating his bottle in the pan of hot water she always kept ready on the trivet. 'Mummy will make you better, sweetheart,' she soothed as she wrapped him up and offered him his bottle. At first he sucked feebly but then opened his mouth and yelled, the bottle forgotten. She lay on the bed and comforted him in her arms until he finally fell into a shallow sleep, but his breathing was laboured.

On Monday morning she was waiting outside the doctor's surgery at five minutes to eight. It seemed like an hour before the doors opened and the doctor arrived.

'No, nothing to worry about,' he said after examining David. 'It's a nasty cold and his chest is congested. Half my patients are down with it, especially the young ones. Just keep him warm and propped up with pillows, and give him a teaspoonful of this every four hours,' he said, sticking a white label on a bottle of red liquid he had taken from his glass cupboard.

'Oh, thank you, doctor.' She felt like hugging him and thanked God silently. It wasn't serious, but he was suffering; she must keep him at home until he was better. How could she let them know at work why she was absent? She couldn't take him there in this cold; she must go straight home. Maybe the landlady would sit with him while she went to work to explain. Although she hated the thought of the sick old woman coughing and wheezing over him when he was already ill, she had no choice.

She met the new foreman, as he was still called, on his way out of the shop. Although he had been there for over two years, the workers still didn't accept him. He was a brusque, surly little man in his late forties, with beady, fly-like eyes that seemed to see in all directions at once. Since his arrival, production had speeded up but morale had declined. The women resented the new dictator, whom they knew reported to the boss every minor misdemeanour, such as talking on the job or being half a minute late back from break. Mary approached him nervously. 'I'm sorry I can't come to work today; my baby's ill. I just came to let you know. I hope to be back in a few days.'

His busy eyes stopped darting and fixed on her. 'As far as I know, you needn't have bothered comin' in anyhow. Your cards is waitin' at the office. Your time-keepin's been gettin' worse an' worse, and we've no room for lackadaisicals like you when there's plenty o' wounded lads that needs jobs now. The boss was goin' to give you a week's notice the day anyway, but when I told him you hadn't bothered to show up at all, he told the girl to get your cards ready. You might as well pick them up while you're here. An' you needn't bother askin' for a reference. If it wasn't fo' the war, they'd have got rid o' you long ago. Disgracin' yoursel' is bad enough, but lettin' the kid interfere with your work can't be allowed. I've never trusted that toffee-nosed voice and manner o' yours anyway. You've got nothing to be so snooty about, especially since you've proved you're no better than you should be.'

The tears and the anger gushed at the same time, and Mary let go of all the pent-up dislike she had held for this man for so long; she had nothing to lose now. 'You sneaky little man,' she shouted. 'They all know you spy on them and report them if they so much as stop to take a breath. They're ganging up on you, Mr Bigwig that you think you are. It won't be long before it's *your* turn.'

She turned and ran blindly towards the office for her cards. She could do better than that rotten job anyway. They could stick it up their jumpers, she sobbed to herself.

Chapter Twenty

The cold air helped to clear her thoughts as she walked home. What now? She stopped to look at the advertisements in several tobacconists' windows. Not a single job was advertised, only items for sale. The so-called post-war boom had been dramatically short-lived, and now there were even rumours that a revolution was in the offing. She bought a newspaper and hurried home to get David into his warm cot as quickly as possible. The landlady had insisted on keeping him in his pram in the hall. Her immediate anger having now subsided, she was thinking more rationally and less optimistically. Why hadn't she thought of it earlier? She'd been fired, not laid off; how would she get another job without references? All she had were the remains of Mr Cowley's money – exactly six pounds – and the five her uncle had sent her. And then there would be the half-crown a week Joe had promised for David. No! Joe would have to do better than that; he owed more than a pittance a week to his own son. She couldn't afford to be stupid where David was concerned; she would have to become stronger.

At home, she tucked David into his cot, using the moth-eaten but warm knitted blanket from her own bed, and added some newspapers and coal to the little mound of dead ash in the grate. After the smoke had subsided and the fire had begun to glow feebly, she set the remains of the pan of broth from the day before on the trivet. She didn't want to leave David alone while she went down to the kitchen. After managing to get him to swallow a few spoonfuls of the warm soup, she forced the red medicine down his unwilling throat. Then she dipped a flannel into the cold water in the jug, wringing it out and placing it on his hot forehead. Finally, he slipped into an uneasy sleep, and she sat on the floor in front of the now comforting fire, spreading the newspaper out before her.

Just as she'd finished reading, there was a knock on her door and Doreen burst in, out of breath. 'Hello, luv. That old cow grumbled again about letting me in. Just thought I'd pop in and see how you are. I heard you got the sack.'

'Goodness, news travels fast. And why aren't you at work?'

'Well, I was, luv, but I got the push as well. They got wind that I was moving back to London so they beat me to it. Didn't even get the pleasure of handing in my notice. It doesn't matter for me; it's only a couple of weeks anyway, but you, what are you going to do?' she asked, taking off her coat and joining Mary on the floor in front of the fire.

'I really don't know. I've just looked in the paper but there's nothing for me: one request for a washerwoman, two days a week only, and two positions as housekeeper – doesn't say where though, there's just a box number to write to. No factory or shopgirl work, which pays better than domestic jobs. I suppose they can't hire new people till all these strikes are over. Life is getting harder, not easier, since the war.' She glanced again at the housekeeper jobs, remembering with distaste her experience in service. 'Listen to these: "Experienced live-in housekeeper wanted for single businessman. Must be good cook. Normal household duties and cooking, including serving at business dinners. Sundays off."'

'Well, that doesn't sound bad, luv. Try it.' Doreen's voice was eager.

'No, I don't think so. I can cook good, wholesome food, but I couldn't cope with fancy dinner parties and, anyway, a single man most likely wouldn't want a child in the house. The other seems more likely. Listen: "Widower with family seeks live-in housekeeper." If he already has a family, surely another child wouldn't make much difference? It would probably involve a lot more work than the other job but at least I'm experienced at looking after children, thanks to Mrs Moynihan.'

'Well, I'd write to both, luv, and take whatever comes up. You can always learn to cook from a cookery book.'

'I suppose I'd better,' Mary said hopelessly.

'Are you going to tell them about David?'

'No, I'll break that news gently when I see them. If they see me first they might be more kindly disposed to making allowances. I know men like me, though so far it's only got me into trouble. I'll use my looks to get a job if I have to in order to keep David, but no man's going to lay a finger on me again. I've had enough of men and their selfish ways.'

'What's wrong with David? He's being very quiet for ten o'clock in the morning.' Doreen indicated the silent cot with her head.

'Yes, he's got a bad cold. The medicine the doctor gave him seems to have knocked him out. I had to keep him at home today and that was the last straw for the foreman. But I was going to get it anyway. He let me have a mouthful about what he thought of my morals.'

'The rotten bastard! At least we don't have to put up with him no longer, luv.'

'That's true, I suppose; but I still wish I'd be seeing his ugly face tomorrow. What we have to do for a wage packet!' she added sourly. 'Look,' she jumped up. 'If I write these letters now, would you mind posting them on your way home? I can't go out and leave David.'

''Course, luv. I've got all the time in the world from now on. I'll go down and get some more coal for you before the fire goes out,' she said, picking up the scuttle. 'You get on with the letters and then I'll be off. I'm not relishing telling Mam the news.'

'Thanks, Doreen. You're a gem. I'm going to miss you when you go back to London,' she said to the retreating figure.

Two days later she received replies to both her letters. Her hopes rose as she saw her name on the envelopes propped up in front of the sad aspidistra on the rickety cane hall table. The valiant plant somehow managed to eke out a bare existence from the frugal light filtering down from the fanlight. Even with David's weight squirming in her arms, in her eagerness she ran upstairs.

Tearing the envelopes open, she glanced quickly through the contents, slightly dismayed by the impersonal tone of both. They each acknowledged her letter and said they would be seeing applicants on Thursday and Friday evenings of that week, if she wished to present herself for an interview. She brooded; they'd probably be drowning in applications. So what! She would go anyway. There'd been nothing new in the paper since Monday. She glanced at the addresses. One was at Whitley Bay, on the coast – a good forty minutes' journey. That must be the businessman, she reasoned. It would be nice to live by the sea, and the air would be good for David. The other was on Edward Street. She knew the street well and grimaced. It was two streets away from Beauchamps Street and was much the same – a row of grimy little terrace houses glued together. The only difference was that these were at least houses and not flats; the bedrooms were upstairs and the back yards were bigger. David was getting better now; she could walk over to Doris's to see, if she could look after him on Thursday.

Doris's flat was an almost identical copy of Mary's old flat in Beauchamps Street. Doris's mother had died of pneumonia ten years earlier at the age of forty-four, so Doris, although only eighteen, carried the responsibility of her father and baby like a mature woman, in addition to working three mornings a week from home, baking bread and scones which she sold to the neighbours. At least, thought Mary a trifle enviously as she knocked on the door, she had a real home to live in and her father's pension. Good God! She must stop these thoughts. What was she doing envying Doris the income from her poor, sick father? The door opened and Doris's head peeked out.

'Hello, luv. What a nice surprise!' She had Jimmy tucked under one arm and a bundle of wet rags in her free hand. 'Come on in. You're just in time for a cup.' She was wearing a wrap-round, print pinafore like all the housewives wore and a scarf tied in a knot on top of her head, one red curl peeping out disobediently.

Mary laughed. 'You're beginning to look like all the other mothers around here. What are you up to?'

'Ask me what I'm not up to an' I can tell you better. I'm scrubbin' the scullery floor, givin' the bairn his bottle, and givin' me da his tea, all at once. I could do with a sit down. I'm glad to see you . . . anythin' the matter?'

'No, not since I saw you on Tuesday. I've had replies from those two jobs I told you about.'

By now they had penetrated the gloom of the hall and reached the kitchen, where the fire was glowing cheerfully in the big black stove, the kettle on the trivet puffing out clouds of steam.

'Sit yoursel' down, an' put him on the floor. I've just

washed in here as well, so he won't get dirty.'

She dumped Jimmy on the floor and, throwing the cleaning rags through the door into the scullery, relieved Mary of David and plunked him down beside her own. Mary looked around the shabby but immaculate kitchen, smiling. 'You *have* been busy,' she said. It was furnished similarly to the old kitchen at Beauchamps Street, except for the addition of an ancient settee against the back wall. She sank into one of the chairs by the fire, glad to be rid of David's ever increasing weight.

'Where's your father?' she asked, glad he wasn't in the room.

'Oh, he's back in bed. I couldn't stand him bein' in here all day an' gettin' in me hair, so I bought him two hot water bottles; at least he can't complain he's cold now. Take your coat off an' make yoursel' at home.' Doris was spooning tea from the caddy on the mantelpiece into a large brown teapot and tipping the kettle into it, when the boiling water spurted over the sides and splashed on to her hand. 'Damn and blast!' she bawled, sucking the offended fingers. 'When am I goin' to learn?'

'You try to do too many things at once,' Mary soothed. 'Let me see your hand.'

'No, its all right, luv. Me hands have had skin like an elephant's since me ma died. One o' these days, when I marry me prince charmin', I'm goin' to pay somebody to do my work. So what about these housekeeper jobs then? Tell me all about it in a minute. I'll just take me da a cup o' tea an' a scone to stop him whinin' on. He's been drivin' me nuts all day.'

She disappeared into the bedroom off the kitchen and Mary poured the tea. The infants were happily occupied, pulling the fraying strands off the braided rag mat on the floor.

'Nothing more to tell,' Mary replied, as Doris

emerged from the bedroom and collapsed into the other armchair. 'I just got the letters. I'd like to go early on Thursday and wondered, if you're not doing anything, if you'd look after David for me?'

'Eey, luv, I'm sorry but I can't.' Doris looked apologetic. 'You see, a handsome, rich stranger came up to me while I was scrubbin' the front step this mornin' an' said me pretty mug had captivated his heart an' would I like to dine with him at the Ritz the morrow. He's sendin' his coach an' horses to collect me.' Her bright eyes, reflecting the firelight, twinkled even more, and she exploded into laughter. 'What the hell do you *think* I'd be doin', you nut? Same as I'm doin' every night – nothin'! That is, if you don't count feedin' the bairn, washin' him, and puttin' him to bed; feedin' me da, washin' him, and puttin' him to bed; then feedin' mesel', washin' mesel', and *fallin'* into bed.'

Mary laughed. 'Thanks. I'll drop him off at five. I'm going to go to the Whitley Bay one first; it'll take a while to get there, and I intend to be the first one on the doorstep. I can't be first at both but I should still be early enough for the other one.'

David and Jimmy were getting bored with pulling the mat apart and one had started whining, setting the other off. 'Here, you kids.' Doris took two scones and rammed one into each miniature mouth. 'Anything for a bit o' peace,' she sighed, handing Mary the scone plate. 'I made them this mornin'.'

Mary took one. 'I'll have to do a lot more cooking if I get one of these jobs. I wish I liked it,' she added.

'An' cleanin',' her friend reminded her, 'an' shoppin', an' wipin' dirty bums.'

'There'll be no bum-wiping at the coast job,' Mary said.

'Oh, aye, no bairns. But watch out fo' those businessmen. It's *your* bum they'll be after.'

'Doris, do you have to be so coarse?' Mary laughed. 'No prince charming is going to carry you off unless you clean up your mouth.'

'Oh, in that case, get the carbolic. Dear God,' she looked up reverently and mimicked Mary's voice, 'I promise I shall never utter another smutty word in my entire life if you will only send me my rich prince charming soon, before I have to bloody well settle for any penniless old bugger that comes along,' she added, the pair of them crumpling with laughter and Mary choking on her scone crumbs.

Doris's expression suddenly turned serious. 'Talkin' o' buggers, has Joe been round since Saturday?'

'No, he hasn't, the sod, and the only way I can find out his address is to go to the office at work. Even then, I doubt they'd let me have it – employee's right to privacy, or whatever they call it. If he doesn't come with the money when he gets his pay packet, I'll just have to go and blast him out at the factory and show him up for what he is.'

'Eey, you'd think he'd have the decency to see how you were doin' when he heard you'd been fired. Strikes me, there's something not quite right about that bugger. I think you're better off not marryin' him anyway.'

Mary ignored the remark and stood up. 'I've got to go, Doris; it's past David's bedtime. I'll drop him off at about five tomorrow, then. Thanks for taking him.'

'I've told you a million times, luv, I'll take him any time you like. I'll never know why you insisted on spending good money on that baby-minder woman when I'm here all day anyway.'

'Yes, and you never stop for a minute all day. You've got too many responsibilities anyway without my adding to them. David's a full-time job.'

Mary had still not been able to tell Doris that she didn't like to leave David for long periods in that house. The thought of the father's deadly disease still struck her with horror. She also worried about being there herself; if anything happened to her, what would happen to David? But she couldn't possibly cut her friend out of her life because of that possibility. Doris meant too much to her.

'Have it your own way. You always do. Good luck with the jobs. I hope you get the rich businessman, and ask him if he's got a friend fo' me. Goodnight, luv. See you the morrow.'

By now at the door, Mary let herself out and hurriedly put David in his pram. She walked home quickly; what if Joe had been while she was out? But he hadn't.

The next evening at five she was back on Doris's doorstep, dressed in her new outfit, the white blouse now embellished with a black velvet ribbon round the demure neckline. Her black overcoat was shabby, but she'd turned up the fraying cuffs and brushed and pressed it, and her grey boater looked elegant yet businesslike. Despite the cold evening, she'd left the coat collar unbuttoned to show off the blouse.

'Thanks, Doris,' she said hurriedly, as the door opened. 'May I just leave the pram out here? I'd hate to miss that train.'

'Aye, luv,' Doris answered, heaving David out from under his blankets. 'Good luck on the first one!' And Mary darted away into the darkness towards the station.

She found the house with little trouble. It was a big, detached house, just beyond the main promenade and overlooking the sea. Every light in the house was on and two hissing gas lamps at the gate lighted her way up the front path. A grey-haired woman in her fifties, wearing a white lace bonnet and a crisp, white, starched apron, answered Mary's hesitant pull on the doorbell almost immediately – unfortunately, a little too soon, as Mary was busy adjusting her hat and pushing out of sight the stray strands of hair the blustery sea wind had dislodged from their neat anchor. 'Good evening,' Mary started, but was cut short by the woman.

'First room on the left,' and she indicated with her head as if Mary didn't know which way was left.

She found herself in a small but elegant room, with dark blue velvet upholstered Victorian wing chairs and carved mahogany occasional tables scattered over a blue and pink embossed Chinese rug. Magazines and newspapers were arranged neatly on the tables. This was obviously a waiting room and, dismayed, she saw that she wasn't the only one waiting, although it was still only five minutes to six. She nodded her head and mumbled 'Good evening' to the half-dozen or so waiting faces that turned in her direction, then made her way to the nearest vacant chair. So, despite her efforts, she'd been beaten to the post. Oh, well. She'd just have to sit it out, although it meant she'd be very late for the second interview.

At six thirty by the ormolu clock on the mantelpiece, her turn came at last. He certainly hadn't taken long with the others. Were they not satisfactory, or had he already decided? No! He wouldn't waste time seeing more if he'd made a final decision, and there were now a dozen new faces waiting eagerly for their turn. She followed the old woman up the curved staircase and into a large, book-lined room, with green leather chairs and a matching, hand-tooled leather-topped desk. The figure, bent over some papers on the desk, looked up as she entered. He looked about forty, with sideburns turning to a steel grey, and thinning, brownish hair revealing streaks of pink scalp. His round gold spectacles glittered in the gaslight as his gaze fixed on her. 'Please sit down,' he said clearing his throat.

Was she mistaken, or had he liked what he'd seen? She'd noticed his expression change as he looked up.

Sitting opposite him, she fixed her large green eyes on his spectacles, and held her shoulders erect. She wished she'd been invited to take off her coat so he could see her blouse and skirt, rather than the shabby overcoat, but his eyes were still fixed on her face anyway.

'Your name?' he asked, with another little cough.

'Mary Maddison,' she answered.

'You look rather young for this job. Had any experience?'

'Oh, yes. I was in service for two years as parlour maid,' she lied, and hoped he wouldn't ask for a reference.

'Had any experience at cooking and entertaining?'

'A little,' she exaggerated.

'I need someone who knows how to cook for and serve guests, some dinner parties and some business luncheons, usually no more than a dozen guests at the table. A typical menu would be oyster or brown Windsor soup, followed by jugged hare, roast venison or grouse, and for dessert perhaps cherry cobbler or flummery, and a good Stilton with the port. Occasionally I give parties for up to thirty or so, but then I usually serve canapés and a cold buffet that can be prepared the day before. Could you handle that?'

'Oh, yes. I served at my last job, and I used to help Cook and stand in for her when she was ill. She was ill a lot,' she added lamely, lowering her eyes for the first time. She knew she had gone too far. Good Lord! What *was* flummery? How do you make jugged hare?

'You don't sound as though you're from these parts.' His voice was soft and cultured and she noticed that the fingers stroking his thin moustache were white, with manicured nails.

'No, I'm from London, originally,' she lied. 'I came up here with my husband.'

'Your husband?' he queried.

'Yes, he was killed in the war,' she lied again. Strange how easily the lies came, she thought.

'Oh, I see. I'm sorry.' He was leaning over the desk now, looking sympathetic.

Now for it, she decided; she couldn't lie about this one. 'And I have a small child.' She looked at him appealingly, but her voice was deliberately matter-of-fact. 'But he's well-behaved and no trouble . . . and I'd make sure to keep him out of your way if I got the job.'

'I see.' The hand stroking the moustache hesitated a moment and then continued. 'I hadn't anticipated a child in the house, but I suppose it's big enough for you to keep him out of the way, especially when I have visitors.'

'Oh, I have someone who would look after him whenever necessary,' she added. 'But he wouldn't be in your way.' So, the worst was over; he wasn't completely put off by the child.

The leather creaked as he leaned back in his chair. 'I did have someone older in mind, but you seem very sure of yourself. I think you would handle the entertaining duties well, and it would be a nice change to have someone young and lively about the place – even a child, at convenient hours, that is,' he added. 'It's like a mausoleum in here at times. Do you have any references from your old job?'

'I'm afraid not; the old lady died, sir.'

'That's unfortunate but not a big problem,' he said, and then, standing up, 'I still have people downstairs I must see tonight, but I shall make my final decision tomorrow. No sense in dragging it out another day. I take it your address is on your letter?'

'Yes, sir.'

'Good, I'll write and confirm my choice, but you

should know that I am seriously considering your application. When would you be free to start?' he asked, as she stood up.

'I'm free now,' she replied, realising that he had spent twice as long with her as with the others and feeling a sense of triumph.

'That's splendid,' he said, walking with her to the door.

She didn't hear the door close and she guessed he was watching her as she walked down the stairs.

Outside, she took a deep gulp of the salty sea air, her poised act crumbling and her spirits sinking like a soggy soufflé. Where had she got the nerve from? She could only cook roasts and stews and simple dishes. Fancy dinners for twelve and cold buffets and canapés for thirty! Was she out of her mind? Well, at least she'd made an impression on him, but she'd need time to think about it. In the meantime, she'd better hurry to the other interview.

Back in Newcastle, she had no trouble finding the house on Edward Street. The area was only too painfully familiar to her. Even in the dark she could see that the step hadn't been scrubbed for some time and that the paint was peeling off the door. A man wearing familiar blue overalls answered her knock. She felt a strange and unexpected relief at being back among working people. What had happened to her mother's ambitions for her to raise herself back to her old status? Well, she would, but this just wasn't the right time. Finding a job she could cope with and where she could keep David was her immediate concern. 'I've come about the job,' she eventually announced to the waiting figure, realising that he was staring at her in the light of the hallway.

'Come in.' She followed him into a small and typical kitchen. A striking blonde woman was holding a small baby on her lap, while a two-year-old boy with a mass of blond hair and the same blue eyes as the woman sucked his thumb and nestled shyly among her skirts.

'Please sit down.' The man indicated one of the chairs around the oilcloth-covered table and sat facing her. In the gaslight she noticed his dark good looks. His features, beneath a shock of black hair, were delicate and refined, his almond-shaped eyes dark and piercing, and his nose slightly Grecian. Only the mouth belied the neatness of the face: the lips were full and sensuous, denying the slightly downward curve at the sides of the mouth, which could have otherwise appeared cruel. He was looking at her intently. She wasn't aware that the cold sea breeze had stirred a pink glow into her cheeks and had liberated damp locks of glistening hair from their restraining bun, allowing them to fall freely around her face. She lowered her eyes at the intensity of his stare, but had already estimated his age at about thirty.

'I'm lookin' for someone to live in and cook, clean, and generally take over the runnin' of the house and the children. My wife died giving birth to this one.' He nodded in the direction of the baby on the woman's lap. 'This is my sister-in-law; she's helpin' out at the moment. The rest are stayin' with their grandmother until I get things arranged.' His voice had only a suggestion of the north country lilt; he didn't sound like a true local.

'I'm good with children and it's the sort of job I'm looking for,' Mary responded.

'Why a housekeepin' job at your age? Why do you want to lumber yourself with bairns when you could be free?'

His blunt questions afforded Mary the opportunity to come to the point. 'I have a child of my own,' she announced, returning his stare boldly, 'and I need a job and a place to live where I can keep him with me.'

The thick black eyebrows rose, but he didn't bother

to ask about the father. 'A child!' He paused a moment. 'As if I haven't got enough.'

'How many do you have?' inquired Mary, steadily returning his gaze, emboldened by the fact that he still hadn't taken his eyes off her.

'Two more besides these two. A girl nine and a boy seven.'

'Oh, that's nothing! I can easily cope with five. And the others are older – that's always a help. I'm used to big families.'

For the first time the blonde woman spoke. 'I think you'd find this lot difficult, luv. They just lost their mother six weeks ago, and you seem a bit young to handle problems like that. Granny and I have been takin' turns so far, but now the ulcers on her leg are worse and she can't walk. At any rate,' she sighed, 'I couldn't have gone on much longer; I've got me own family to see to as well. We knew we'd have to get someone permanent anyhow, after the bairns had got over the worst of losin' their mam, but they're still upset and can be a bit hard to deal with at times, especially this one,' she said, indicating the toddler. She didn't like the way her brother-in-law looked at this girl, and besides, she thought her much too young for such responsibility.

'I lost my own mother when I was young,' Mary asserted, 'so I know all about those problems.'

'I think she knows better what she can handle and what she can't, Jane,' the man addressed his sister-in-law. 'The younger they are, the more energy they have. That last one we saw could hardly have made it up the stairs on her own, never mind carry bairns up with her. I don't suppose one more bairn in the house would make that much difference. How old is it?' His eyes were back on Mary.

'He'll be two in May and he's very good. He's close enough to your little one here.' She looked towards the toddler, still sucking his thumb and eyeing her.

'Aye, he's almost three and all over the place. So long as you know how to keep them in check. I'm usually tired when I get home from work and need some peace and quiet. Got any references?'

'Unfortunately, my last employer died.' The lie was even easier the second time.

'When could you start?'

She was surprised by the abrupt question but didn't hesitate to reply. 'Tomorrow, if you want.'

'Aye, that would be all right. She's got to get back to her own place as soon as she can.' He nodded in the direction of his sister-in-law. 'You get room and board and four shillin' a week. It would have been more, but there's goin' to be an extra mouth to feed with another bairn in the house.'

Mary calculated quickly. That wasn't much, but with the money she'd get from Joe and no rent or food to pay for, she'd be better off than she was at the factory after paying the baby minder – and she could keep David with her all day.

'That would be all right to start,' she agreed. She wasn't going to let him think she would stay at that wage for ever.

'All right then. Come round tomorrow afternoon and Jane'll show you where things are. The other two won't be home from school till after four, and I get home from work at six. My wife always fed the bairns first and had my dinner ready at six.'

'Thank you. I could come in the morning if you like,' Mary offered.

'Aye, you might as well.'

As she stood up to leave, his gaze travelled down to her black-gaitered ankles.

'My name's Mary Maddison, by the way,' she added, not quite knowing how to make her exit.

'Oh, aye, I forgot about the formalities. I'm Walter

Dolan. Jane'll see you out.'

Carrying the infant, Jane showed her to the door in silence. 'See you tomorrow then, I suppose,' she said in a resigned voice.

Once again out in the cold night air, Mary's head cleared and she wondered what she'd got herself into. A widower with four children! Was she crazy? And living in! Thank God her mother wasn't alive to know about it. But it was a home for her and David and at least it would be familiar work. She thought nostalgically of living in the beautiful house at the coast and having only one man to look after – but all those dinner parties and luncheons. No! She'd just make a fool of herself and lose the job. Children she knew she could deal with. But what about him? She thought about his penetrating stare as she hurried to Doris's house to pick up David.

Chapter Twenty-one

The next morning Doris arrived to help Mary pack and move her few belongings to Edward Street. She was worried about Mary. 'It doesn't mean 'cause I'm helpin' you to move that I think you're doin' the right thing, you know. I think you're crazy! A widower with four bairns, when you could have had a rich, single man.'

'Doris, stop nagging. We went through all that last night.' Mary was harassed and didn't want to deal with her friend's disapproval.

'No, we didn't go through it all; I'm not finished yet. You've still got time to go round and leave a note to say you've changed your mind, and wait till you hear from the rich one. Sounds to me like you've got that swanky one up your sleeve already, an' you're givin' it all up for a penniless labourer.'

'I didn't say he was a labourer, and anyway, if I took the other one I wouldn't last a day before he found out I couldn't cook.'

'I think they're both more interested in your talents in the bedroom than your talents in the kitchen, an' in any case, you could easily get some cookery books and read up on fancy dishes. If you're goin' to use your body just to get a roof over your head, you might as well make it a rich man's roof.'

'Doris, how many times do I have to tell you, I'm *not* going to *use* my body, I'm going to *work* for my living. You know I'll do whatever it takes to keep

David with me, but not that. My looks may have
helped me get the job, but that's where it ends.' Mary's
agitation was rapidly becoming irritation. Why
wouldn't Doris mind her own business? It was decided
now and final; she had no choice. Doris had a home
and money coming in every week; she didn't understand what it was like to be homeless and desperate.
Mary noisily plunked the kettle inside the saucepan
and thrust them at her friend – anything to change the
subject. 'You might as well have these, Doris. I shan't
be needing them.'

Doris accepted the gifts without a word and continued: 'I have to say what I have to say, an' then I'm
done and we'll forget about it, but I think you've got
a sneaky fancy for that labourer.'

'Doris, don't be ridiculous!' Mary flung a pile of
David's clothes into the already full, pink pigskin
travelling bag that had belonged to her mother and
missed it. 'Blast,' she muttered, bending down to pick
up the heap and cram it into the bag.

'Then why get your knickers in a twist when I mention it? I heard all about his good looks last night, but
I never heard nothin' about the businessman.'

Mary straightened up and turned to face Doris,
weary of her friend's concern. 'All right, Doris. The
businessman was six feet tall, dark, handsome, and
around twenty-five, I'd say. He was, in fact, the most
handsome man I've ever met. However, I decided to
turn him down in favour of the much less handsome
labourer because I'm not qualified for the job and I'm
afraid of getting into a bigger mess than the one I'm
in already. Do you understand me?'

'Yes, I get your meaning – shut me trap and mind
me own business.'

Mary penitently put her arms round her friend.
'Oh, Doris, I know you're just worried about me, but
honestly, I can take care of myself. Why don't you

stop worrying and help me get some of this stuff down to the hall, there's a dear?'

She rescued David who had crawled to the empty fire grate and was happily munching on a cinder, while Jimmy had made his way to the bag and was busy unpacking David's clothes. 'Look at the mess! We should have been keeping an eye on these two instead of arguing. Let's get them down first.'

With the boys safely strapped in their prams outside the front door, they brought down Mary's bag and David's clothes, now stuffed into a pillow case, and a pile of blankets. Mary was out of breath. 'We'll have to dump these two off first and come back for the cot and mattress. I hope that woman doesn't mind looking after them for a while.'

Jane greeted them politely, but she seemed very strained.

'This is my friend, Doris. She's helping me move,' Mary explained. 'Do you mind if we drop this stuff off and leave the children while we go back for the rest?'

'Aye, that's all right. Bring them in.'

Mary noticed the kitchen for the first time. It was painted a light green, with white lace curtains at the window. The furniture consisted of the usual shabby but comfortable settee, two wooden armchairs by the fire, and the dining table where she'd sat the evening before. Some loving hand had painted the room and made the curtains, she thought.

Jane helped them get the bundles and the babies inside and said in the same restrained yet not unkind voice. 'You might as well leave the stuff down here and I'll show you up to your room when you get back. I'll look after the bairns.' She was already unbuttoning Jimmy's coat. 'Are they hungry?'

'No, they should be all right for a while, thanks.' Mary liked this quiet, distant woman, but she had a strong feeling that the woman didn't like her.

The two girls wheeled the prams back to the lodging house to pick up the cot and mattress. They perched the wooden frame precariously over one pram and draped the mattress over the other. 'I'll just go up and get your kettle and saucepan,' Mary gasped to Doris. She wouldn't be sorry to be living on the ground floor again. 'Oh, and you can have the glasses and dishes. I don't think I shall need them.'

'Thanks, luv. I'll keep them for you, but I'm not takin' them for good. I don't think you're goin' to last there long – at least I hope not.'

Mary ignored the remark and ran upstairs for the remaining glasses and dishes, which she loaded carefully under the mattress. She then took from her pocket a sealed envelope and a piece of paper, placing them on the hall table.

'Wouldn't do to forget those. I wrote to Joe last night telling him where I am and that he could come over tomorrow with David's money.'

'I hope it does some good.' Doris shook her head. 'What's the paper for?'

'That's my forwarding address in case I get any post.'

'I think you'll have to come round an' get it. I can't see the old crow bothering to forward nothin' to you.'

'For the first time today, I think you're right, Doris. She grumbled that she wanted a week's notice last night, and said that I should pay an extra week's rent instead. I gave her one and tenpence, all the change I had. It shouldn't take her more than a couple of days to fill the room.' She glanced up at the window, 'Goodbye, little attic. I can't say I'm sorry to leave you.'

The girls moved on slowly, pushing their unwieldy cargoes. When they returned to Edward Street, Jane had made tea and liverpaste sandwiches for them; the boys, seated by the fire with the toddler from the night before, were already tucking into large wedges of bread and jam.

'I'll show you up to your room when you've had this. You must be tired and hungry,' she said, seating them at the table and joining them. 'You're probably wondering about the job.' She looked hard at Mary. 'I'll tell you honestly, I don't think you're suited for it.'

'Why not? I'm used to hard work.' Mary was on the defensive.

'You're young and pretty, luv. This isn't the sort of job for the likes of you; you need to have some fun and some free time, not be cooped up lookin' after someone else's bairns. They miss their mam and so does Walter. He loved her in his way, though he had a funny way of showin' it at times. He's not always an easy man to live with, you know, though he's not a bad man.'

Even in her agitation, Mary noticed again that the woman spoke rather like the man, softly, with only a suggestion of the local accent. She was curious about this family. 'He seemed very nice,' she countered, beginning to feel depressed.

'Aye, he's all right, but he's got some funny streaks in him. You'd better know now.'

'What sort of streaks?' By now Mary was worried.

'Oh, nothin' that I want to dig into, luv. Let's just say that he can be a bit selfish at times and he likes a good time. Though he did love our Annie, I admit, life wasn't always easy for her. Just make sure you get your pay out of him and keep yourself to yourself. Maybe it'll work out,' she sighed, getting up to clear away the dishes.

Doris glared at Mary from across the table with an 'I told you so' look and Mary, her heart sinking, said, more to convince herself than the others, 'I've worked with a lot of people in my time and none of them was perfect either. Don't worry, it'll work out.' She glared back at Doris, who got the message and stood up.

'Well, I'd better get back then.' And then boldly to Mary, 'Sure you don't want to come with me, Mary?'

'Don't be silly, Doris. Thanks for your help. I'll pop over on my day off.'

'Aye, that's another thing you should have sorted out with him,' Jane interrupted. 'Make sure you get Sundays off and maybe Saturday nights. He needs to spend more time with the bairns anyway, now that Annie's gone.'

'I will, don't worry,' Mary asserted, more to herself than anyone else. ''Bye, Doris. Thanks again.'

With Jane's help, Mary spent the afternoon making herself and David comfortable in their upstairs room, acquainting herself with the two young ones' routines and needs, and making a mutton stew and rice pudding for dinner.

She ate with the children when the two older ones arrived home from school at four thirty. They were both blonde with fine features and looked like their aunt; the girl was especially pretty, with pale blue eyes and a sad smile. They were a little shy at first, but seemed to take to her all right. Nevertheless, Mary noticed that they clung to their aunt and seemed to be reluctant to let her go when she finally decided to take her leave. 'I've got to go now, luv. Their father'll be home soon and I think it best that you all get acquainted without me around.'

Mary felt her stomach jump. Now for her first real trial on the job. Remembering Walter's words, she had the baby and David in their cots and the others scrubbed and in their nightclothes by the time he arrived home at six. His dinner was keeping hot on a plate over a pan of water on the stove; the rice pudding she would heat up while he ate the first course.

She saw a shadow cross the kitchen window and

heard the scullery door open and close. Her stomach jumped again.

'Hello! How've you been managing?' His voice was soft and courteous.

What had she been worrying about and why was everyone trying to put her off this man and this job? 'Fine, no problems so far. Your dinner's ready and there's some hot water on the stove if you want to wash first.' She noticed that his soiled blue overalls were covered in oil stains, and his hands and face were smeared with factory grime, so he probably was a labourer.

The two older children were seated on the settee, the girl with the toddler on her lap. She'd been telling him a story, to which the older boy was also listening, but they looked up when their father came in. 'Aren't you going to say hello to your father?' Mary inquired.

'Hello, Dad,' chorused the older two, while the toddler continued sucking his thumb.

'Hello! Have you been good for your new auntie?'

'Yes, Dad,' came the chorus again, as the little one removed his thumb from his mouth and nodded agreement.

Mary quickly confirmed their answer. 'Yes, they've been very good, and Anne helped me make dinner and set the table.'

'That's good. I see you're all ready for bed. A bit early, isn't it?' As he spoke he unbuttoned and stepped out of his overalls in the kitchen, revealing a shabby grey cotton shirt and frayed black trousers held up by grey and red striped braces.

'I just thought I'd get them ready early so they could relax a little before bed.' Had she done something wrong?

'Aye, that's all right. I'll just have a wash and then I'll have me dinner.' He kicked the overalls through the scullery door and followed them.

'Here,' she said, picking up the kettle from the hob and following him to the scullery sink. 'I've heated you some water.'

Continuing to roll up his sleeves, he thanked her and then took the kettle from her. 'And there's a clean towel on the peg behind the door,' she said over her shoulder as she quickly made her exit, on the way picking up the soiled overalls and stuffing them into the tub under the scullery bench. It was strange being so familiar with a man she didn't know.

When he returned he'd resumed his good looks of the night before, his face and hands freshly soaped and scrubbed and his black hair combed and neatly parted down the centre.

'What's to eat then?' He sat in his same place at the table and noticed the single place setting. 'Aren't you goin' to eat tonight?'

'I had mine with the children.' Should she have waited for him? 'Yours is ready,' she said, setting the plate down in front of him.

'Well, you don't have to do that. I don't mind a bit of company with me dinner.' He started eating his mutton stew and propped the evening paper up against the salt jar in front of his plate.

She noticed that the children were amusing themselves quietly; they were obviously well trained. The older boy was rereading a two-week-old comic and the girl was rocking the toddler in her lap; he was already half asleep. 'Why don't I take him upstairs now, Anne? It looks as though he's ready.'

'I'll come with you.' The child seemed glad of something to do.

'All right, you come and help.' She looked over her shoulder as she lifted the limp, living weight from the girl's arms. 'I'll get your pudding when I come back,' she said to the silent figure at the table. All she heard was the rustling of the paper, but she noticed that the plate was almost empty.

After getting Billie into bed, she checked the infant and David in their cots. David was restless and far from sleepy. It was much too early for his bedtime but Mary hadn't wanted to make his presence too obvious the first evening. She left Anne upstairs to soothe him while she went down to serve the rice pudding.

'Nice dinner,' he said, pushing his plate away. 'Any more stew left?'

'Well, there is, if you don't mind waiting till I heat it up.' He had a large appetite; she must remember to serve up more in future.

'No, that's all right. I'll just have my puddin' then.'

While he ate the rice pudding, she sat beside Michael on the sofa and pretended to read his comic with him, but all the time her mind was racing. How would they get through a whole evening?

She needn't have worried, however. As soon as he was finished, his chair scraped backward across the linoleum and he announced calmly, 'Well, I'll be off to the pub for a drink. I'll be back after ten.'

Mary didn't know whether she was delighted or dismayed. Was he a pub crawler? Well, what if he was? It was none of her business and, at least, it helped to get the first awkward evening over. Besides, it was Friday evening and he'd had a hard working week, not to mention his recent bereavement. He probably needed some livelier company than hers. She'd make sure that she was in bed by the time he got back. Tomorrow would be easier.

Chapter Twenty-two

Mary opened her eyes the next morning to the grey light striving through the thin white cotton curtains. She looked around the strange bedroom. David was standing in his familiar green cot, rattling the bars and babbling his usual early morning greeting: 'Mummy, Mummy.'

'Yes, sweetheart,' she murmured sleepily as she looked at the clock. Good gracious! It was six o'clock, time to get up. The new baby was still sleeping soundly in his cot, thank goodness. She'd had to get up twice for him during the night. All part of the job, she thought ruefully. Just when David was beginning to stay dry through most nights, she had to start again with another. Pulling off her nightdress and washing in the cold water, her mind ran through the events of the evening before, or rather the non-events.

She had busied herself clearing away the dishes, getting the children off to bed and answering the door to four would-be applicants for the job. She had felt no small pleasure in telling them the position had already been filled; nevertheless, each time she had opened the door her heart had sunk in disappointment. It wasn't Joe! But he would surely come today after work. She hadn't even heard Walter coming home last night. So far, so good.

She shivered as she grabbed her old grey flannel dress; the morning air was frigid. She picked up David; his night-time nappy was damp. Quickly sponging down and dressing him in some warm leggings and a hand-knitted wool sweater – a gift from Mrs Moynihan – she tucked him under one arm and made her way downstairs to the outside privy. 'Good boy, David,' she cajoled. 'You go potty like a big boy.'

'Me went potty in bed,' he argued, trying to wriggle off the wooden seat.

'Yes, I know you did, but now it's time to go potty like a big boy.' She persevered, to no avail, longing for the day when he would be completely toilet trained.

Back indoors, she quickly laid the fire and put on some water to boil for tea and porridge, and to heat up the baby's bottle. Oh, my goodness! She'd forgotten Billie. Just then Anne appeared, dressed, and leading Billie down the stairs in his pyjamas. Mary had also forgotten to leave clean clothes out for him. 'Good morning, Anne. How's Billie this morning?' she asked, trying not to sound flustered.

'He wet the bed again,' Anne said matter-of-factly. 'I'll hang the sheets outside if you like.'

'Thank you, Anne. I'll take him.' He started to cry as she peeled off his damp layers. 'Now a big boy like you shouldn't be making such a fuss, Billie, and shouldn't be wetting the bed either. You stay there by the fire while I get you some dry clothes.'

'They're in the airing cupboard. He's only been doing this since Mam died; sometimes he has to be changed umpteen times a day. Auntie Jane's been seein' to him.' Anne's big blue eyes were anxious. Was Mary going to scold him?

Dear God, thought Mary, as she grabbed some underwear and a sweater and some short trousers from the cupboard by the stove. He was obviously distressed about his mother, and she didn't have time to give him the special attention he needed, poor little mite. Doris had certainly been right about 'wiping

258

dirty bums'. On second thoughts, she pulled a nappy off the baby's pile. 'We're just going to put one of these on you for now, Billie, until you learn how to be a big boy again and go potty. You and David can learn together.'

'No!' Billie kicked and yelled. 'I'm a big boy – no nappy.'

Mary gritted her teeth and put the nappy back on the shelf. 'All right, if you show us that you're a big boy by going potty before you wet your pants, we won't use a nappy. Is that better?'

'No nappy,' he screamed again. 'No nappy!'

'All right, sweetheart,' she cajoled, taking him on her knee. 'No nappy if you don't want it. Now stop those tears, there's my big boy.'

'What's going on in here?' The dark head loomed above her. With all the noise, she hadn't heard him enter the room.

'Just a problem with Billie wetting himself. I'm dealing with it.' She tried to keep her voice calm – of all the times for him to arrive!

'Never mind about him now. What's for breakfast? I'll be late for work.'

Flustered, Mary said, 'I'm making porridge and tea; they'll be ready in a minute, and there's some bread and marmalade on the table. Perhaps you could start with that.' She quickly dried Billie's eyes with her handkerchief and sat him on the sofa, giving him a kiss on the forehead. 'There now! Billie's a big boy.' Please God, let him stop crying soon.

'Aye, I'll start with that; I have to leave in twenty minutes.'

Dear God! What had made her think she could cope with five children and a man? Doris was right.

Mary took advantage of Anne's return from hanging out the sheets. 'Anne, just keep an eye on these two while I make breakfast, will you, please? It'll be ready in a couple of minutes.' Thank goodness the girl was sensible.

So, she thought, as she stirred the porridge, I have a choice of a wet child or a screaming child. How am I going to deal with the poor little chap? Her head was spinning but she kept her face calm as she poured the tea. 'Here you are,' she said apologetically, serving Walter. 'Sorry it took a while.'

'That's all right; you'll soon get the hang of it. Billie's just missing his mother. He'll get over it soon enough.'

'Well, that's good to know.' She was still puzzled by this man, his quiet lilting voice, his refined features, and his long slim hands, calloused from hard work. He didn't seem to fit his role. Where did he come from? His children, too, weren't rough like the neighbourhood children, yet they obviously belonged here. Her thoughts were interrupted by Michael coming into the kitchen. Oh, God! She'd forgotten Michael – and the baby!

'Michael, here's your porridge. You'd better get down earlier in future or you'll be late for breakfast.' She handed him a bowl of porridge and poured another cup of tea.

'Ta,' was all he said.

David was still sitting on the settee eating his bread and jam; she'd have to see to him later. She must feed the baby now; the milk should be warm enough. 'Would you all just mind keeping an eye on David while I go up to feed the baby?' she asked hesitantly.

'Aye, Anne'll watch out for him. Nice lookin' boy. I'm off to work now. Where are me overalls?'

'Oh, I put them in the washtub; I thought they needed washing.' Had she done something else wrong?

'Aye, they do. But I usually wear them out on

Saturday mornings and start a new pair on Mondays.'

'I'll get them, then.' She hurriedly put the bottle on the table and rescued the overalls from the tub of dirty washing. The familiar smell of grease and oil reminded her of Jack, and she wished fervently that Mrs Moynihan were here to help her.

As he stood up, she draped them over the back of his chair and retrieved the bottle from the table. It would be an escape and a half-hour break to go upstairs and feed the baby. No, on second thoughts, she'd better bring him down by the fire; the bedroom was cold.

By the time she had brought the complaining infant down, Walter had gone. She put the bottle back in the pan of hot water on the hob to keep warm. This one needed changing, too. Was there ever going to be an end to dirty nappies?

She was glad the children had no school today so she could leave Anne in charge while she went shopping. As she opened the door, she was surprised to see Doris, hand raised, about to knock.

'Goodness, you startled me! What are you doing here?' she asked, still buttoning her coat.

'I was on me way to the shops and thought I'd see if there was anything you want,' Doris replied peering closely into her friend's face.

'What are you looking at me like that for?' Mary laughed. 'I know I look a bit frazzled, but I can't look that bad.'

'Well, to tell the truth, luv, I was so bloody curious I just had to come to see how you were doin' an' if he kept his grimy paws off you last night.'

'Of course he did, you idiot. I told you he's all right. Still, I'm glad you've come. Where's Jimmy?'

'Me da's lookin' after him. It's not often Da feels well enough so I took the chance to get out on me own.'

'Wonderful, we can go to the shops together. I can't deny I'm glad to see a familiar face.' Mary tucked Doris's arm in hers as they started down the street.

'How was it then?'

'Oh, it was all right, nothing I didn't expect. But he's forgotten to give me any money so I'll just have to use my own for the shopping.'

'Well, that's a great start! Make sure you keep track of it an' get it back. Remember that woman warned you about money.'

'Don't you worry,' said Mary determinedly. 'I'm going to talk to him about the money and my time off this afternoon. Let's go to the pork butcher. I'm going to get some pease pudding and saveloys; at least it'll save cooking lunch,' Mary added, remembering Mrs Moynihan's system.

'Aye, I think I will as well, but we'd better leave that till last or it'll get cold. I know Mrs Boyd at the shop; she'll lend us some basins if we take them back on Monday.'

'All right, let's go to the greengrocer first. I thought of cabbage and bacon soup for tonight.'

As they approached the greengrocer's window, Doris exclaimed in horror. 'Hey, look! The cabbage is thruppence a head. They must be kiddin'.'

'I don't care,' countered Mary, grabbing one. 'The soup's quick and easy to make and I don't feel like spending hours over the stove. I have to admit, the first day was a drain on me.'

'Aye, an' so will all the others be, if you ask me.'

'Well, I'm not asking you, Doris. Have you time to come to the baker's with me before we get the pease pudding? Then I'd better get back. I'm worried about leaving Anne in charge for too long; she's a sensible girl, but she's only nine.'

'Aye, luv, I have to get back an' all. Them two don't like it when I'm out long neither.'

There was a queue at the pork butcher's and they had to wait. After ten minutes, they grabbed their steaming basins and parted at the end of Mary's street.

"Bye, luv. Pop round when you have a minute.' At the same time, Doris was dipping her fingers into the pease pudding and sampling it.

'I'll try to make it tomorrow if I can get Sundays off. Saturday nights too I hope.'

'You'll be lucky, luv, but no harm in tryin'. See you when I see you. Ta, ta, then.' But she turned and called after Mary's retreating figure: 'Hey, Mary! Daft bugger that I am, I clean forgot. I stopped at your old house on the way to see if there was any post for you and there was.' With her free hand she pulled a small white envelope from her coat pocket and handed it to Mary.

The postmark was blurred and Mary didn't recognise the handwriting. 'It must be about that job,' she said, staring at the envelope.

'Well, open it, you ninny, quick; it's not too late to take it if you've got it.'

Mary put her shopping basket and the basin on the pavement while she opened the envelope and read the letter it contained. 'He wants me to start on Monday,' she said dully.

'Well, thank God for that. You can still do it. Just tell the old labourer man you're sorry but the job's too much for you. He's still got time to get one of his other applicants.'

'No, Doris,' said Mary, replacing the letter in the envelope, 'I couldn't. I'm less able to cope with that job than I am with this one. I'm staying where I am. I'll just write and say I've found another position.'

'Aw, Mary, give it a try at least.'

'If I give it a try I risk finding myself out of work again, *and* out of a home this time. No thanks! I'm safe where I am.'

'You daft bugger, where's your sense of adventure?' Doris's tone was challenging.

'I can't afford to be adventurous with David to think of.'

'Have it your own way, then,' Doris sighed. 'But I think you're being stupid.'

'Then I'm stupid, as you say. Thanks for picking up the letter anyway. 'Bye, Doris. I've got to go.'

''Bye, then, but I hope you change your mind.'

As Mary hurried home with her purchases, she planned her day. By lunch time the beds were made, David and baby Walter, well wrapped up, were out in the yard in their prams, the older ones were playing in the front street, and the lunch was keeping hot on the stove. She washed her face, combed her hair, and put a little rouge on her cheeks; it wouldn't do to be looking so pale and tired when he arrived. She didn't want him to think the job was too much for her.

Twelve thirty came, one o'clock, two thirty, before the figure crossed the kitchen window. She and the children had already eaten. As he entered the kitchen, the smell of beer mingled with the oil on the overalls.

'Hello, how's it been?' His voice sounded sober enough.

'Fine, but I'm afraid your lunch is a bit dried up. I expected you home earlier.'

'Aye, I stopped off with the lads for a couple of drinks. I usually do of a Saturday.' He sat in his chair, still wearing his overalls. 'I'm tired; I'll have it now.'

She served up the spicy sausage and pease pudding, having made sure to keep a large portion back for him this time.

'Where did you get this?'

'I went shopping. You owe me some money,' she dared. 'Here's the list,' she added, placing it beside his plate.

'Aye, money. I get paid on Saturdays so that's when you get your housekeepin'.'

'Well, may I have it now, plus the shopping money? I've nothing left,' she lied.

He put his hands inside his overall pocket and withdrew a small brown envelope, carefully counting out the coins into three small piles.

She picked up the money, trying to appear casual, and put it in her pocket. 'And while we're talking business, we haven't sorted out my off-duty time yet. I need Saturday evenings and Sundays free,' she blurted, amazed at her own daring.

'Saturday evenings, *and* Sundays! And when do I get a break at weekends then? I work all week too, you know. You can have either Saturday afternoons and evenings, or Sundays, but not both.'

'I'll take Sundays then,' she grabbed quickly. At least that was a whole day. 'But I will need an occasional Saturday evening.'

'Oh, aye! What for?'

'That's the only time I can see my friend – she works on Sundays,' she lied again. She could see she was going to have to be firm from the start with this man.

'Well, tell you what. Maybe you can arrange with Jane to come and sit for an occasional Saturday night, but that'll be between you and her. Your official day off is Sunday.' His eyes never left his plate and he propped up the *Gazette* in front of the sugar bowl to signal the interview was over.

Well, she thought, so much for his falling for her charm and being after her body; Doris was wrong there. He had made it quite plain that she was a paid employee only.

After lunch he went to the front parlour (which served as his bedroom) for a nap and didn't reappear till tea time. The children were already seated round the table. She had stuffed the two chair cushions underneath David so he could just reach the table top, tying a strap round his shoulders to the back of the chair so he wouldn't fall off. He would be less conspicuous now he had joined the family.

'What's for tea, then?' Walter yawned, seating himself in his usual place. His hair was tousled and his face slightly puffy from sleep, yet he still looked handsome.

'It's bacon and cabbage soup.' She waited for a complaint but none came. At least he seemed easy enough to please with his food.

'How's your first day been then?' Was he really interested or just trying to make conversation?

'Busy,' she replied. She wasn't going to let him think it had been easy. This was a hard job for the money he was paying.

'Aye, it always is. You either slave in a factory all day or slave in the house all day. That's the only difference between men and women.'

'I think I found the factory easier.' Whoops! She'd better not go too far or he'd think she was complaining. 'Nuts and bolts are easier to handle than children,' she added, smiling.

'So that's what you did before. You don't seem the type for that sort of work, nor for this sort, for that matter.'

'Well, I'm the type that has to eat, and if you have to eat, you have to work.'

'Got nobody, then?'

'I've got friends,' she replied quickly. It wouldn't do to let him think she was completely alone and helpless.

'What about his father?' He nodded in David's direction.

'He's dead.' Why did she lie to this man? She had a feeling it wouldn't make any difference to him anyway. Well, too late, the lie was out now; she'd have to stick with it. She'd become too accustomed to having to lie about Joe.

'Oh, I see,' was all he said, his eyes fixed on her face as they had been the first night.

Uncomfortable, she got up to clear the table.

'Anne, give your new auntie a hand with the dishes.'

'Yes, Dad.' The child obediently got up and started carrying plates through to the scullery. The children were certainly well behaved when he was around. Did they respect him or were they afraid of him? Well, whatever the reason, she appreciated their silence and co-operation in his presence. When he was out, they were normal, noisy, children, bickering and playing alternately, and she was finding them difficult to cope with, especially Billie and the baby, who needed the most attention. If it had been just the two older ones, her life would have been much easier.

The clock on the mantelpiece said half past five. 'Well, I'm off now.' He scraped his chair back from the table in his customary fashion. 'Any hot water for a wash? And I need a clean shirt.'

'There's some water on the hob,' she said with her back to him as she took a clean, ironed white shirt from the airing cupboard. 'Here's a shirt.'

'Thanks,' he said, unbuttoning his grey flannel shirt of the day before. He took the new one and retreated to the scullery. Mary looked away. Did he always change in the scullery like this? He undressed down to his body shirt and she heard the sounds of splashing in the scullery. She'd have to leave the dishes till later. He passed through the kitchen again, still in his body shirt, and carried the clean garment to the front parlour. Thank goodness! It wasn't proper that he undressed in front of her, a complete stranger.

In five minutes he returned, wearing a dark blue serge suit, a blue and grey striped tie, and the white shirt. The transformation was startling. He looked

like any well-off businessman going to the office in the
morning, until he stopped at the outer scullery door,
pulling from the pegs a grey muffler and grey cloth
cap. The working man's uniform, Mary thought as she
studied him. Yet they didn't detract much from his
image, they simply added a touch of incongruity. She
caught herself staring and busied herself at the scullery sink. 'I'll wash and you dry, Anne. Thank you for
helping me.'

'That's all right; I used to help me mam.'

Poor child, Mary thought, as she filled the sink with
hot water from the kettle. She remembered well what
it was like to have your mother die, and Anne was even
younger than she'd been.

Nine o'clock and she'd got the children upstairs to
bed and finished her evening chores. She'd just sit
downstairs for a while and have a cup of cocoa before
retiring. It had been a hard day. The kettle started
hissing just as someone knocked on the front door.
Joe, it had to be Joe! Her heart pounded as she
ran down the hall to answer the door. Joe loomed in
the doorway and, as usual, she smelled beer on his
breath.

'Hello, Mary.' His voice was steady; he hadn't had
too much. 'I got your note. Sorry I couldn't come any
earlier. I've brought the money.'

She opened the door wider, 'Come in, I'm alone.'
She was nervous about letting him into the house, but
it would be worse if the neighbours saw her talking to
a man at the door. Walter would be bound to hear
about it sooner or later.

'I can only stay a few minutes . . . got some mates
waiting. How's the new job, then?' he asked, following her into the kitchen and standing with his back to
the fire.

'I suppose I'll get used to it,' she replied, standing
facing him. 'Looking after five children, a house, and

a man isn't easy, especially when three of them are under three years old.'

'A man, eh? What's he like? Has he made a pass at you yet?'

'Oh, Joe! You're just like everybody else. No! And he's not going to. He's hired me as a housekeeper, that's all.'

'I'll bet that's not all he's got in mind. Just you wait.'

'Don't judge everyone by yourself, Joe. What about the money? I'm getting tired of this conversation.'

'Oh, don't get grumpy. I'm just concerned for your welfare, Mary.' He moved towards her and put his arm round her shoulders. 'It's a sticky situation for a pretty young girl to be acting as housekeeper to a single bloke. I take it he is single.'

'Widowed, and since when did you care a damn about my welfare?' she shrugged his arm off her shoulders, but she had left it there long enough to feel his presence again. Damn him! Why was her heart racing, still, the way it used to? Her head was swimming with confused emotions. This man had got her into trouble and had left her in the lurch; why did his touch still disturb her so? She should have frozen and, instead, she'd felt herself begin to melt. 'The money, Joe, I need it more than ever now – or rather your son needs it,' she said firmly, squaring her shoulders.

'I'm sorry, luv, but that's as much as I can make it – two bob. Blasted landlady's just put the rent up. I'm going to have to look for a cheaper place.'

Mary looked down at the florin he had placed in her hand. 'Well, you'd better, and in a hurry, because I can't manage on this for long.' Now she hated him again. That was better; she was back on solid ground.

'You're really getting frosty in your old age, Mary. I'm not obliged to pay anything, you know.'

'I'm not frosty; I just have to be a lot more sensible than I used to be now that I have a child to bring up, and he's your son as well, Joe. Don't you feel any responsibility at all for him?'

'No, Mary. He's your son, your choice, and your responsibility. I'll help out for as long as I can but I can't keep this up for ever. You made your decision; you'll have to learn to live with it. If I'd had my way he'd have been adopted into a comfortable home by now.'

'Oh, and you think that's so easy, finding warm-hearted, rich people to give your son the love and security you deny him.'

'Look, Mary, I didn't come round to argue. You've got your money and now I'll be on my way. My mates are waiting and the pubs'll be closing soon. I'd hate to miss last call. We're going to give the Prince Albert on the corner a try. I take it that's where your new man is. What's he like, so I can say hello and introduce myself?'

'He's not "my man" and it's none of your business where he is. You'd better go before he comes home and knocks your block off.' In her anger she rushed down the hallway and opened the door.

'Ooh, you look attractive when you're angry, Mary. Can't say I like the temper but I like the way it makes you look, all hot and bothered and beautiful.' He chucked her under the chin and, once again, his brief touch and his proximity stirred her in a way she'd hoped her body had forgotten.

'See you next week, Joe. And how about coming earlier, before you have time to get drunk?'

'I'm not drunk, but you've just reminded me. I brought this for you, a sort of housewarming present.' He pulled a bottle of sherry from his pocket and thrust it at her. 'I'd hoped to break the bottle with you, but never mind, my mates'll be waiting with a pint. Take it up to bed, luv. It'll help to keep you warm; the nights are chilly.'

She took the proffered bottle without even saying thank you, banging the door closed and leaning against it. She knew she was behaving badly but she couldn't help her anger, and she wasn't only angry with him but with herself too. Why did he still have the power to affect her the way he did?

Oh well, she'd have some sherry instead of the cocoa; perhaps it would help her to sleep. She'd better hide it in her room though; it wouldn't do to let anyone get the wrong impression.

Sitting alone by the fire with a glass of the sherry, she sighed and shivered, thinking of how his touch had affected her. No! She mustn't ever let him affect her that way again or she'd be heading for more trouble. The past was the past; she must be more responsible now that she had David to think of, and Joe had made it quite plain that he wanted neither to marry her nor to accept responsibility for his son. She would see him every week to get financial help for David, but that was all.

Chapter Twenty-three

A month had passed and Mary was off on her Sunday visit to Doris. Feeling too tired to go to the park, she was happy to sit in the kitchen and relax over tea and cheese sandwiches, leaving David at home with the others in Jane's care.

'Well, now, let's have it all,' said Doris, settling herself comfortably in the opposite chair with her tea, the plate of sandwiches on the floor between them.

'I think it's going better now. Life is beginning to take on a routine, though there's too much to do. The baby's fretful, and Billie's still wetting his pants and refuses to wear a nappy. Thank God the other two are older; they're pretty well-behaved, really, and Anne helps me quite a bit looking after the others and helping out with the chores. I'm thankful to have her, and they're all nice children – not like the spoiled brats I had to put up with the last time I was in service.'

'I have to hand it to you, hinny. I didn't think you'd last this long. How's the old bugger behavin' himsel'?' Doris inquired through a mouthful of sandwich.

'I still can't work him out, Doris. His obstinate streak seems to surface mainly when I ask him for money, but otherwise he's quite pleasant really. I've discovered if I wait to ask till he comes back from the pub he's much more affable about it and more generous – that is, if he hasn't had too much. At those times we all keep out of his way.' She sipped her tea thoughtfully. 'Not that he gets violent or angry or anything, he just goes quiet and expects everybody else to keep quiet too. You can imagine how hard it is on the children. When the weather's all right they usually disappear into the lane. They seem to know it's better to keep out of his way; sometimes they even go to bed early without being asked. For some reason they seem to respect his authority, yet I've never seen him being unkind to them in any way. Sometimes, his moods remind me of Joe's, except that Joe was always in a loud mood when he'd had a drink.'

Doris stood up and stretched, then reached for the teapot on the hob while Mary held out her cup for more. 'Never mind about that bugger, I want to hear about the other one first. Do you mean he still hasn't tried anythin'?'

'No, Walter's been a perfect gentleman, although he still looks at me with those penetrating eyes of his. Sometimes I feel as though they're searing through my flesh, but he hasn't laid a hand on me. So, you see, I was right, Doris.'

'Well, time will tell about that, hinny. What about Joe, then? Anythin' juicy to report?'

'Yes . . . Joe . . . he's another story. I still just live for his Saturday-night visits and yet I know he's only coming because he has to bring David's money. I hate myself for it. He stayed longer than usual last week though and had a glass of sherry with me. I wondered if he was beginning to feel something for me again, although I've told myself a million times I'd be stupid to have any more to do with him.'

'Is he any better with the bairn, then?' Doris's tone was concerned.

'No, not really. I always keep David downstairs so Joe can get to know him, but he still doesn't show any fatherly interest.' Mary put down her teacup with a sigh. 'Which reminds me, I'm not showing much interest today either. I'd better get back; I promised to take him to the station to see the trains today and I thought I'd take Billie too. He seems to be the one who's suffering the most from his mother's death, although it's hard to tell with children. Jane's taking the others to visit their grandmother.'

'Eey, well, luv, I enjoyed the chat. The only excitement I get is hearin' your chatter of a Sunday.' Doris rose from her chair.

'Some excitement!' Mary grimaced, as she hugged her friend goodbye. 'See you next week with the latest exciting episode. Don't worry, I'll let myself out.'

It was eight o'clock the following Saturday evening and she'd just got the children upstairs. They complained about going to bed early on a Saturday, but Mary was forced to be strict on that point. If news of Joe's weekly visits got to their father and he learned that David's father was still alive and paying two shillings a week to help support him, her lie would be out. That was the terrible thing about having to lie to survive, once you'd told a lie you had to stick to it and one lie inevitably begot another. Walter hadn't seemed to notice that she hadn't yet exercised her right to have an occasional Saturday evening off. Just as well, for the moment at least. It was eight fifteen now; she just had time to put some rouge on her cheeks and slip into the blue dress she'd picked up at the market; it would be a useful workdress later on. Joe would be here any minute and she couldn't help the usual surge of excitement the anticipation brought.

She'd barely had time to change and tidy up David when the doorbell rang. He was early.

'Hello, beautiful. You look smashing in that dress. How are things? The old man still keeping his paws off his lovely housekeeper?'

'Things are fine and he's not old and he doesn't have paws. Come in and don't shout like that in the street. Do you want all the neighbours to hear?'

'Oh, you and the bloody neighbours.' He cupped his hands to his mouth in a mock attempt to broadcast his presence. She caught his arm and dragged him into the kitchen, where he seated himself by the fire, warming his hands.

'I'm surprised you don't have me skulking in through the back lane like the coal man.'

'They're more likely to see you that way than at the front. I don't know why people seem to spend their lives in their back kitchens; they only use their front parlours on Sunday afternoons,' she said, sitting in the chair opposite.

'Don't be a snob, Mary. Your front parlour's a bedroom anyway.'

'That's only because David and little Walter and I have Walter's room.'

'Well, for the moment, anyhow.'

'And what's that supposed to mean?'

'Well, if he hasn't already, it won't be long before he starts sneaking upstairs in the middle of the night. You watch out for him – if you want to, that is.'

'Could it be that you're jealous?'

'Nooo, just realistic!'

'You have a dirty mind, Joe.'

'Hello, titch,' he greeted David, who was sitting on the floor eating a slice of bread. 'Brought you a present.' He pulled out a bottle of port from his coat pocket and presented it to the child, who grabbed it eagerly with his free hand. 'Never too young to start, me lad.'

Mary rescued the bottle. 'Oh, port, what a nice change. I've got some lemonade; would you like a port and lemon?'

'No, I'll have mine straight, me bonny lass.'

'Joe, that's pub talk. What's happening to you? You're getting as bad as your cronies.'

'If I were like my cronies I wouldn't be sitting here like a gentleman with a lovely lady like you in the room. I'd be up on my hind legs, pouncing on you like a predatory lion.' He jumped up and began a mock assault on her, grabbing her by both shoulders.

'Joe,' she giggled, 'stop playing the fool and keep your voice down.' But his touch disturbed and excited her. 'The children will hear you. Behave yourself till I get the drinks.'

Returning with the drinks, she sat on the settee and he moved from the armchair to join her. 'Cheers, me lovely lady; bottoms up.'

'You're in an unusually good mood, Joe. How much have you had already?' Again his proximity distracted her; she felt lightheaded even before she'd taken a drink.

'Just a couple of beers at lunch time and maybe two or three at the pub just now. Oh, yes, and one of my mates is getting married so we all drowned his sorrows with a couple of rounds of bitter and a couple of chasers. Come on, drink up. I like you better when you've had a drink; you're less grouchy.'

She took a long draft of the refreshing mixture. She'd felt hot and flustered before he arrived and, now that he was here, even more so. 'What about what you came for, Joe?' she asked, remembering her resolution.

'What I came for? Oh, yes, the money! I might have known that would be the first thing on your mind. Here you are, luv, two bob's worth of my hard-earned pittance. The papers are reporting a marked decline in drunkenness – no bloody wonder with booze going up all the time and income tax at five bob in the pound.' He placed the coins in her empty hand, cupping it and kissing it exaggeratedly.

Mary withdrew her hand, flushed, and put the coins in her pocket. She wished she weren't so hot. She finished the cool drink, rubbing the empty glass against her forehead to stem the throbbing in her veins.

'You look hot, luv. Let me get you another drink.'

'Yes, please. That's a nice change from sherry.'

He returned with two full glasses and sank down beside her again, spilling some of the red liquid over the new blue dress. 'Oh, dear, let me clean that up for you.' He disappeared and returned with a damp towel from the scullery and began sponging the dark stain on her skirt. She could feel the cold damp cloth on her thigh and his warm hand as he held the skirt in place while he dabbed and stroked. She was vaguely aware that the cold sensation had ceased and the warm one was slowly moving up her thigh. And then she felt his mouth on hers.

She didn't even pretend to fight; she knew she was lost. She kissed him back fiercely, and he needed no encouragement. In an instant his kisses were all over her face and his hands all over her body. She gave herself up completely and hopelessly as he gently laid her back on the settee. Why pretend with him any more? She wanted him and, besides, maybe he would change his mind and want her back. after he'd experienced their wonderful lovemaking again. 'Wait, Joe!' She suddenly remembered David. 'Let me put David to bed.'

Reluctantly leaving Joe's arms, she ran upstairs with David, tucking him into bed with his clothes on and giving him a perfunctory goodnight kiss. 'Sleep well, my darling,' she whispered breathlessly, any guilt she might have felt was overwhelmed by her desire to get back to Joe.

He pulled her down beside him again and, once more, her sense of reality was obliterated. Oh, God! She'd forgotten what it was like to be transported to that other dimension; nothing else existed except Joe's body pressing against hers, his hands caressing her, their lips joined, and then their bodies. She quivered, and then froze. 'Joe, you will be careful.'

'Yes, yes, yes, I will,' he murmured into her hair. And she was lost again.

Afterwards, she lay in a trance, losing track of time, while Joe slumbered peacefully beside her. Good Lord! Time! What time was it? The clock on the mantelpiece said ten o'clock. 'Quick, Joe, quick.' She shook him roughly. 'You've got to go. The pubs are closing; he'll be back soon.'

Joe blinked sleepily and sat up. 'I suppose you're right. I mean, we don't want the big bad wolf to come back and find out I've been eating his porridge, or was it sleeping in his bed?'

'Joe, stop being an idiot. Get dressed, and hurry!'

'Yes, ma'am! I'm as good as out of the door,' he said, carrying his jacket and coat and buttoning his trousers as he retreated down the hall.

'Same time next week?' she asked, trying to sound casual.

'I don't know about that. Now that you've decided to be human again, how about asking for one of those overdue nights off? We'll have a few drinks and then go to my place. It's a hell of a lot more comfortable than that settee, and there are no kids around,' he said as he finished dressing before opening the door.

He was actually asking her out again. She had done the right thing after all. 'Yes, I will, but I'd better drop you a line when I know for sure.'

She quickly closed the door behind him and raced to the kitchen, plumping the cushions on the settee and clearing away and washing the glasses. She didn't want the pungent odour of the port to tell any tales. She picked up the bottle and ran upstairs, closing the door and breathing heavily. Footsteps sounded in the back yard and she heard the scullery door open.

Thank God, she'd made it in time. She must be more careful in future. Then she heard voices, male and female. He wasn't alone. And they were loud, jovial, inebriated voices. It seemed his mourning period was officially over.

Quickly throwing off her crumpled dress and tossing it with her camisole and petticoats on to the bedside chair, she fell into bed, breathing heavily. Not two minutes later there was a knock on her door. 'I'm in bed. What is it?'

His familiar lilting voice rang through the door. 'We're having a little party downstairs; I just wondered if you'd like to join us. It's time you did something other than work . . . time you enjoyed yourself a bit.'

'Thank you, but I was asleep . . . another time, maybe. I'm much too tired now.'

'All right then. Sorry about the noise, hope it doesn't disturb you.'

Disturb me? she thought. What about the children? The baby was already beginning to whimper and it was another two hours before his bottle was due. If he kept that up he'd wake David. She got up and took the infant into bed with her, patting his back gently to soothe him. She had grown fond of all the children, but Billie and little Walter were constant problems; she wished they were as easy as David. She lay wide awake, patting the baby's back until his complaining finally subsided, her mind going over the events of the evening.

Joe wanted her again! It had been wonderful for both of them. Surely he would want to see more of her now. She must just be patient and he would change his mind eventually about getting married. She hadn't realised how much she'd missed the musky smell of his body and the feel of his lips against hers. The memory of the intimacy of the evening made her shudder again with excitement.

Also, the noise from downstairs disturbed her. Walter was right. She did need to enjoy herself more; the sound of gaiety and the music sparked an emotion in her. Was it envy? Yes, she would have liked to go down and join them and have some fun; it was so long since she'd had fun. It was a pity that everything seemed to happen at once. Next time, she would go to the party; working long hours without some pleasure in life was dreary, and heaven knew, her life had been dreary quite long enough. She was the housekeeper; surely, there would be nothing wrong in her joining in an occasional party.

Chapter Twenty-four

The next day Mary sang as she washed and dressed David. Joe had made love to her, it was her day off, the sun seemed to be succeeding in poking its way through the clouds, and she was on her way to see Doris and go to the park. Life was beginning to get better at last. Jane had already arrived with her three- and five-year-old daughters to take over the family for the day; Mary would ask her when she went down if she would take over next Saturday evening as well. It was a long time since she'd felt so happy.

Jane shook her fair head, and her soft voice was apologetic but firm: 'I'm sorry but I can't, luv. It's me birthday and me old man's takin' me to the music hall. Me niece is comin' to look after my two, but she's only twelve herself and couldn't cope with this lot. I'll be happy to take over for you next Saturday, though.'

Mary felt as though she'd been struck a blow in the face; all her plans were shattered. Now she'd have to wait another week – an eternity. 'All right, thanks, Jane,' she said, trying not to show her disappointment; after all, Jane had a good reason.

Outside, she took out the centre section of the pram and sat David upright in it. He was getting too big for it and was toddling well enough now to walk with reins, but he got tired easily and then she had to carry him. He'd have to make do with the pram for a while longer and, besides, he'd get enough exercise when they got to the park.

She knocked on Doris's door and her friend yelled from within: 'I'm comin'! Keep your wool on! Don't knock the bloody door down. What's up?' she asked, as she opened the door and noticed Mary's long face. 'Your face'll trip you up if you're not careful.'

'Why is it things never seem to go the way I want them to, Doris?'

'Well, come in and tell me what things first, luv, and then maybe I can give you an answer. You look nice in that blue dress. New?'

'Yes, I got it at the market.' Mary hauled David out of his pram and manoeuvred him down the hall. 'I got him down to a shilling because it had a bad stain on the bodice. I told him all it was good for was to cut up for the skirt material, but I managed to get the stain out.'

'Eey, even at a bob, I don't know where you get the money from, Mary. And new shoes last week. You seem to be gettin' a hole in your pocket since you started gettin' David's money.'

Mary looked hurt. 'Well, everyone's telling me it's about time I started treating myself more and enjoying myself more, and besides, David's got more clothes than I have. I only ever buy secondhand clothes from the market, Doris; you could hardly call that extravagant.'

'Aye, I know, hinny. Just don't go off the deep end and wind up in debt like me. You're right! It *is* bloody time you had a bit more fun; I reckon you've paid in advance for any good times you might have comin'. It's got to be your turn one o' these days, and mine an' all. Just put David on the mat with Jimmy.'

Jimmy was playing with an old, battered, red wooden engine which David immediately snatched, causing Jimmy to discharge a wail of anger and frustration.

Doris pulled down her full mouth at the corners

and, shaking her head, asked: 'Bloody kids. Why did we do it, Mary?'

Mary rolled her eyes while Doris rescued the engine, returning it to Jimmy and thrusting a doll made of clothes pegs into David's grasping hands. 'That should keep them quiet for two minutes at least,' Doris said with relief. But it didn't. David was adamant that he wanted the engine and let it be known by emitting an angry scream and throwing the peg doll at Jimmy.

'For God's sake, you two, shut up!' Doris's tone silenced David long enough for her to rescue an old wooden car from under the table and throw it towards him. That did the trick. He grabbed it and, for the moment, both children seemed satisfied with their prizes.

'Now, what's got you all upset? You're even spreadin' your bad mood to your bairn. Let's sit down and talk about it.'

'I'm not in a bad mood, Doris; I'm just disappointed. I asked Jane for *one* Saturday night off – the first in the two months I've been there – and she said she couldn't.'

'Why not? That seems a bit stiff,' Doris consoled.

'She said it's her birthday and her husband's taking her to the music hall. I understand, but that doesn't stop me from being disappointed.'

'Why, you're right, hinny. That's fair enough. If it's her birthday and her old man's takin' her out, that's different. I wouldn't cancel a birthday night out with *my* husband to babysit for anyone – if I had a husband, that is. Why did you want the night off, anyway?'

'Joe asked me out.'

'God in heaven, you're not startin' up with him again, are you?'

'If you mean what I think you mean by starting up, yes! And I've already started.'

'You don't mean you let him have his way with you?'

'No, I didn't just let him, I wanted him. If you want to know the truth, I think I actually encouraged him.' Mary clenched her teeth and braced herself for the criticism she knew was bound to come.

'You mean you did it with him at the house? An' you're the one that gave *me* a lecture fo' doin' the same thing.'

'I know, Doris, and I'm sorry about that, but that was then and this is now; I think differently about a lot of things now. And don't worry, he was careful.'

'Well, I'm glad to hear that, but what do you mean, you encouraged him? Strikes me he never needed any encouragement.'

'I didn't even attempt to stop him; that's encouragement, isn't it? I needed him, Doris. I take back what I said to you. A girl needs some excitement in her life and, Lord, did I need Joe. I thought I was going to burst. It's always been good, but never anything like that before. I can't imagine now how I got through life for so long without him.'

'Go on, what happened?' Doris's bright eyes almost popped with excitement. 'Let's have the whole story, and I want *all* the gory details.'

'Doris, it was anything but gory; it was wonderful. It's actually the first time he's even tried since he came back. I was beginning to feel he'd gone completely off me as a woman but it seems he hasn't. So, anyway, when he put his hand on my thigh, I just couldn't stop him. I wanted him anyway, but I also thought it wouldn't hurt to let him see what he's missing by not marrying me. Thought I'd throw a sprat to catch a mackerel, so to speak.'

'Good God, Mary!' Doris laughed. 'I never thought you'd turn into a designing woman, but good for you! It's about time you started taking your life into your own hands and stopped letting other people push you around. I'm glad you're finally getting a bit wiser; it's *who* you've got your designs on that worries me. I never trusted the bugger from what you told me. I just hope it works out all right for you and, for pity's sake, be careful! You don't want to end up in the club again.'

'Do you think I'm still that stupid, you ninny? Once is enough! I thought I'd go and see Maggie, one of the girls at the factory; she knows all the tricks and hasn't got caught so far.'

'Good idea.' Doris stood up and went to the scullery. 'I'll just make some tea and a sandwich and then we can take the bairns out. That should last them till tea time. I've got to take me da somethin' an' all. He's bad again, up all night hackin' an' coughin'. I can't be out very long 'cause I don't like to leave him on his own too much.'

'Oh, I'm sorry. I thought he was feeling better,' Mary said, suppressing a shudder; she could hear the poor old man coughing in the bedroom. Thank God he was in another room.

'No, he has his ups and downs, but on the whole he's not gettin' any better. Doctor doesn't say much but I know what he's thinkin'.'

After ministering to her father's needs, Doris returned with a large platter of dripping sandwiches and a pot of tea. 'Come on, bairns, tuck in, you're at your granny's,' she declared, ramming a large sandwich into each eager fist. 'If you eat all these up, you can have a cake at the cafe.' At least their full mouths silenced their noisy, playful chatter and they sat quietly munching. The two children were good friends by now.

The park was crowded. The sun dodged the remaining few billowy cumulus clouds, shedding dappled yellow spots on the grass under the naked birch trees. It was cool but a fine day for a walk. Doris, having now shed her pinafore and workclothes, vibrated in a vivid green dress with tiny black buttons down the bodice, her shoals of red curls shimmering in the sun underneath her black hat. Mary's blue dress, white skin, and deep auburn curls, topped with the ubiquitous boater, now trimmed with a blue ribbon to match the dress, formed an attractive contrast. The February day was so unusually fine they had dispensed with their overcoats and barely needed the wool shawls they had tossed round their shoulders. Many admiring eyes turned in their direction.

Unhappily, many of the eyes, though set in young faces, were old and tired. The depression was getting no better; there was a dramatic wave of strikes, and no work to be had even for many of those soldiers who had returned fit to work.

The girls were too busily engrossed in their conversation to take any notice of their admirers, yet Doris granted a warm smile to a handsome, blond youth, who doffed his cap as they approached the bench he was sitting on. But as they passed him, she averted her gaze. 'Poor bugger's only got one leg. If he had two good pins I could fancy him, but I'm not gettin' stuck with any more invalids.'

'No more kids, either. You were right about that, Doris; I love David and I've grown very fond of the other children, but I sometimes wonder if that's all there is in life. I never have time to relax and have fun and just be myself, I'm always being somebody's mother. That's one of the reasons it was so wonderful being with Joe again; for a blissful hour, only the two of us existed and I forgot about all my worries.'

'Aye, although I love Jimmy and me da, sometimes I'd like to run away from them both and just find out what it's like to have no responsibilities.'

'Of course there are rewards, but if only children didn't need such constant attention. It would be wonderful just to have an hour to myself during the day and put my feet up and read the newspaper. The only time I have alone with my thoughts is one hour in the evening before bed and by then I'm so tired, I barely have enough energy to drink my cocoa, stare into the fire, and drag myself up to bed.'

'Aye, I know, but it's a woman's lot, luv.'

Mary put a restraining hand on her hat as a slight breeze attempted to dislodge it from its pins. 'I didn't mind helping Mrs Moynihan with her children because they were still her responsibility; the problem now is that I'm totally responsible for them all, and sometimes I feel so inadequate.'

'Well, I told you, didn't I? Why not look for another job then?'

'But most housekeeping jobs are going to mean looking after children. There aren't many jobs like that one with the businessman; and I'm not qualified for those.'

'Oh Mary, get away with you; you're just talkin' through your hat. You could have managed that job if you'd had the nerve to take it, but it's no good moanin' about it now. I'd rather talk about what went on last night.'

Mary laughed. 'It's obvious you're not getting any; you're totally obsessed with sex. If you must know, I actually had two offers last night.'

'Two! You don't mean the old bugger had a go at you as well?' Doris stopped dead, her face aghast.

'No, not that,' Mary laughed, propelling her friend forward again, 'but he asked me to join him and his friends; he was having a party . . . and I keep telling you, he's not *old*.'

'Eey, I can't get over you, Mary. I know you needed to change up to a point, but are you changin' into a whore overnight?'

Mary laughed again. 'Don't be an idiot, Doris; you

should know me better than that. It was only a party, and I said no anyway.'

'Why did you say no, then?'

'I couldn't go. I looked a mess after Joe had finished with me, but otherwise I would have loved to. I felt like having a good time last night, and why not? I haven't had one for too bloody long.'

'Swearin' now, an' all. I never thought I'd live to hear it. I think that man's a bad influence on you, an' Joe, too.'

Mary giggled. 'Tut, tut, Doris, since when was your language so pure? If I've picked up anything, it's probably from you.'

'But you wouldn't want to start anythin' up with him, would you? He's a widower with four kids, remember, and what about Joe?'

Mary paused, thoughtfully, and gave her friend a wicked grin. 'Just maybe it wouldn't hurt Joe to think he had a rival, might make him jealous and speed him up a bit.'

'So you're thinkin' of playin' one off against the other. You're turnin' into a schemin' wench, Mary, but good for *you*. That is, if you don't get yoursel' into even more trouble.'

'Don't be silly, Doris. I wouldn't *do* anything with Walter; I was only joking. But you're giving me ideas; perhaps it wouldn't hurt to flirt a bit and have a good time. It sounded like a riotous party; I was quite envious, lying in my bed with only two crying babies for company.'

'Aye, so would I have been. To tell the truth, *I'm* quite envious; I'd give me eyeballs to have a man interested in me again and here you are with two after you.'

'Look, I may be a fallen woman but I have my limits: one at a time's more than I can handle. I have no intention of having anything to do with Walter like that, but joining in his next party couldn't hurt; it was just a room full of people having fun and singing. It feels like centuries since I did anything like that, and I'm too young to bury myself yet.'

'Me an' all. Maybe you could get me an invitation. The last time I was at a party was Jimmy's birthday, ha ha! I spent the afternoon doling out lemonade an' cakes an' moppin' up after them when they spewed up or filled their pants. Wonderful time I had.'

'Poor Doris. It *is* time you had some fun. I wish you could meet a nice man who'd sweep you off your feet and cherish you for ever.'

'Aye, well, that day might come, but it's wishful thinkin'. At least you've got Joe in the here an' now. Though I think he's a bastard for what he did to you, you obviously still care about him, an' I'd give my right nostril to feel like that about a man again.'

'It's funny, Doris, I know he's been a bastard to me but when he held me in his arms again I forgot everything bad he'd ever done. I mustn't let my emotions rule me this time, though; I've got to keep my wits about me, if only for David's sake. Last time, Joe had unlimited power over me, but this time I've got to make an effort to exert some power of my own. I'm not the stupid little girl he used to know, thanks to him.'

'Aye, you're talkin' sense for once, Mary, especially with a fella like him. He's done you no good once; you'd better be on your metal this time.'

By now they had reached the Tea Rooms in the park. 'Let's have tea now and sit outside,' Mary suggested. 'It's a nice enough day.' They retrieved a discarded newspaper from the waste basket nearby and dusted off the dirty wooden table and chairs which hadn't been used since the previous summer. Then they ordered tea and four cakes and put the children on the grass to play while they seated themselves at the table.

'So, how are you goin' to egg old Walter on and keep him at bay at the same time? I never thought I'd learn any tricks of the trade from *you*. An' don't think you can give him any of that old tommy-rot about not being that sort of girl when you've already got one bairn to prove you are.'

'Doris, I didn't say I was going to egg him on, and I don't intend to get into any romantic situation with him, but if he tries anything, I shall simply say that, in future, no man will lay a hand on me until he marries me,' Mary giggled.

'But you don't want to marry him, do you?'

'Doris, you *are* dense today. Of course not. That would simply be my reason for not getting into bed with him, and he'd have to respect that. I'm just having daydreams that if Joe *thought* another man was interested in me, it might wake him up a bit.'

'Well, I think you'd be playin' with fire, playin' off one man against another, especially that Joe fella. I don't know the other one but I know that Joe's no one to fool around with. An' talkin' about Joe, there's somebody comin' over and he fits his description to a T.'

At that moment Joe approached the table, looking very debonair in his black suit and grey waistcoat, with a black and grey spotted cravat tied neatly under his high pointed collar and his straw hat cocked at a jaunty angle. 'Afternoon, ladies. Mind if I join you?'

Doris looked flustered, but Mary was amazed at how composed she felt. 'Yes, please do.' She indicated the chair opposite.

Joe flicked the worst of the dust off the chair with his handkerchief and sat down. 'I was just on my way home and thought I'd walk through the park, it's such an incredible day. What would you like, ladies?'

'We've already ordered, thank you. Doris, this is Joe Cowley, David's father,' she added deliberately to make him uncomfortable, and succeeded. 'This is Doris Leeming, my best friend.'

'How do you do, ma'am.' Joe doffed his hat, a trifle red in the face, and Mary couldn't fathom whether it was embarrassment or anger. But he seemed affable enough as he remarked that the two children played well together, bending down to tweak each nose by way of greeting.

'I can't get Saturday evening off,' Mary told him. 'Jane's going out; I was going to drop you a line. But I can get the following one off,' she added quickly, determined not to give him a chance to slide out of his invitation.

The waitress brought their order and Joe asked for an extra pot of tea; then, turning to Mary, 'That's all right, then. We'll make it the following week. I'll just pop round with the money as usual this Saturday – maybe a bit earlier,' he added, giving her a suggestion of a wink that he hoped Doris didn't see.

Mary kicked Doris's foot triumphantly underneath the table and Doris stifled a wince. So, thought Mary, he does want to see more of me now. It worked! She was delighted with and emboldened by her success, enough to push it even further. 'I thought that instead of just going to the pub we could go to the music hall first. They've got a new singer and a new master of ceremonies. That's where Jane's going on Saturday. And,' she added, even more boldly, 'I could always say that I was staying at Doris's, so I wouldn't have to leave early. Sunday's my free day anyway.'

Joe raised his eyebrows, obviously taken aback. 'Well, it's a thought, I suppose, but it'll have to be the gallery; I can't afford the stalls.'

'That's fine,' Mary responded, satisfied with her achievement. He hadn't mentioned anything about her staying overnight with him, but she supposed that was simply because of Doris.

He finished his tea and took out his pocket watch. 'Well, I must be running along, ladies. I'll take care of the bill. Nice to have met you, Doris.'

As soon as his back was turned, Doris dropped her jaw and raised her eyebrows in exaggerated amazement. Finally, she found her voice. 'Well, clever clogs, good for you! Where did you learn to do that? Talk about wheelin' and dealin' with a man! The poor sod didn't have a chance to say no if he'd wanted to.'

'But he didn't want to, did he?' Mary was jubilant. 'I must admit I was shaking in my shoes, but do you think I handled it all right, then?'

'Handled it right? You were a bloody miracle! I don't know what he wanted, and I don't think he did either. But I'm glad you got your own way. Atta girl! Start the way you mean to go on this time. Lord above! I know what you see in him now – quite a charmer, and a good-looker. They're the dangerous ones, though. Why don't you get yoursel' a nice ordinary lad that you know'll keep his eyes at home?'

'But I don't want an ordinary lad; I want Joe, and how about taking a bet that I get him this time?'

'All right, luv, a bob on you to win. And talkin' about being on, I'd better be off. Me da's been on his own too long already.'

'I'll walk back with you as far as the gates and then I think I'll go and see if Maggie's at home and ask her advice. I'll let you know if she has any tips.'

On the way back they saw the blond young man who had smiled at them. He was now on his feet, or rather on his crutches, his trouser leg pinned up over his right leg which was missing from the knee. He stopped in front of them to light a cigarette and, in doing so, dropped one of the crutches.

'Here, hold the pram, luv; I'll just go and help that

poor lad.' Doris skipped ahead and bent down to pick up the crutch. 'Here you are,' she said shyly, embarrassed in case she'd made him feel helpless. But he took the crutch and wedged it under his right arm gratefully. 'Thanks, I'm not much good without them.'

'That's all right,' and she made to return to Mary who was still behind, pushing both prams awkwardly.

He turned with her. 'Can I walk with you? I can walk all right, you know, as long as I've got two of them,' he said, indicating his crutches with his head and smiling again, revealing even white teeth.

Doris took in the broad, fair, rugged face and the laughing grey eyes that yet showed a suggestion of pain. 'Aye, why not? We're just walkin' home now.'

Mary had by now caught up with them and Doris made the introductions. 'This is me friend, Mary Maddison, and I'm Doris Leeming, and these are our two brats.'

'Pleased to meet you, and you too.' He smiled at the little ones. 'I'm Frank Riley. And please don't slow down for me; I can keep up with you. Lovely day for a walk. I come out here for some fresh air every day when it's fine. I've seen you both often on Sundays. I suppose you leave the men at home sleepin' the booze off.'

'There aren't any men,' Doris replied.

'Oh, I'm sorry. I didn't mean to be nosy, I just thought—'

'Never mind about that, *we* don't,' Doris cut in to ease his embarrassment. To change the subject she said, 'I suppose you got that in the war.'

'Aye, this and a pension. They gave me a temporary wooden one but it didn' fit right an' I kept fallin' backwards so now they're makin' me a new one. It's been six weeks already. There's a long waitin' list, they say.'

Mary finally broke her silence as they reached the gate. 'If you'll excuse me, I have to leave you now. Doris, why don't you pop over one day next week? Nice to have met you, Frank.' She turned on her way and waved.

'Your friend talks posh, doesn't she?'

'Well, you might say she's seen better days and had a good education, but she's all right, she's not as snooty as she sounds.'

'No, I didn' mean that. She just talks nice, that's all. And you sound nice an' all,' he added.

'Soft-soap,' she laughed. 'Me da says I sound about as refined as a fishwife bawlin' her wares. Anyways, we're good friends, me and Mary. We're pretty close because we're both in the same boat, I suppose. It's not easy bringin' up bairns on your own.'

'Aye, now especially; nothin's easy now. So much for freedom and prosperity.'

'I'll bet the pension they gave you fo' that just about keeps you in cigarettes.'

'Aye, and a few pints a week, but there's a rise comin' soon, so they say. I get the dole too 'cause I'm still employable at a sittin' job, and when I get me new leg I can maybe do somethin' more like a real job.'

The pair chatted eagerly and, lost in their conversation, Doris suddenly realised she'd passed her door. 'Hey, I've gone two doors past me house and me da's waitin' for his tea an' I'm late already.' She turned the pram and retraced her steps. He turned with her. She hesitated at the door. 'If you'd like a cup o' tea, you're welcome. You must be tired, walkin' on them stilts.' She giggled, to hide her embarrassment at being so forward as to invite him into the house.

'Aye, I'd love one, and a bit of a sit before I go back. That's good o' you.'

As Doris opened the door she prayed her father would still be in bed. Whatever would he say about her bringing a strange young man home from the park, and a one-legged one at that?

Mary knocked on Maggie's door and a girl of about fourteen answered, a Maggie in miniature.

'Is Maggie at home?' Mary asked.

'No, she's gone to Lilly's.' Even the strident voice was the same.

'Well, perhaps I'll go over and see her there. It's not important but in case I miss her, would you tell her Mary called?'

'Aye, I'll tell her. Mary who?'

'Mary Maddison. Thanks.'

'That's all right.'

The door closed and Mary retraced her steps. Lilly lived on Hilary Street, close to Edward Street; she could have saved herself a long walk. This time the door was opened by Lilly.

'Why, hello, Mary. What a surprise! Nice to see you. Come on in, just park the pram, Maggie's here.'

'Yes, I went to her house and her sister told me she was here.'

Lilly led her into the front parlour, which, like most parlours, had a bunk bed in the corner. Maggie was curled up in one of the wooden-armed chairs by the fire, the Sunday paper on her lap.

'Why, our Mary!' she said, straightening up with surprise. 'You never pay me a visit.'

'In fact I did, and your sister told me you were here, so I thought I'd pop round and see you both.'

'Eey, well, we're glad you did, luv,' said Lilly. 'Sit yoursel' down. Can I get you anythin'?'

'No thanks,' said Mary, flopping into the other chair. 'I've just had tea in the park.'

'An' we've just finished Sunday dinner. We're stuffed,' said Maggie, burping. 'I came over for a quiet afternoon to get over last night's hangover and now

I've got a belly-ache as well as a bad head. What's new with you, luv? Haven't seen you for ages. I heard all about your new job from Enid. How's it goin'?'

'Oh, fine. It's hard work but I think I'll survive it.'

'Eey, we're really pleased to see you, Mary,' Maggie said. 'I'd rather hear your gossip any day than read the scandals: "Man Attacks Wife's Lover with Coal Shovel",' she read from the *News of the World*. 'Got anythin' juicier than that?' She threw the newspaper to the floor and gazed expectantly at Mary.

'Nothing so violent, I'm pleased to say. I need some advice and I couldn't think of anyone more qualified than you to give it, Maggie, and now, even better, I'll get some of Lilly's old-fashioned wisdom, too,' Mary laughed.

'Well, I can think of only one kind of advice you'd want from me,' Maggie said, straightening up in her chair with interest. 'Don't tell us you've got a new man finally.'

'Not quite. At least, he's not really new.'

'Joe!' the girls both exclaimed at once, and Lilly, who had been sitting on the bed, stood up and flung her arms round Mary.

'You're goin' to get hitched at long last?'

'Not exactly . . . at least not yet, but, as from last night, we're back together and I'm hoping he'll get around to asking me.'

'Eey, I hope so, luv. That would be good news, an' little David would have his real da. So what can we do for you?' Maggie asked.

'Well, I don't want David to have a little brother or sister before he has a father, so I thought you could give me some tips. I can't afford to be as stupid as I was last time.'

'Why, you've certainly come to the right place, luv. What have you been doin' so far?'

'Well, there was only last night, and Joe was careful.'

'Careful, be blowed! Don't rely on him to be careful, hinny, or any man. You want to make him go to the chemist an' get some French letters, an' get some yoursel' just in case he ever forgets them. Don't be caught short like last time. I always carry a packet; they've been dead easy to get since the war ended.'

'Aye, luv, I always carry some an' all – not that I need them as much as our Maggie, though, but you never know me luck!'

'Oh, I couldn't go into a chemist and ask for them. I'd die!'

'Well, get Joe to get some for you to keep, an' in the meantime you can have my packet,' Lilly said, rising. 'The chemist knows me now an' always has them ready for me in a brown paper bag so I don't have to ask in front of the other customers.'

'Well, if you insist, thank you, Lilly, but let me pay you for them.'

'Not on your nelly! They're a present, luv. I don't want to see you in the club again.' She left the room and returned with a brown paper bag. 'Here you are,' she said, handing Mary the bag. 'Worth their weight in gold.'

'Ugh!' said Mary, peering into the bag at the pink objects peeking through their cellophane packet. 'They look disgusting.'

'Don't you worry about what they look like, luv; you just make sure he wears them. They're not completely safe but they're the best you can do.'

'Talk about ruining the magic moment,' Mary said, taking one of the offending articles out of its packet to examine it. 'I couldn't see Joe doing that!'

'You see he does it afore the magic moment starts, hinny. That makes sure he doesn't get carried away.'

'But I'm seeing him on Saturday. I can't just present

them to him like that. It looks so . . . so . . . cold and calculating.'

'Better than him presenting *you* with somethin', hinny.' Lilly wagged her finger. 'Don't forget the last time!'

'You're right,' said Mary, tucking the bag into her pocket. 'Thank you both so much. I'd love to stay a bit longer but I have to go now.'

'Aw, can't you stay and have a bit more natter, an' tell us some more about Joe? We're dyin' to hear all the details.'

'I wish I could, but I have to get back to work. The woman who takes over from me has to leave early today. I promise I'll pop in and see you another Sunday when I have more time.'

'Aye, that would be nice, luv. Ta ta, then,' Maggie said as Lilly showed Mary to the door.

''Bye, Maggie! 'Bye, Lilly. See you soon, and thanks.'

Chapter Twenty-five

Joe brought the money, as usual, the following Saturday evening, and this time Mary had put David to bed beforehand. Seated on the settee with Joe's arm round her, sipping the sherry he'd poured for her, Mary decided now was the time to broach the subject: 'I went to see Maggie and Lilly last Sunday, Joe.'

'Umhh,' he said, nuzzling her neck.

She moved her head away; she must talk to him before he got amorous. 'I wanted some advice on birth control, and they gave me some things.'

'Umhh, what things?' he asked, now brushing her cheek with his lips.

'French letters,' she blurted out, 'but *you'll* have to get them in future.'

'Oh, no, not those things. They ruin a wonderful experience.' He was sitting up straight now.

She ignored the fact that he had obviously used them before with some other woman; after all, she knew there must have been other women during the war, and went on: 'I don't call getting pregnant a wonderful experience, and I don't intend it to happen again.'

'But I promise I'll be more careful now.'

'Being careful isn't enough, Joe; you must use them for my sake.'

'Aw, well, if that's the price I have to pay, I suppose you're right. And, while we're on the subject, why are we wasting time talking?' he murmured, enclosing her in his arms and kissing her till her head swam. She kissed him back fiercely.

Afterwards they lay on the settee; nothing else and no one else existed while they were in each other's arms, yet a warning bell sounded in her ear at five minutes to ten.

'It's time, Joe,' she whispered, raising herself and gathering her clothes.

'Blast!' he said, sitting up. 'I wish we didn't have to be so sneaky about it.'

'Me too, but now please be quick and leave,' she said fastening the last of her blouse buttons.

He was dressed and gone by ten and Mary quickly went up to bed before Walter returned. She had just closed her door when she heard the back door open. Good! She didn't like to face Walter after having just made love with Joe.

The week went by slowly; Mary could hardly wait for the visit to the music hall with Joe on Saturday. On Friday, she sat watching the soup bubbling in the sooty pot, her mind tracing over the events of the previous Saturday with Joe. Their bodies were made for each other; it had been as marvellous as ever. Why, she wondered, had she tried to conceal the strength of her feelings from him before David had arrived? Had he known the true intensity of her passion then, perhaps he would never have left her. It was your influence, Mother, she thought, telling me that nice girls kept themselves to themselves until they were married. Her mother had finally broached that subject just before she'd died – a timely warning, Mary supposed – yet she'd never explained to her what 'keeping oneself to oneself' meant. A stab of pain still went through her whenever she thought of her mother.

But I'm *not* a bad girl, Mary thought, and I like

giving myself, if that's what it is. What's wrong with that? It's perfectly natural! She checked her thoughts. Was she a nice girl? Her mother certainly wouldn't think so now. She was in disgrace in society's eyes and was deliberately giving her body to Joe out of wedlock and running the risk of history repeating itself, and she didn't care. Was she truly becoming a wanton woman? No! It seemed so right to be with Joe.

On the other hand, there was Walter. She was afraid of her reaction to him. He hadn't brought people home since the party, but he was acting more and more intimately towards her. Several times he had brushed past her so closely that their bodies had touched for a brief second and she had felt sparks pass from him to her. Had he touched her deliberately? Should she, a *good* girl, have felt that spark? What would her mother think about that? And what about the time he had placed his hand on her shoulder to draw her attention while she was bending over the oven? She had felt a tremor pass through her then, too.

So she had finally discovered and acknowledged her body, and she was glad. But she mustn't let it rule her. She truly loved Joe, so if she did feel any physical reaction to another man it must be perfectly normal; however, she must be careful to keep her distance from Walter for, normal though it might be, it would be dangerous to let him see he affected her in that way.

'Penny for your thoughts.'

The voice startled her. 'Oh,' she gasped, pushing some stray strands of hair back from her face and smoothing her skirt. 'I was just thinking . . . I must go upstairs and tidy myself up before dinner.'

'You look fine, as always, to me,' Walter said, slumping in his accustomed chair at the table.

'Oh,' she said, flustered.

'What's for dinner?' He'd changed the subject but his eyes had not left her face.

Even more flustered, she gabbled, 'It's beef and barley soup and macaroni pudding.'

'Fine! I'll have the soup, but you can skip the macaroni for me.'

He rose and, brushing past her, disappeared into the parlour. Damn him! He'd done it again. She was shaking. And she had the uneasy feeling that this man knew her thoughts without asking.

'Where are the bairns?' he asked, returning a moment later, his brown eyes again boring through her.

'They're all out in the front street playing,' she said, trying to ignore his stare.

'Good. They need to get more fresh air and it's nice to have some peace and quiet in the house for a change.'

Oh dear! She'd better bring them in soon. She felt uneasy being alone in the house with this man.

He retreated to the scullery to wash and then resumed his seat at the table, clad in his grey workshirt and old blue serge trousers. Mary served his dinner and then said: 'I'd better get the children in now; it's beginning to get dark.'

'Aye, I suppose so,' was all he said.

When Saturday finally arrived, Mary was vibrant with excitement at the prospect of the evening ahead. She wore the blue dress and looked with satisfaction at her reflection in the full-length mirror on the wardrobe door, although she felt a twinge of guilt at the shilling it had cost when money was so short. But she'd definitely need it when summer came, so it wasn't an extravagance. And it was her own money she was spending – and Joe's money. The children would also need some summer clothes soon. She would have to ask Walter for some clothing money.

The doorbell rang and it was Jane, with the girls, to take over for the evening. 'Why, you do look nice, hinny. New dress?' Jane's voice was neutral but Mary's guilty conscience caused her to lie. Jane was kind to her but that didn't give her the right to know all her private affairs.

'No, it's an old one I patched up; you've seen it before,' she said and turned her face away. She changed the subject as she led the way into the kitchen. 'They're all excited and ready for you, so I'll be off now,' she announced, grabbing her hat and coat from the hooks on the scullery door and wishing she could just wear her shawl as she had the previous Sunday, but winter had resumed its normal chill. 'I'll be back about lunch time tomorrow. I'm staying over with Doris and going for a walk after breakfast and then we're going to church,' she lied even further. 'Thanks for standing in for me, Jane.' Her conscience stricken and her face flushed from her lies, she hastened out. What would her mother have thought of all her lies? But a girl had to survive, especially when she was alone in the world with a child to take care of. And then she remembered that her mother knew well what that was like, and wondered if she, too, had had to lie to survive.

Joe was waiting for her at the corner as arranged. Walking arm in arm, Mary thought happily that now they were truly walking out together.

In a gay mood, Joe announced, 'We just have time for one at the pub before the music hall starts, and then we can have some sandwiches at my place. I bought a boiled bacon shank. I'm afraid I can't run to a meal out as well.'

'Oh, that's all right, Joe. The tickets must have cost a fortune.' Mary wouldn't have cared if they hadn't eaten at all. They were together and they were going out to have fun; that was all that mattered. Yet she was concerned about leaving David; it would be his first night without her. 'I'm a bit worried about leaving David overnight, though. What if he wakes up and cries for me?'

'Oh, don't worry about him; kids are hardy little creatures.'

'Is that what you think, Joe? That shows how much you know about children; that's just exactly what they're not.' Was she expecting too much that he might show some concern for his son? She wouldn't continue this discussion now, though; she mustn't spoil the special evening. Nevertheless, she would bring up the subject again when the time was right; maybe a little prodding might make Joe take more notice of his child.

The music hall was exciting. The new singer was a plump, jolly, middle-aged woman, who sang 'Goodbye Little Yellow Bird' with the voice of a choirboy and 'My Old Man's a Dustman' with the voice of a street vendor, and the master of ceremonies kept the audience laughing and singing between acts. Mary couldn't remember laughing so much in one evening and begged to do it again soon.

Back in Joe's room, he opened the wardrobe door with a flourish and produced two bottles of stout, a bottle of port and a bottle of lemonade, which he set on the bedside table, and then from his underwear drawer he took out paper bags containing bread, butter, and the bacon shank. These he placed on the dresser and brandished a knife before her. 'This, madam, is the kitchen,' pointing with the knife to the dresser, 'and that is your domain. The bar is mine,' he joked, taking two tumblers from the mantelpiece and setting them on the cane bedside table with the bottles. 'Get busy with dinner, woman.'

Despite his lightheartedness, Mary hung on his words. She felt as if they were playing house. If only it were real, and if only David were sleeping in the next room, waking up in the morning and climbing into bed with them for cuddles before enjoying a family breakfast.

'And after dinner,' Joe continued, 'we shall adjourn to the bedroom, which is over there,' pointing to the single bed in the corner. 'Sorry it's not a little larger, but it's cosy.'

Mary hummed 'Goodbye Little Yellow Bird' as she made the sandwiches and sipped her drink. She would be with Joe for the rest of the night and half of tomorrow and there was no one to interrupt them. She mustn't dwell on the negative aspects; she'd never imagined this day would come, and yet it had. She must be thankful for what she had now, and she could still hope for the future. She felt truly happy.

The next morning she woke up with a slight headache from the port, but Joe was beside her, so nothing else mattered. He was clutching her round the waist and snoring loudly. Was it an embrace or a desperate attempt to avoid falling off the narrow bed? She smiled fondly at him and stroked his brow, causing him to grunt and open his eyes. 'Morning, Joe. How's your head?'

'Like a stairhead,' he grunted, rubbing his eyes. 'How's yours?'

'The same.' They both giggled and he rolled over and grabbed her waist tighter. She pretended to struggle, coyly, but soon was lost in his embrace again, headache forgotten.

At eleven o'clock Joe sat up and stretched. 'We'd better finish off that bread and bacon. Breakfast's over at nine on Sundays and, anyway, I couldn't take you down.'

They both attacked the remains of the previous evening's dinner with voracious appetites, sharpened by their prolonged lovemaking.

'Oh, Joe, it's so wonderful – no babies crying, no children to dress and feed, just you and me having breakfast. I don't want it to end. But that doesn't mean I wouldn't want David to be here,' she added hastily.

'Can't you relax and stop worrying about him for one night? He's in good hands. And end it has to, my love. I've got to be at the Black Bull by twelve and you've got to get back.'

Reality! He'd made arrangements to meet his friends so soon. She'd hoped they could at least have taken a walk in the park together. She didn't have to be home until about one o'clock and had left the time of her return deliberately vague to allow for this. Did he put his male friends before her still? She sighed. 'I need the lavatory and I'd like a wash.'

'The back door's not bolted. And don't worry about anyone seeing you. The old girl's a sport, she doesn't mind about lady guests, just refuses to feed them, that's all.'

Afterwards, on the street, Mary shivered. The day was raw and she now felt a little fragile from lack of sleep and too much port. Well, back to reality, but first she'd pop in and see Doris on the way home. She hadn't seen her since the Sunday in the park when she'd met that young man and she wondered how things were progressing, if at all.

Doris's eyes popped when she saw her. 'Well, I didn't expect to see you today. Isn't this your day with Joe?'

'It is . . . was. He had to leave early to see his friends.'

'Well, come on in, luv. Is anything the matter? You look done in a bit.'

'I'd love a cup of tea and then I've got to run. I'm just feeling a bit wrung out after last night – too much port and not enough sleep, I suppose. But it was wonderful.'

'I'm glad to hear it. You look as if you're comin' from a funeral, not a night of love and laughter.'

'I suppose I'm out of training,' Mary grimaced, taking off her coat and seating herself by the fire. She tousled Jimmy's hair. 'Hello, imp! How are you today?' Not waiting for an answer, she turned to Doris. 'How's the new boy friend?'

'He's very nice, luv, but I don't think I want to get any more involved. I'm tired o' lookin' after invalids an' bairns. First me ma, an' then me da an' Jimmy.'

'But he's not really an invalid and he's going to get a new wooden leg soon; he'll be more independent then.' Mary didn't want to encourage the relationship but she felt sorry for Doris, who appeared to like the boy, and she wanted to comfort her. 'It sounds hopeful to me; he'll be able to get around better.'

'It's just that I can't stand him bein' in so much pain still, even where he's got no leg.'

'Yes, I've heard about that, but surely it won't be for long.'

'Eey, I don't know, and I don't really know how I feel about him. It could just be that I'm gettin' so bloody bored and lonely bein' stuck here, but he is sort of growin' on me. We still haven't done anything though; he's very shy. It took him all his time to give me a peck on the cheek last night an' that's the third time I've seen him.'

'He didn't seem shy in the park,' Mary countered.

'No, I know he didn't; that's what's so funny. I think he thinks that because he's a cripple I wouldn't fancy him that way. But I do, you know, leg or no leg. He's got a lovely face an' a good body, and he's so *nice* – very well-mannered an' all that.'

'Well, if you like him, why don't you just let him set

the pace and if something's going to grow out of it, it will.'

Doris was pouring the tea and Mary took the proffered cup gratefully.

'Lord, I need this. I couldn't have any for breakfast, just last night's leftover food.' She emptied the cup and poured herself another.

'Moses, you *are* thirsty! Booze makes you thirsty, you know. How much did you have?'

'A lot! It's always a lot when I'm with Joe. He's getting me into bad habits, but at least it's only once a week.'

'Aye, at the moment, but mind you don't start gettin' a taste for it like me ma. That's what sent her to the grave early.'

Mary laughed. 'If I go to my grave early it'll be because of overwork. Now I have to go back and face the mob again. This is the longest I've been away from David; I hope he's all right. I'm feeling guilty about the others, too; they're beginning to get attached to me. They still haven't got over their mother but they seem to be accepting me as a substitute. I hate to think what will happen to them if and when I leave that job.'

'You're not thinking of leaving, are you?'

'No, of course not. Where else could I go? But it might come one day if Joe decides to pop the question.'

'I wouldn't bank on that, luv.'

'I know I might have my head in the clouds, but it's so wonderful when we're together and I know he enjoys being with me, too. I can't help but hope that he'll eventually want to be with me always. After all, he is a little more mature than he was last time.'

'Older, perhaps, but that doesn't necessarily mean more mature, you know. Strikes me he's still a good-time boy. But I must admit I'd hang on to those hopes as well.'

'Then you don't think I'm being stupid in hoping?'

''Course I do, but I'd be just as stupid. It's hope that keeps us going in this life, luv; if we didn't have hope there'd be no point in going on. An' if by any chance he did ask you, you'd be bloody stupid to hang on to that job for the sake o' those bairns.'

'I know, but the thought still worries me. It would be like another bereavement for them, and they'd have to start getting used to someone else all over again. I've just got Billie to the point where he's stopped wetting his pants and he'd probably start again. They're all just beginning to feel secure with me. I'm trying to give them the same attention they used to get from their mother, though I do admit it wears me out sometimes.'

'There's no such thing as a bairn that doesn't need attention, hinny. I warned you about takin' on that job.'

'Oh, let's not go into that again. I've made my bed and now I have to cry on it.' She smiled ruefully. 'It's not so bad really, except that I have so little chance of a private life. I'm always scared stiff in case one of them comes down when Joe's there. I've told them if they need anything to knock on the floor and I'll come up. If they saw Joe and let it slip to their father, I'd probably be out of a job again.'

'Well, now that you're walkin' out with him again, you don't need to do it on your own doorstep any more.'

'But how often am I going to see him, Doris? I can't get every Saturday off, and he made it plain today that he still intends to see his friends on Sundays.'

'Aye, you're not goin' to push him any faster than he wants to go, luv. You'll just have to be patient.'

'Patient! What do you think I've been all these years? I'm not just going to sit around waiting for another three years or more until he decides he's ready. I have to be a bit cleverer this time. I was too soft on him last time, Doris, just as you were with Harry, and now you're getting soft on Frank because you're sorry for him.'

'No! That's not why . . . I mean, I'm not gettin' soft on him 'cause I feel sorry for him; I'm gettin' soft on him 'cause he's nice.'

'I can see you're in over your head already. But try to watch out for yourself – just make sure you don't get hurt again.' She stood up and put on her coat. 'Well, I've got to go now or I'll be out of a job. Pop over on Tuesday before the children get home from school.'

Lunch was over when Mary arrived home and Jane and Anne were washing up the dishes. 'I thought you'd be home earlier.' For the first time Jane's voice was a little curt, and Mary bridled.

'I said around lunch time and it's only one o'clock.'

'Well, you know we eat at twelve. Yours is on the pot on the stove keepin' hot and Walter's is on a plate – just put it on the pot when you take yours off. I have to be off now. I promised I'd take the girls to see their gran on the way home.'

'Oh, can I come as well, please?' asked Anne, excitedly. 'I haven't seen her for two weeks.'

'Me too,' begged Michael. 'Gran always makes jam tarts on Sundays.'

'Well, of course you can. But I can't walk all the way back with you. I've got to get home and make me old man his tea. I wasn't there for his Sunday dinner today; he'll think I've run away and left him.'

Was that another jibe at her for being away so long? Mary wondered. Surely she deserved *some* free time. Still, she'd better play her cards right if she wanted to remain on good terms with this woman; she liked her and needed her help and goodwill.

'I'm sorry. I'll make it earlier next time,' Mary apologised.

'Aye, that'd be better. I can't stop too long; I've got me own things to see to an' all. Well,' she addressed Anne and Jimmy, 'I'll take you two if Mary can come an' get you after three. Walter'll be home then and can keep an eye on the little ones for half an hour.'

Oh, no, thought Mary. She'd been hoping to have a quiet lie down when Walter had his Sunday afternoon nap and now she'd have to go out for the children. Anne and Michael were old enough to walk home by themselves; it was the same way they came home from school every day. Why was Jane treating them like infants still? But she decided not to show her displeasure. Something about Jane's attitude was beginning to make her uneasy, so she smiled while groaning inside. 'That's all right. I'll bring the babies and Billy with me. Some fresh air will do them good.'

After Jane and the children had left, she picked up David, who had been tugging at her skirt for attention. 'All right, sweetheart! Have you been a good boy and had a nice lunch? Would you like some of mine now?'

She put the plate on the table and sat with David on her lap. She had missed him. Billie sat on the settee with his thumb in his mouth and his big eyes on them both. Mary turned, feeling guilty. Good God! She'd forgotten about Billie! She mustn't let the poor child feel left out. Picking up a carrot from her plate, she said, 'Here, sweetheart, come and sit on my knee, too.' The child silently stood up, walked to the table and climbed on to her knee, taking the proffered carrot. Mary sighed; so much for a peaceful Sunday afternoon and a nap.

Chapter Twenty-six

It wasn't until Mary went to bed that night that she had time alone to think and she realised with distress that the parting with Joe had been so hasty, they hadn't made arrangements for the following week. How could she have been so stupid not to think of it? He hadn't mentioned seeing her again. Oh, please let him ask her out for Sunday when he came on Saturday evening; she couldn't ask for two Saturdays in a row anyway. When she saw Doris on Tuesday she'd tell her that if she didn't arrive by eleven on Sunday, she would be seeing Joe. Doris would understand; she might even be seeing Frank anyway. Yet Mary felt a little uneasy at dropping her friend at the last moment. She knew it wasn't polite, but they were so close now, she didn't think Doris would mind. It was wonderful to have such a loving friend. Perhaps this was what it was like to have a sister.

Mary didn't have to wait until Tuesday; at Monday lunchtime Doris called in on her way to the shops.

'Oh, nice to see you, Doris,' Mary said with pleasure as she answered the door. 'Come in and sit down. I'm just making lunch. Would you like some?'

'No thanks, luv, I had a sandwich before I left, but you go ahead. I just felt like a bit of a chat.'

'There's nothing wrong, is there?'

'Not much more than usual,' Doris sighed as she removed her coat and slumped into a chair. Then she said brightly to David and Billie, who were seated at the table, 'Hello, you two. Bein' good today?'

They chorused, 'Yes,' but Mary contradicted them.

'Not really, they had a fight this morning over a comic. I had to tear it in half and give them each a piece to keep them quiet, and then each wanted the other's half. Little monsters! I'll just give them their soup and then I'll sit down with you and have mine.' Mary heaved the enormous pot off the fire, setting it on a trivet on the table and ladling out three bowls.

'Smells wonderful,' said Doris, 'I think I will have a bowl after all.'

Mary filled an extra bowl and handed Doris one, sitting opposite her. 'Well, now! Why the unexpected visit? I don't like the look of you; you look pale.'

'Aye, I feel pale, luv . . . it's Frank . . . he came round yesterday after you left, an' he had a terrible cough, sounded just like me da. By four o'clock he was feelin' so poorly he had to go home. I went round first thing this mornin' to see how he was an' he couldn't even get out o' bed. He's got a bad fever an' all. His mother had sent for the doctor at eight o'clock but he had so many calls to make because o' this new flu goin' round, he can't get there till this afternoon. I'm callin' in again on me way back to see if he's been yet.'

'Oh, I'm sorry, Doris. I heard about a new flu, but it's not like last year's epidemic.'

'Aye, that's what they say, but the doctor told Frank's mother different, says folk are droppin' like flies around here. He says it's just as bad as the last one only it's not country-wide – at least not yet.'

'But Frank's a strong chap, apart from his leg; he should be able to fight it off.'

'That's just the point, he's not. His mother talked to me this mornin' and she says he's been gettin' everythin' that's goin' since he got back from the war. She told me he got gassed as well, the time he lost his leg. Not a lethal dose, o' course, but enough to affect his lungs. She says he's embarrassed enough at the sympathy he gets for his leg, so he doesn't tell people about what they can't see.'

'Oh, Doris, I'm so sorry, and you were determined not to get involved with another invalid.'

'Well, I am involved now, luv. It's too late. I just hope he's not sick all the time like me da; it just tears me to pieces to see someone I love sufferin'.'

'So you *do* love him, Doris!'

'Aye, an' I didn't realise how much till I saw him poorly yesterday.'

'Oh, you poor thing! But you mustn't dwell on the black side. Why don't you go straight back there now and be there when the doctor arrives; then you can find out what's wrong straight from him, and you can ask how much Frank's lungs have suffered from the gas. It might be very little, in which case you won't go on worrying so much about it.'

'Aye, you're right. I'll go straight back there now. Me da's lookin' after Jimmy anyway.' She put down her empty bowl and put her coat on.

'I'll pop over in the morning to hear what the doctor says,' Mary promised. ' 'Bye, luv, and I hope it's good news.'

The two hugged at the door and Mary went back to the kitchen to see to the boys. They were both tired and needed a nap. She placed one at each end of the settee and covered them with a blanket; then she heated up some milk and water and went for little Walter, who had been sleeping in his pram in the hall. Not until she sat down to feed him did she have time to let her mind dwell on Doris's news. It was bad news all round, not only for Frank. Another epidemic! She and David had miraculously escaped the last one, but now she had five children to worry about . . . and Joe . . . and Walter, of course. If one got it, they'd most likely all go down with it.

The next morning she put little Walter in the pram; it wasn't far to Doris's so David and Billie could walk on the reins. She knocked on the door and, as soon as Doris's face, emerged, she asked, 'How is he, Doris? Did you talk to the doctor?'

'Aye, I did. Come in, luv.' Doris took the two boys while Mary lifted the baby from the pram. She waited until they were all settled in the kitchen before announcing, 'It's not good news.'

'Oh!' Mary said, her jaw dropping. 'What is it then?'

'Well, the doctor says the damage to Frank's lungs is permanent, although it's not all that severe. He says as long as he avoids infections, he could live a normal lifespan, but he'll always have to take care o' his lungs and he mustn't do heavy work of any kind.' She sighed, 'It's Doris's luck, isn't it? I'm too far gone on him to turn back now, Mary. I want to marry him and take care o' him.'

'Oh, you poor thing,' Mary said, kneeling down and taking her friend's hand. 'It's ironical, another lung problem in your life. But if you love him, you have no choice. He's young; he could have a long life ahead of him yet.'

'Bad lungs *and* only one leg! I do pick 'em, don't I? But I don't want no rich prince charming any more; I want Frank. I'll just have to stop worryin' an' take what comes. I'm lucky to have found such a nice fella, healthy or not. Now, that's enough about me, luv. When are you goin' out with Joe again?'

'I don't know. Joe didn't ask me out for this weekend. But we parted in such a rush, it could be that.'

'Aye, I'm sure it is, hinny, but if you're worried, why don't you write him a letter an' find out?'

'I'd thought I might do that. You don't think it would be too pushy for a woman to take the initiative?'

318

'Why, from what I saw that day in the park, you weren't worried about being pushy then.'

'You're right, but that was desperation; I had to grab him while I had the chance. This time I've had more time to think, and that's when I get nervous.'

'All right, why don't I get you a pen and paper and you can do it now and post it on your way home?'

'Oh, Doris, you *are* a gem. I just needed someone to tell me that I wouldn't be overstepping the limits of ladylike behaviour. When a woman's too forward it can put a man off.'

'Don't worry,' said Doris, rising, 'if that man's made up his mind to stop walking out with you, then there's no changing his mind anyway, but if he just forgot, then there's no harm in jogging his memory. Here, get on with it,' she said, handing Mary a sheet of paper and an envelope she'd miraculously acquired from somewhere in the scullery. Only Doris would keep stationery in the scullery.

Mary began, hesitantly:

Dear Joe,

I want to thank you for a wonderful time last weekend. It would be nice to do something together next weekend, too. Although I can't get another Saturday night off so soon, I've got Sunday free. Please write and let me know so that I can plan my day off. See you on Saturday evening as usual.

Love,
Mary

'Do you think it sounds all right, Doris?' she asked nervously after reading it aloud.

'Bloody marvellous, luv. I wish I could express myself like that. I'd have probably said somethin' like:

319

You bugger, you didn't ask me out last time. Do you want to see me again or not?'

Laughing, Mary said, 'I don't think you'll ever have to remind Frank to ask you out; it seems he's truly smitten with you.'

'Aye, he is! I can hardly believe it mesel'. It's wonderful to have someone that crazy about you.'

'You're right there; Joe's never been the type to show his true feelings – if he has any, that is. Well, I'll be off now. I have to go for some groceries anyway, so I'll stop at the post office and get a stamp and post this.'

'I'll help you out with the bairns.' Doris retrieved the two boys from the settee, where they had been happily reading comics and chatting to each other, while Mary rewrapped the baby, who had spent the time lying on the floor gurgling and kicking off his blankets.

Mary waited impatiently for Joe's reply during the next few days. It arrived on Thursday; he must have written immediately he received her letter. Her fingers trembled as she read the scrawled note:

Dear Mary,
    Yes, it would be nice to see you on Sunday afternoon. I'm back from the pub at two, so why don't you come over then? I'm glad you wrote because I forgot to tell you that I can't come this Saturday evening. One of my mates is getting married, so we're all giving him a send-off.
    See you Sunday,

Joe

Mary put the note down, confused. Should she be pleased or not? He couldn't come on Saturday evening because he preferred to see his damned mates, and he wanted her at his place after seeing them at the pub on

Sunday, no doubt mainly to fill his sexual needs. Well, she supposed she should just be grateful she was seeing him at all and, anyway, she had no objection to filling his needs, she thought, sighing. But she'd miss seeing him on Saturday night.

On Sunday afternoon at two, Mary knocked on Joe's lodging-house door. The landlady opened it. Mary, startled because she'd expected to see Joe, said, 'Oh, I'm here to see Joe. He's expecting me.'

'I don't think he's back yet, hinny. I haven't seen him come in. But why don't you come in; you can wait in his room. If he's expectin' you he shouldn't be long.'

'Thank you,' Mary said, disappointed, following the woman up the stairs. He'd said two o'clock. Why couldn't he be on time? She sat on the bed and waited till two-thirty, three o'clock, and he still wasn't back. She was beginning to worry that something had happened to him when the door opened and he staggered in.

'Oops, my lovely! Sorry I'm a bit late.'

'Joe, did you forget?' she asked.

'No, my sweet,' he said, flopping on the bed beside her, the smell of beer and whisky mingling on his breath. 'How could I forget seeing you? Bob's leaving tomorrow to work in Glasgow, so after the pub the lads all took him home, and he'd bought a bottle of whisky to complete the send-off, so I had to stay and finish the job, didn't I? I knew the landlady would let you in; it's not as though I left you waiting on the street.'

Mary drew in her breath. 'Joe, you bastard! How could you keep me waiting a whole hour, no matter where? You always put the lads, as you call them, before me. Don't I count at all?' She was on the verge of tears but she bit her lip.

'Of course you count, my sweet. Why do you think

I left early to come and see you? The other lads all stayed on.'

'That's not the point, Joe. When you make arrangements to see me, you should stick to them. You know I'd never let you down.'

'Well, that's your problem, Mary. If you had something special to do, I'd understand. Now come on and give me a cuddle. Be your own sweet self.'

She didn't budge, but he moved closer and put his arm round her, kissing her cheek.

'Joe!' She shrugged him off. 'You smell like a bar room – it's nauseating.'

'Oh, come on,' he cajoled her. 'You don't complain when we drink together.' He turned her head and kissed her on the mouth. At first she didn't respond but, as he persisted, she melted. Dear God! Why was she so weak with him?

'There! That's more like my Mary,' he said, laying her back on the bed.

Mary sighed but didn't resist. Their precious time together had got off to a bad start; she mustn't make things worse. But his thoughtlessness hurt her; would he ever be as loving and considerate towards her as she was towards him?

Chapter Twenty-seven

Mary was dismayed when, the following week, Walter asked her if she would prepare some special sandwiches for Saturday night. It was his birthday and he and his friends would be having a quick drink at the pub and then returning with some bottles to have a party from about eight o'clock. Damn! Joe would just have time to drop the money off and disappear. Why did it have to be Saturday, the one day in the week Joe could come? Well, she decided, she'd make up for it by asking for the following Saturday off.

'That's fine,' she said affably, 'but I'd like the following Saturday off, if that would be all right?'

'Aye, that's all right; just ask Jane to come over again. You'll enjoy the party; they're a good crowd, and we'll be having music and a sing-song. It's time we had a bit more jollity around here. You must get awfully bored just visiting your girl friend once a week.'

Mary blushed. She'd forgotten that lie. So, he was concerned about her having fun, and last night he'd expressed concern at her looking tired. He'd been showing a much more personal interest in her well-being lately; she must be careful it didn't become *too* personal. 'I'm usually too tired or too busy, or both, to be bored,' she laughed, in an effort to steer the conversation back to her work and her place in this house.

'Well, it's time to let your hair down and have a bit o' fun while you're still young and pretty. Just have the bairns in bed and somethin' to eat ready by eight o'clock. And why don't you wear that blue dress you look so nice in?'

She blushed again; that was Joe's favourite dress. In order to avoid any further conversation, she went into the scullery to get the cocoa and returned with the tin and one cup. 'I'm just going to make my cocoa and take it upstairs. Is there anything you want before I go to bed?'

'Aye, I'll have a cup o' cocoa with you. Stay and have it down here. I could do with a bit o' company.'

So much for that effort, she thought. Next time she wouldn't ask if he wanted anything.

They sat at each side of the fire, and he began to talk as he never had before – about himself. 'Annie and I used to do this sometimes when the bairns were in bed.'

'You must miss her very much,' she said, touched by the nostalgia in his voice.

'Aye, I do, but you get used to anything in time. I've even got used to the shipyard and I thought it was the end o' the world at the time.'

'You mean you don't like working there?'

'Like it! It's not a question of liking – it's necessity. Weldin's hard work but it pays, and that's what matters. That's why me father made me do it. Times were hard then and he knew they were goin' to get harder, so he put all us boys into a trade after he went bankrupt.'

'Your father went bankrupt?' Her voice showed her surprise; you had to *have* money before you could go bankrupt. So that's why this man sounded better educated than most and why he spent most of his free time reading books and newspapers.

'Aye, me father was a colonel in the Army and put a lot of store by education . . . quite a hero in the Boer war. But after he came out of it, he sort o' fell apart and started drinkin' and that was the end of the family's education. We had to get out and earn a living. I used to want to be a politician,' he laughed. 'Those were the days. I was thirteen when I started at the shipyards and I've been there ever since, six days a week, every week o' me life. I don't expect to make it to the House of Commons now,' he laughed again.

There was no self-pity, just resignation, in his voice, and Mary began to respect his attitude. They had something in common, both having suffered a severe drop in status. There was one difference though: she didn't intend to remain at the bottom for ever, and it seemed as if this man had simply accepted his misfortune. But she was younger and only had one child to feed; Walter had four. There was not much chance of his being able to break away from the shipyards and better himself, although he might have stood a chance if he'd abandoned his children as some men did in his situation. He must be more fond of them than she'd thought, or at least he was a good enough father to respect his responsibilities, which was more than Joe did. It was interesting, after all, to learn something about him. At least it would help her to understand him better. No wonder he drank to alleviate his boredom and frustration, and perhaps it explained why he was so loath to part with his hard-earned money.

'It must have been hard for you to give up all your ambitions,' she commiserated.

'Aye, at the time, but now I'm used to things as they are; they could be worse. I could have no job at all. At least we've got bread on the table and I've got you to help with the bairns. I don't know what I'd do without you.'

Mary thought quickly; this would be an appropriate time to bring up the subject of a wage increase. 'While we're on the subject, Walter, I'm finding it very hard to manage on the money you pay me and the housekeepir.g allowance. Remember, when I first came you said it would only be to start with. I really do need more now. Everything's going up every week.'

His face took on that guarded look that was so familiar to her now whenever she asked for money. Yet, like Joe, he didn't seem to mind how much he spent at the pub. She'd never understand men.

'Aye,' he sighed. 'I've been expectin' it. From next week, I'll give you an extra half-crown for the house-keeping, but I'm afraid you'll have to wait a while longer for more wages. You don't seem to do too badly on what I give you, anyway, and you only go out once a week. I don't know what you're complainin' about.'

'But I have to spend some of the money you give me on food and the rest barely keeps David and me clothed. I don't have any money to spend on going out; the only thing I can afford to do is go out to tea with my friend once a week.' It was only half a lie, she thought; if she'd had to rely on his money, that would be the situation. Thank God for Joe's extra help, little though it was, and thank God also that Walter didn't know about it or she'd probably get a reduction rather than a rise.

'Aye, I'm sorry, lass, but I just can't run to it right now. As soon as I get me next rise we'll talk about it again.'

'Yes, we will,' she said firmly, but then added calmly, 'Well, I suppose I'd better go up now; I'm very tired. I enjoyed our chat. Goodnight.'

'Aye, goodnight, so did I. We should do it more often.' He remained seated, his deep stare fixed on her as she rose.

The following Saturday was busy and Mary was nervous. After breakfast she took Anne aside. 'Anne, would you mind going to the butcher for a leg of mutton and an ox tongue, and to the baker for three large loaves?'

'No, I don't mind,' said Anne, 'but you asked me to look after David and Billie and the baby this morning.'

'Oh, I forgot. Never mind, this is more important. It's for your dad's birthday party. I'll just have to keep an eye on them all while I cook. And I shan't have time to make lunch today, so later on would you mind going to the pork butcher for some pease pudding and saveloys?'

'Oh, all right.'

Was there a note of resentment in her voice? Mary wondered; she knew she would have resented running errands at Anne's age, but there was no alternative. She sighed, as her thoughts began racing through the rest of the chores for the day.

When Anne returned, Mary put the mutton in the oven to roast and the tongue in a pan to boil, hoping there would be enough cold meat left over for Sunday lunch, and then she started making jam tarts and apple pies.

At eleven thirty she reminded Anne, 'It's time to go to the pork shop now, Anne.'

'Why can't Michael go?' the child complained. 'I've done all the other shopping and he's out playing.'

'I know, Anne, being a girl is tough, you have to learn to do womanly things. Why don't you go and tell Michael to come in. I asked him to fill the coal scuttle; he knows we've got visitors coming tonight.'

Anne obeyed, eyes downcast. Why did grown-ups have all the fun? She and Michael had to help with the work but they weren't even allowed to stay up for the party. Life wasn't fair.

'And mind you come straight home from the pork shop, no dilly-dallying or it'll get cold,' Mary said, flustered by having to do so many things at once.

'Can we have some pickled onions with it?' Anne asked eagerly, her favourite treat.

Mary sighed. 'I'm sorry, Anne, we simply can't afford pickles for lunch, but I'm glad you reminded me, we shall need some for tonight. Here's another bowl. Get it half full, please.' She saw Anne's face drop and relented. 'As you're being so good and going for them, why don't you have a couple on the way home, and tell Michael he has to go with you to help you carry them, and he can have a couple, too. And if you're a good girl and come back quickly, you can feed the baby after lunch.' That was one chore Anne loved to do. She loved her baby brother and often changed and fed him without being asked. She was a good girl and Mary hated to impose on her, but at times she had no choice. There was simply too much to do for one pair of hands. Sometimes she wished she could let her standards drop and bother less, as some women did, but she couldn't stand the thought of a grubby house or grubby children. She could do less baking and cooking, but ready-cooked food was expensive. And the washing, perhaps one day she'd be able to afford to take that to a washerwoman, but funds certainly didn't run to it at the moment.

She was busy rolling the pastry for the tarts as Anne put her coat on. 'And when you get back, Anne, would you bring in David and Billie from the yard. They'll be filthy by now.' She'd better have the baking out of the way and the table cleared before they got back. If she was lucky, she might be finished in time to grab a short rest before this evening. She was feeling awfully tired again today.

By seven o'clock the table was laden with sandwiches and pickles and tarts, and the glasses and plates were out. Mary sat in front of the fire and sipped a cup of tea. The children were playing in the yard and it was dark; she'd have to get them in for bed and then get herself dressed for the party. What was she going to do about Joe? She prayed that he would come before the guests arrived and after the children were in bed. But she had a plan ready should he arrive late: she'd just have to say that someone got the wrong address.

At ten past eight there was a knock on the front door. Please, God, let it be Joe, she thought as she ran to answer the door. It was! Breathlessly, she told him the news. 'You can't come in tonight, Joe; he's having a party. I've got next Saturday off, so I'll meet you on the corner at six. Just give me the money now, please, and go; I can't have him seeing you here.'

'Whoah, hold on! So I'm being stood up for the boss, am I? Just leave the money and *go*, *Joe*,' he rhymed sarcastically. 'Aren't you going to invite me to the party? You'll probably need a bodyguard to keep old what's-his-name's hands off you anyway.'

'Don't be silly, Joe, and I'm sorry to chase you away, but I can't help it. I could lose my job if he sees you here, and I can spend the whole night next Saturday instead. That'll be more fun. Please, go now; I hear voices in the back.'

'All right, sweetheart, I know when I'm not wanted. See you next week then.' He pecked her on the cheek and turned to go.

'Joe! The money.'

'Oh, yes, I forgot. Here you are, luv.' He fished in his pocket and planted the two coins firmly in her hand. 'Don't put them down your bodice; he might find them,' he joked.

'Joe! That's enough nonsense. Thanks, and see you next week.' The sound of voices was definitely coming from the back yard now. She quickly hid the money under the vase on the hall table, smoothed down her hair and straightened her shoulders. This was her first time playing hostess; at least she hadn't had to make jugged hare or *pot au feu*.

The evening started off more easily than she'd anticipated. The people were friendly and complimented her on her table. Walter, like most of them, was just a little bit tipsy, and the party spirit was already in full swing when they arrived. Walter loaded the sideboard with at least two dozen bottles of brown ale, a large bottle of White Horse whisky, a bottle of port, one of sherry and three pint bottles of lemonade. Mary's eyes boggled; she'd never seen so many bottles at once outside a pub. Where had he got the money from? Walter must have read her thoughts, for he said, gaily, 'The lads all chipped in at the pub. Not a bad spread, eh? What would you like, Mary?'

'I'll have a port and lemon, please.' She needed something to relax her and put her in a livelier mood. She was exhausted after her day's work.

He introduced her to the crowd. All were his workmates and their wives or girl friends, except for Jane and her husband, Jim.

'Everyone, help themselves,' Walter announced, 'while I help my lovely housekeeper.' Mary blushed. At least a dozen pairs of eyes turned in her direction.

'A toast to the cook!' he announced after they had all filled their glasses, and he raised his glass to Mary. They all did the same and, in her confusion, Mary took a large sip of port, realising too late that she wasn't supposed to toast herself; however, nobody seemed to notice and soon the table and glasses were half empty.

'Time for a song,' shouted Maude, a tall, dark-haired woman of about thirty, whom Mary had noticed particularly as she never seemed to be far from Walter's side. She was strikingly good-looking, with aquiline features, a deep red rouged mouth, and a husky voice. Mary wondered which man was her husband.

The port was beginning to relax her and warm her up now and she soon gave up trying to match man to wife and joined in the song: 'Whoa, me lads, ye should o' seen them gannin' . . .' She'd heard the 'Blaydon Races' often enough at Mrs Moynihan's to know the words by now. It reminded her of her old friend, whom she hadn't seen for weeks, and she resolved to pay her a visit as soon as possible.

Walter was kept busy refilling glasses while the man with the accordion played 'Greensleeves', a song her mother used to sing often. Again she joined in. This was more fun than she'd expected and the people were all very nice.

As the party got merrier, the bottles got emptier, and soon the port and sherry were finished. 'Well,' Walter laughed, 'we should have got more for the ladies. I'm afraid you'll all just have to drink whisky now. Let me refill your glass, Mary.'

'Thank you,' she said, automatically holding out her empty glass.

'And for you, Jane,' he said as he went round the women with the bottle.

'No thanks, Walter. I've had enough; I'll just have some lemonade.' As Jane spoke she glanced in Mary's direction. Was it a look of disapproval, Mary wondered, taking a sip of whisky? It was none of Jane's business to disapprove of what she did in her off-duty time, and she *was* off duty tonight; she'd worked hard all day.

Gradually the chatter of voices and the singing grew louder and then finally lessened as the guests departed two by two. Eventually only Mary and Walter were left with the dirty glasses and dishes and the depleted bottles. 'Well, it was a nice party, Mary. They certainly liked your sandwiches and tarts.'

Mary looked a little dizzily at the load of dirty, empty plates and nodded. She stood up unsteadily. 'I'd better start clearing away,' she muttered, walking but feeling as if she were floating, towards the table. Perhaps she should have stopped drinking when Jane did.

'No,' he caught her arm and led her back to the settee. 'Sit down and rest a bit; you look tired. The dishes can wait till the mornin'.'

'Oh, I really think I'd better,' she started, but he put a restraining hand on her shoulder and sat down beside her.

'I'd rather you had a chat with me; I enjoyed our talk the other night.'

'All right.' Mary was grateful to sink back into the couch, 'But I'll have to get up very early in the morning.'

'Don't worry yourself about that now. How about us having a nightcap,' he said, picking up the almost empty whisky bottle and draining it into two glasses. 'They were good enough to leave us a drop.'

She nodded and accepted the glass he handed her. As he sat down on the settee beside her, his arm rested on her shoulder. 'You've been a grand little lass, tonight, Mary. I didn't know you were such a live wire.'

'Oh, I'm learning to be,' she giggled, 'when I'm given the chance, that is. Funny, isn't it? I've just realised lately that life isn't meant to be all work and no play.'

'That's the spirit!' His grip tightened on her shoulder and for the first time she became aware of the pressure of his arm round her. Good God! Had she let him do that? Why hadn't she stopped him? But she liked his touch; that electric feeling pulsated through her again.

Encouraged by her acceptance, he pulled her closer and kissed her perfunctorily on the cheek. 'Thanks for doin' all that work for my birthday.'

'Oh, it was nothing.' Again, why was the touch of his lips on her face so pleasant? She loved Joe! This was wrong! Her mother had always said 'when drink's in, wit's out'. She'd better be careful her wits didn't desert her tonight.

He interrupted her thoughts: 'Well, it was something to me, and thank you again.' This time he put down his glass, and turning her face towards him with his roughened hands, kissed her full on the mouth. Her conscience said no but, against her will, her senses reeled and her body responded. He gently removed her glass from her hand and pulled her slowly towards him, and she became totally lost in the physical mystery of this man and returned his kiss. His pressure grew harder and his hands gently strayed to her breasts. No! What was she doing? Was she crazy? She pulled herself away and stood up shakily. 'I shouldn't have let you do that, Walter. It was stupid of me. It . . . it must be the whisky. I must go now. Goodnight.'

She stumbled up the stairs and shivered as she quickly undressed and crawled into bed. What on earth had got into her? Dear God, she mustn't let Walter come near her again. If he did, she'd have to hand in her notice. She'd better not drink in his company either. Her mother had certainly been right about drink. What a mess she'd got herself into!

Chapter Twenty-eight

The next morning she woke up feeling exhausted and guilt-ridden. Pulling on her grey workdress and trailing downstairs to light the fire and start cleaning up the mess, she still questioned herself: why had she done it?

By the time Walter appeared at breakfast, she and the children were eating their porridge, and Mary kept her head and her eyes down over her own bowl.

'Hello, gang,' he greeted the children cheerfully, and then to Mary, 'Mornin'! It's a grand day, eh?' as if nothing had happened.

She acknowledged his greeting but kept her head down. Thank goodness she could get out of the house soon. This was her day off. She would escape to Doris's as soon as breakfast was cleared away. Joe had gone to Carlisle for the day, to attend the funeral of his best friend's father and, in a way, she was glad she wouldn't be seeing him so soon after her episode with Walter. She knew she wasn't good enough at acting to hide her fresh guilt, and telling Joe would be out of the question if she wanted to keep him – and she did. She'd acted stupidly because she'd been drunk and she'd never make that mistake again.

Mercifully, after breakfast Walter retired to his room to read the Sunday paper in peace and quiet, as the children were being particularly active.

At nine o'clock, when Jane arrived, Mary had all the children washed, scrubbed, shining clean and dressed in their best clothes.

'Hello, I'm glad to see you,' Mary said cheerfully, but she couldn't look Jane in the face after getting drunk at the party. Thank God the woman didn't know the rest of the story.

'Aye, mornin'. The bairns all look nice.'

'Thank you. They were all ready for a good scrub; I didn't have much time to see to them yesterday.'

'Aye, you must have been busy. Nice spread you made.'

'I'm glad you enjoyed it. I've saved the bones and enough meat to make a stew for lunch.'

'Aye, that's good. I'll start it now,' she said, rolling up her sleeves.

So Jane wasn't going to mention anything else about the party, thank goodness. Mary quickly grabbed her hat and coat. 'I'll be off then, Jane. I'm taking David today to see his friend; he hasn't seen him for a while.'

'Aye, it's a nice day; enjoy the fresh air. I'll take the rest out when I've got the stew on.'

Arriving at Doris's, she rapped the door knocker sharply. She was still tired and not feeling well and wanted nothing more than a sit-down and a cup of tea. David was walking with his reins and she wished, too late, that she had brought the pram for support.

'Why, hinny, you look done in. Been at it again all night?'

'As a matter of fact, I almost have. Does it show that much?' Mary sat down wearily, pulling David on to her knee to undo his reins.

'But I thought it was party night and you weren't seein' Joe.'

'It was and I didn't, except to get the money.'

'Good God, Mary, you don't mean to say—'

'No, I don't,' interrupted Mary, rising to take squirming, whining David to join Jimmy in the yard. 'But I almost did. I let him kiss me . . . I suppose you're shocked.'

'You know me, hinny. It would take more than that to shock me. I suppose surprised would be a better word, but not much o' that neither. I seen it comin' an' I told you so. I knew that man had a fancy for you an' I knew you had a sneakin' fancy for him an' all, right from the start.'

'Well, I might have to leave now, if he tries again. And I don't think he'll stop at one attempt. I'd better be prepared and start looking for something straight away.' Mary's voice was drained of emotion as she again wondered what her mother would think now. She loved one man, yet had allowed another to kiss her passionately. 'You know, Doris, it's strange; even though my mother is dead I keep worrying about what she would think of me. I feel as though I've let her down.'

'Aw, rubbish! Stop punishin' yoursel'. She's dead now an' you've got to think o' your own life, but next time you get a housekeepin' job, make sure you get an old, ugly man; it seems you can't resist a handsome face. Cup o' tea, then? It doesn't look like you'll want to go walkin' the day. Let's just have a cosy afternoon by the fire. Me da's in bed and likely to stay there, an' I've got some nice drippin' sandwiches; I cooked the joint yesterday 'cause Frank came round. He's comin' again the night. He's really back to his old self now – jokin', laughin' an' feelin' sexy again.'

'Oh, so you've been busy, too,' Mary joked. 'I'm glad he's feeling better. We were lucky none of us got it.'

'Aye, thank God! It's been a hard time but the

doctor says he's almost as good as new now and should be fine as long as he keeps his strength up and doesn't get any more infections.'

'That's wonderful, Doris.' Mary got up and hugged her friend. 'I'm so relieved for you – and Frank. You both deserve some good fortune. Has Harry reappeared yet to see Jimmy?'

'No, that bugger's disappeared off the face of the earth; the last time he came was three weeks before I met Frank, so if he thinks he's got any claims on me he's got another think comin'. An' you know, Mary, you wouldn't believe it, but it's sort of different with Frank . . . *he's* sort of different. We've still only had a few kisses and cuddles, nothin' else. I know he'd like more; I can feel his charlie against me, so you might say there are times when he's got two good legs,' she giggled, 'but he never tries. I think he respects me morals, even though I've got Jimmy to prove I haven't got any.'

'Maybe there are some men left who respect women, after all. Not that I could ever respect myself again,' Mary added despondently.

'Oh, Mary, don't be hard on yoursel'. You made a mistake, that's all.'

'More than one, and I'm worried. The fact is, Doris, I have trouble stopping myself. I lose my head so quickly.'

'If you didn't drink booze, you'd hang on to your head better, you know.'

'I know. My mother used to warn me against the dangers of alcohol.'

'Back to your bloody mother again, are we? I've told you, don't get your drawers in a knot over her now. She's dead an' gone, hinny, an' life is for the livin'. I don't want to hear no more talk about your mother. When are you seein' Joe again?'

'On Saturday. I got the evening off for doing my

party duty,' she answered wryly. 'As it turned out, I was glad he went to that funeral; I didn't feel like facing him today.'

'Are you goin' to tell him?'

'Doris, do you think I'm crazy? Of course not! I'd lose him in a shot.'

'Well, he's goin' to want to know why if you suddenly decide to leave your job.'

'I can't tell him. If Walter tries again and I have to leave, I'll just tell Joe the work was too much for me. He's always suspected Walter's intentions towards me anyway.'

'Anyone in their right mind would, except you. I'm goin' to make a bite now and see to me da. Why don't you put your feet up and have a rest and then we'll get some fresh air after all? You could do with some colour in them cheeks.'

'Thanks, Doris. I don't know what I'd do without you.'

The week flew by and soon it was Saturday. Mary was looking forward to her night off with Joe. It had been a strain keeping Walter at arm's length, but she had managed it, avoiding being alone with him. Billie was suffering from a cold and was sleeping on the settee in the warm kitchen, so that had helped. Nevertheless, Walter had been much more personal with her and several times had deliberately brushed past her or sat beside her – too close for Mary's peace of mind.

She had scanned the papers every day and had checked the shop window advertisements but there was no work she could do. The entire week had been stressful and she was ready for an evening out with Joe. She decided against wearing the blue dress and wore her white blouse and black skirt. Then, diving into her coat and pinning on her hat, she rushed out to meet Joe, who was waiting at their usual corner.

'Hello, luv, let's go and have a noggin at the local. I'm frozen to death standing here,' he said, stamping his feet.

'No, let's not go to the local. Let's go to the Black Bull. The walk will warm you up. Sorry I'm late.' She dreaded the thought of seeing Walter or any of his friends at the local. The idea of the two men meeting filled her with horror.

'All right, the Black Bull it is; at least they'll have a fire on in there. And then we'll go to my place for more booze and food. I stocked up earlier at the off-licence; it's a lot cheaper than the pub, and we can pick up some fish and chips on the way home.'

The modest evening ahead sounded delightful to Mary and she was happy as they sat together near the pub fire sipping their drinks. After warming up, they picked up the fish and chips, steaming hot from the fish shop, and rushed home before the meal got cold. Sitting on the bed, curled up with Joe, and eating a tasty meal that she hadn't had to cook was heaven. Remembering her headache from whisky the previous week, she'd decided to stick to port, and soon she felt enveloped in its warm glow. Life was not so bad after all.

'I've got some news, Mary.' Joe's voice interrupted her contented thoughts. 'I'm going back to London.'

She went suddenly cold. 'But why, Joe? You've got a good job here . . . and what about me?'

'That's just the point, I haven't got a good job here. It's a dead end. I'll never make more than shop foreman, like my dad. This new job is with a smaller factory with more chance to move up to management, especially as I've got most of my night classes behind me now. That's how I got the job – the only applicant with more than shop floor experience. Besides, I need to get out of this hole; it's beginning to depress me. The weather's better and life's a lot more exciting down there. I wouldn't have come back except that I had a job to come to.'

'But what about me?' Mary queried again, her face white and horror-stricken.

'I know, luv, and I'll miss you, but you knew I wasn't going to stay put very long. I'll be coming back sometimes to see my mates and you, and you can come and visit me.'

'Why can't we get married and go together?' she cried, unable to believe that he was deserting her again.

'Mary, you know how I feel about marriage; it's out of the question. Let's not go into that again.'

'So, you're going to leave me again, and David. When?' Her voice was dead.

'Next week. I had to give a week's notice. I'm catching the two o'clock train on Saturday; the job starts on Monday. I have no choice, Mary; I simply have to do what I have to do. I wouldn't be doing you any favours by marrying you; it just wouldn't work for me, so it would be no good for you either. Can't you see that?'

'All I can see is that you're going off and leaving me again. And next Saturday! That means this is our last time together.' She was sobbing now. 'You never really loved me, did you, Joe?'

'I'm very fond of you, Mary,' he said awkwardly, 'but what you mean by love, I just don't know about. If it simply means wanting to get married and settle down with that person and bring up a family, then it can't be love I feel, but something else. I just don't know. Maybe one of these days I'll want to settle down, but I couldn't at the moment. I'm simply not ready for it. Look, I'd like to see you one night during the week if you could get a night off.'

'You know that's impossible, Joe.'

'All right, so we'll just have to make it a fond farewell this time. Now be a dear and drink up your port and don't spoil our last fun together.'

'Yes, that's your motto, Joe. Drink up! Have a good time! To hell with real life and responsibilities! Well, there's one responsibility you're not going to get out of and that's your son. You'll keep on paying for him, won't you?' She must think of David, despite her own misery.

'Of course I will, and I'll write to you and see you when I come back to visit.'

'I hope you're better at writing than you were the last time, Joe.' She burst into tears and took a long draught of port to calm her nerves. She knew she'd never hear from him again.

'Oh, come on, Mary. I haven't gone yet, and it's not the end of the world.'

'Maybe not for you,' Mary wailed, taking another drink to stem her sobs. 'This is the second time you've left me in the lurch.'

'Lurch, what lurch? I never promised you anything except a good time, Mary. That's all I can offer.'

She took a deep breath and the sobs subsided, anger taking their place. 'Yes,' she said coldly, 'and now you're going to offer that to someone else in London. I've no doubt it won't take you long to find a substitute.' As the words came out, memories of the previous Saturday flooded back. Who was she to talk? Well, it served him right. If he didn't want her, other men did. Other men thought she was worth having. But it was only Joe she wanted. 'I know you won't come back.' She broke down again, burying her face in his chest, the tears flowing.

He put his arms round her and rocked her, covering her face with kisses. 'Come on, Mary, cheer up. I've told you I will, and I haven't gone yet. Give me a kiss . . . There, that's better,' he soothed, kissing her damp lips. As he lowered her onto the pillow and stroked her face and arms, she responded wildly, clinging to him. But although she felt his body in her arms, in her mind she felt as if he'd already left her.

The next morning they stayed in bed even longer than usual. She longed to spend the whole day with him, but when she had Saturday nights off she had to get back by lunch time to relieve Jane. It wasn't fair to expect the woman to do Saturday nights and all day Sunday. At eleven o'clock she reluctantly dragged herself away from his embrace. They'd hardly said a word all morning and they'd never made love so often in such a short time; she'd clung to him feverishly half the night and the next morning. He was feeling extra ardent, too. Could it be that he really didn't want to leave her? No. Of course he did or he wouldn't be going. 'I have to go soon, Joe. I promised I'd be home by lunch time.' Her voice quavered and she shivered as she left the warmth of the bed.

'Don't look so sad, Mary; I've told you, I'll be back to see you.'

'I know, Joe,' she said, wishing she could truly believe it.

'I've got some cold sausages and a fresh loaf. I'll make you something to eat.'

'No, don't bother, Joe. I'm not hungry anyway.'

She searched for her clothes in the heap on the floor, where, in their hasty passion, they had flung them the night before. Then she pulled on her garments slowly, mechanically, and splashed her face at the bowl. She would wash properly when she got home; she simply couldn't be bothered now. And she was even glad she wouldn't have time to call in on

Doris; all she wanted to do at this moment was to hide and lick her wounds.

'I'll see you to your door, then,' he said, rising and stepping into his longjohns.

'No, Joe. I couldn't bear to say goodbye in the street. I'll leave you here.'

He strode over to her, looking comical in the undergarment. Normally, she'd have laughed but she didn't feel like laughing today.

'If that's what you want, then,' he said, holding her gently round the waist as she pinned up her hair at the mirror. 'I'm missing you already, Mary,' he whispered, kissing the nape of her neck.

'Well, it's your choice, Joe, not mine. I'm ready, I must go now.'

He grabbed her and kissed her fiercely until she had to push herself away to breathe.

'Farewell, dearest Mary, until we meet again,' he whispered, brushing his cheek against hers.

'Goodbye, Joe,' she sobbed, prising herself away and rushing blindly to the door. She couldn't bear to drag out the parting any longer. Until we meet again, she thought, closing the door quickly behind her. That's a joke!

Back at the house she felt miserable and empty.

'Hello, Mary, you're just in time for lunch.' Jane was stirring a large pot of rabbit stew and the smell of food nauseated Mary.

'I'm not hungry, thanks. Actually, I'm not feeling very well. Would you mind if I lie down for half an hour?'

'Not at all, luv. I'm going to eat with the bairns anyway. I'll put Walter's on a pot to keep warm and give you a call when I'm ready to go.'

'Thank you, Jane,' she said gratefully; she'd be better able to cope with the children when she'd pulled herself together. Dragging her feet up the stairs, she lay down on the bed to be alone and think. What now? Well, she wouldn't need to worry about looking for another job. The odds were against her finding anything anyway; both money and jobs were getting even tighter than they were after the first avalanche of homecoming soldiers, and now even Lloyd George couldn't stop the surging wave of strikes. She was probably safer staying where she was.

And what about Walter? Well, with Joe out of the picture again, nothing mattered. Joe had never really loved her anyway; she realised that now. Whatever it was he felt for her was too temporary and sporadic to be real love. And what did she really feel for him? At the moment, only a strange mixture of sadness and anger that he was leaving her again, and this time was final, she knew.

Jane called up the stairs. She looked at Mary strangely when she reappeared but asked no questions.

'They're all fed and I've got to go now, Mary. George's got the bairns and he's waitin' to go to the pub.'

'Yes, of course. Thank you for all you've done.' David and Billie ran to greet her and she gave them both a hug. 'Did you behave yourselves for Auntie Jane?' she addressed all five.

'We always behave ourselves, don't we?' It was Michael, and from his genuine, questioning tone, he seemed to need reassurance.

'Of course you do,' she said, ruffling his hair playfully. 'You're the best behaved children in the whole of Newcastle.' Even distant, independent Michael was becoming more eager to please her.

'Why do you keep on saying "children" an' "lunch" an' other funny words, when everybody else says bairns an' dinner?'

'I've told you, Michael, it's simply what I was

brought up to say, and it's hard to break the habit. Now, do you all want to go outside to play?'

'No,' said Anne, 'it was cold when we were out playin' this mornin'. I want to stay in by the fire an' read comics.'

'All right. And the rest of you?'

'Yes! Comics, an' you read to us,' begged Michael.

Mary sighed, she didn't feel in the mood to read to them, but perhaps it would keep her mind off her misery. She spread a comic on the floor, close but not too close to the fire, and they all grouped round her as she pointed out pictures and read the words. At least she wouldn't be left alone with Walter.

He arrived home at two fifteen. 'Well, you all look very cosy there,' he said. 'I think I'll join you after I've had me dinner.'

Mary groaned inwardly at the thought of his spending the afternoon with them. Thank goodness she'd have the children for protection. 'Your lunch is on the hob; I'll get it now.'

'Thanks. You look a bit tired today; I'll help you with the comics when I've finished.'

When he joined them he sat next to Mary, picking up Billie and settling him on his knee to make room. 'Make way for your old dad,' he said, as he inched closer to Mary, while she tried, unsuccessfully, to inch away.

The evening meal was a noisy affair. Mary couldn't wait for Walter to leave for the pub and for the children's bedtime to arrive. With Anne's help the dishes were cleared in record time and the children soon dressed in clean nightclothes. By eight o'clock Mary was sitting by the fire and thinking about making some cocoa. Billie's cold was better now and Walter wouldn't be back until ten, so, thank goodness, she had the kitchen to herself for a couple of hours. Before sorting out dirty clothes and preparing stacks of clean ones for the next morning, she had an hour and a half to relax.

She was just rising to put the kettle on when the back door creaked. Startled, she saw Walter striding into the kitchen.

'Thought I'd leave the gang early and have a nightcap with you instead. I've had enough of their company for one night and, anyway, I'd rather be with you.'

Flustered, she mumbled that she was just putting the kettle on.

'Never mind the kettle,' he said, taking a bottle of whisky from his coat pocket. 'I brought us somethin' stronger. Let's have some glasses, then,' he added amiably, taking off his coat and throwing it on his chair, then unscrewing the bottle cap. 'You're lookin' very pretty tonight – pale and pretty. Pale suits you, gives you an even more ephemeral look.'

'You talk as though I look like a ghost,' Mary smiled, her spirits raised a little by the compliment. Besides, maybe some company and a whisky would be better for her than moping by herself, although she was careful to take her seat at the fireplace rather than on the settee.

He sat opposite and raised his glass, 'To my lovely housekeeper.'

'Thank you,' she said and, raising hers, responded, 'To my boss.'

'Aw, let's have none of that boss stuff. You live here, Mary, and so do I, and you're a woman and I'm a man. Let's just drink to us instead.'

'All right, to us.'

He pulled his chair closer and took her free hand. 'I haven't forgotten last Saturday, Mary. I've hardly been able to take my eyes off you all week, but we haven't had a minute alone. That's why I came back early tonight, now that Billie's cold's better. It was driving me crazy seeing you every day and not being able to touch you.'

Despite herself, she let her hand remain in his. It was reassuring to feel the touch of a man who wasn't planning to run away and leave her, and the whisky warmed her inside.

'I'm so glad you took the job, Mary. I don't know what the bairns and me would have done without you. You take good care of us all. I'm glad I didn't take me mates' advice when Annie died and put them in a home.'

'Oh, you'd have found someone else, maybe somebody more efficient.'

'No, when I saw you with that white blouse and black ribbon – the same as you're wearin' tonight – just peekin' out from your coat, I tried to imagine you with your coat off.'

He was getting personal again, she thought. Why couldn't he be Joe? 'You have a good memory,' she said automatically.

'For some things only. I'll never forget the way you looked that night, all damp and glistening from the rain. I couldn't believe my luck. I expected to get some hard-bitten old crow who'd try to boss *me* around as much as the bairns.'

'I doubt that anyone could boss you around,' she said, sipping her drink. The whisky and the compliments were making her feel a little better now. At least she felt worthwhile and wanted with this man, *and Joe didn't want her* so she didn't stop Walter when he came and sat on the arm of her chair and put his arm round her shoulders, kissing her gently on the mouth.

'I've wanted you from the first moment I saw you, Mary,' he whispered, pulling her up from the chair and circling her with his arms, kissing her harder this time. She felt secure in his arms, his hard body against hers. The voice in her head repeated: Joe didn't want her, but Walter did. And he wasn't going to run away and leave her. She didn't stop him when he lifted her and carried her into the front parlour which was his bedroom.

Chapter Twenty-nine

During the next few weeks Walter helped to fill the gap of loneliness, yet, even when she was in his arms, Joe's image would often crowd her mind. She hadn't been feeling well for some time and had missed a period again. It had often happened before, but this time she was worried. Her greatest fear increased one morning while blackleading the stove. The fumes from the black polish nauseated her and she vomited. Oh, God, she thought, you couldn't do this to me again! And she'd been so careful. No, it couldn't be possible. But yes it could, she moaned inwardly, and finally decided to ask Maggie's advice; she would call in on her way to Doris's that Sunday.

Maggie, in her usual high spirits, answered Mary's knock, her blonde hair askew and her blue eyes popping with surprise. 'Why, hinny, nice to see you. What's up?' But before Mary could answer, she went on, 'Come on in and have a cup of tea; the kettle's just boilin'. How are you? You don't look so hot.'

'I don't feel so hot, either, Maggie. That's why I came.' Mary's face was pale and her voice strained.

'Eey, Mary! You haven't fallen again, have you?'

'I'm not certain but I'm worried and I wanted to ask if there's anything I can do.'

'Did you use them things I told you about?'

'Yes, but you said yourself that nothing's fool-proof.'

'Aye, you're right, luv,' Maggie sighed. 'It'll be a

bloody miracle if that day ever comes. But there are some things you can do if you're worried, not that I'd like to recommend them, though. How late are you?'

'About six or eight weeks, I'm not sure. I've been so mixed up lately what with Joe leaving and everything else that's been happening. I often miss a month when I get upset, but this time I've been feeling sick too.'

'Sick! Oh Lordy, sounds bad. Take your coat off, luv, and I'll make the tea.'

Mary sat down in the familiar looking kitchen. She'd only been there once before, but from the table at the window covered with worn green oilcloth to the balding velvet armchairs, it looked similar to every kitchen she'd ever been in. As usual, the only cheerful sight in the room was the fire blazing in the black stove. Maggie was pouring the water into the pot and shaking her head.

'Joe again, Mary? You daft thing, where's your sense? Trust him to bugger off and leave you again. Have you tried a hot bath and a bottle o' gin? That might work if you're only late – they don't call it "mothers' ruin" for nothin', you know. It helped me once when I was late. If nothing else, it eases your mind, stops you waitin' an' wonderin'.'

'A whole bottle! But I couldn't drink a whole bottle at once.'

'Well, start off with a half, then, and see what happens. That would be my first shot. Here's your tea, luv. Looks as though you need perkin' up. I'd like to give that Joe a piece o' me tongue.'

Taking the proffered teacup, Mary looked up helplessly at Maggie. 'To tell the truth, Maggie, I can't be certain that it *is* Joe.' Her voice was shaking.

'Good God, Mary! You've got two?' In her astonishment Maggie's tea cup almost toppled from its saucer. 'Who's the other one? Aw, don't tell me, it's your boss. I knew that set-up sounded fishy from the start.'

'Yes, it seems everyone did but me. It's strange, Maggie; I do feel something for him but I don't know what it is. It's not like it was with Joe.'

'Never two the same, luv. Does he know about Joe?'

'No, thank God, and he's not going to. At least I'll have a man behind me this time; I'm tired of being left in the dirt.'

'You mean he's said he'll marry you?'

'I haven't told him yet, but I certainly will if the worst happens. I'll try the gin first. Thanks, Maggie, and for the tea,' Mary said, finishing her tea and standing up. 'I have to go now. I left David at the house, and I have to pick him up before I go to see Doris. And that reminds me, I had a letter from Doreen yesterday.'

'And how's our little virgin friend doin'?'

'She's all right, still pining for her fiancé. The way things sound, she's destined to be an old maid.'

'Aye, maybe it's better than what we're in for, hinny. I'll see you to the door.'

Mary went to the off-licence to buy a half bottle of gin. Thank goodness she had almost the entire week's housekeeping money left; she'd have to cut down on groceries somehow this week. She would drink it and take a hot bath at Doris's, and she'd have the rest of the day to recover. But if she did that, she'd better leave David at home with Jane. Yes, she had to go through with it today; she couldn't stand another week's uncertainty.

'Has it come yet?' Doris asked eagerly as she opened the door, but she could tell from Mary's face that it hadn't. 'Come on in, luv, an' tell me the worst.'

'Well, the worst is that nothing's happened. The only slightly hopeful news is that Maggie said a half bottle of gin and a hot bath might bring it on if it's

only late. So I've bought some and wondered if I could
do it here; I can't do it at home with Jane and the
children there.'

'O' course, luv. I'll just put some pots on to boil
an' get you a clean towel. I've only got carbolic soap,
though.'

'I don't need soap, Doris. This bath's not intended
to clean my outside; the hot soak and the gin are supposed to clean my *inside*. I'll help you fill the pots.'

Together they filled four big saucepans; there was
only room for two to boil on the fire so they placed
the other two in the oven, which was hot enough to
warm them up.

'The kettle's already boiled, so that'll help an' all.
Now we'll go and get the tub,' said Doris, already on
her way out to the yard. Mary followed and together
they heaved the heavy zinc bathtub into the kitchen
and set it down before the fire.

'Sit down, luv,' said Doris, lowering herself into
one of the chairs by the fire. 'We might as well get
comfortable; it'll be a bit of a wait. I'd offer you a cup
o' tea, but we can't use the precious water . . . an'
you've brought your own drink anyway,' she added,
in a feeble attempt at humour.

'Oh, yes,' Mary said, remembering the gin, and taking it from her bag she unscrewed the cork. She put
the bottle gingerly to her nostrils and then took a sip.
'Oh, my God! Maggie didn't tell me it was so foul, and
she didn't tell me whether to drink it in the bath or
before.'

'Well, if it's that awful, I think you should start
takin' it now and get it over with. I'll just get you a
glass; it might go down easier that way. And how
about puttin' some sugar in it?'

'Sounds a wonderful idea but I don't want to add
anything to it that might make me even sicker. Maggie
warned me that it might make me sick.'

Doris handed her a small glass. Mary filled it and, holding her nose, knocked it back. 'Ugh! It tastes worse than medicine; it had better work,' she spluttered and shuddered as her throat burned. 'Why couldn't it be whisky? At least I don't mind the taste of that.'

'Well, I'm goin' to sit here and make sure you get at least some of it down you afore the water's ready.'

Mary held her nose again and took several more draughts before the pots on the hob began to bubble. Doris jumped up and placed them on the hearth. 'I'll just put the two in the oven on the fire now to finish off quickly.'

'Oh, Doris, I forgot about your father and Jimmy. There's no chance they might come in?'

'No, don't worry, luv. Me da's sound asleep and Jimmy's next door at little Andy's birthday party; he won't be back till five.'

'Frank's not likely to call, is he?'

'No, luv, he's not comin' round till the night. There's a reunion on today for what's left of his battalion; no doubt he'll be stinkin' drunk when he does come. An' talkin' about bein' drunk, you're beginnin' to look a bit glassy-eyed, Mary. Let's get your things off and get you into that tub afore you get any worse, though I've had some practice at handling drunken women with me ma.'

'You've had practice at just about everything, Doris,' Mary said, her voice slightly slurred. Rising a little unsteadily, she attempted to undo her bodice buttons.

'Here, you'd better let me help you. You're half cocked already.' Doris rushed to her friend's aid and started undressing her.

'Yes, I didn't notice it so much until I stood up. I do feel a little funny. God knows what I might be like by the time you have to help me out of the bath. Can you manage?'

'Why, I have to hump me da in an' out o' the tub every week. Didn't you just say I'm experienced at everything?' Finally she managed to strip Mary of the last of her underwear, her camisole and drawers, and then gently seated her back in the chair. 'Now you just sit down till I fill that tub; you're not fit to stand on your own.' Swishing her hand around in the tub, Doris grunted with satisfaction. 'Good! It's hot, a little too hot for that delicate skin o' yours; hang on till I add some more cold, an' after I get you in I'll put some more on to boil to keep it hot.'

Mary sat, shivering now, even before the heat of the fire, until Doris had swirled four pans of cold water around the tub. 'Good God, Doris, what's happening to me? What have I sunk to?' She hiccupped as she put her hands to her swimming head.

'Now, you're not doin' nothin' that any girl in your situation wouldn't do, so stop bein' so hard on yoursel'. Now I've got hold o' you, just take it slowly and I'll help you to ease in gently.'

Mary felt the soothing hot water hugging her body, but her head was spinning even more violently now. 'Doris, I don't think I can finish that bottle . . . I feel terrible.'

'Well, if they say it takes half a bottle, that's what it takes, and I'll get it into you if I have to force it down your gullet. No point in startin' the job an' not finishin' it. Auntie Doris is here to look after you so, come on, just knock another one o' these glasses back. You've had so much already, you can't have any taste buds left anyway. There, that wasn't so bad,' Doris soothed, as Mary obediently swallowed the remainder of the gin.

Doris was right; it didn't really taste of anything any more. Was she that drunk that she'd even lost her sense of taste? Oh, but the water felt soothing . . . and her head now felt far away.

When she finally opened her eyes she was lying on the settee, wrapped in blankets. 'What happened? Oh, my head!' she wailed as she tried to raise it.

'I'll tell you what happened: you got drunk out o' your mind an' started thrashing about all over the place. I had a job to hold you down in the bath. Don't you remember?'

'No, I don't even remember getting into the bath.'

'Gettin' you in wasn't all that hard, but gettin' you out was bloody back-breakin'. You finally conked out all together, but it was about time you got out of the water anyway; I couldn't add any more hot 'cause I didn't dare let go o' you. Now, that was a new experience! I've never had to get a dead body out o' the tub before.'

'Thanks, Doris . . . I . . . I think I'm going to be sick.'

'It's all right, I've got a bucket here handy. I thought you probably would.'

Mary lost the contents of her stomach and lay back gasping. 'Oh,' she groaned, holding her head with both hands. 'Maybe now I'm rid of some of that poison, I might sober up a bit quicker.'

'How long before you'll know if it's worked or not?'

'Maggie says it should be soon, at least within a few days.'

'I'll keep poppin' round to see if anythin' happens. And now, luv, you just lie back there an' have another sleep. I'll have a cup o' tea ready and somethin' to eat when you wake up, an' when you're ready I'm going to walk you home. God, you look terrible, Mary!'

'As usual, thank you, Doris,' Mary managed to mutter as sleep overtook her again.

* * *

A week later, she decided to confront Walter with her worst fears. It was definite now. She'd been nauseated every morning; the gin had done nothing but make her ill. She asked him if he'd come home early from the pub on Saturday evening; this was not business she could discuss in front of the children. He arrived home at nine, true to his word, and asked in a matter-of-fact voice, 'Well, what's the matter? What's all the mystery about?'

'It's not a mystery any more . . . I'm sure . . . I'm pregnant.'

He sat down heavily in the armchair, pulling his heavy eyebrows down in a deep frown and closing his eyes for a second. 'How long gone?'

'Over two months.'

'Damn!' he said, angrily, and then, 'Sorry, Mary, it's not all your fault. But that'll be another bairn around the place and we can't even give the ones we've got what we'd like to. Just what we need . . . another one.' His hands, white-knuckled, gripped the chair arms.

'Just what *I* need, you mean,' she replied angrily. 'I'm the one who has to have it. You *will* marry me, won't you?' She tried to keep her voice calm but it quavered.

'Hold on, Mary! I'm not in a position to get married till me wife's been dead a year.' He shook his head slowly. 'It wouldn't be right. That's the last thing I had in mind. I'll stand by you, but I can't marry you yet. We'll just have to go on as usual and to hell with what people say.'

'Well, you may not care what people say, but I do, and this is your baby as much as mine. You'll have to marry me . . . I don't believe you could say no. It wasn't too soon to make love to me but it's too soon to accept the consequences.' Dismayed, she realised that with all this talk of marriage, not one word had been spoken about love and, what was worse, she hadn't really given it any thought herself until now. For all his charm and his compliments, he had never once mentioned the word. She had been so bound up in her misery and confusion about Joe, she hadn't really noticed that this man showed no feeling for her outside the bedroom, although inside those closed doors he was everything a woman could want. But, of course, the children were around the rest of the time, she comforted herself; he couldn't be demonstrative in front of them.

'Don't you have any feelings for me at all?' she asked, longing for a word of love and comfort.

'Well, of course I do, Mary. You're a beautiful woman and any man would be proud to have you. I've grown very fond of you and I *will* marry you, but not until the right time. This is too sudden . . . but I'll look after you, don't worry.'

'Does that mean you won't throw me out?' she asked bitterly. 'What do you think people are going to say about my being pregnant and living under your roof?'

'Oh, come on, Mary! It's not all that bad. You'll have a home and I'll take care of you. Whether we get married sooner or later, it won't make any difference; people are going to talk anyway.'

'Well, if it won't make any difference, why won't you do it sooner?' she pleaded, leaning forward in the chair.

'I said it won't make any difference to what people say. It *will* make a difference to *me*; I just wouldn't feel right about gettin' married again so soon. I have to respect me wife's memory. I'll see you all right, though, don't worry.'

'But your wife's *dead*, I'm alive!'

'Aye, and the least we can do is respect the dead for a decent period.'

Mary couldn't believe that Walter, too, was reluctant to marry her. This was the second time in her life she'd begged a man to make an honest woman of her. What was it about her that made men want to have her but not commit themselves and do the right thing by her? She would never live down this shame. Once was bad enough, but *twice*! She determined to use every means in her power to change Walter's mind; she wasn't going to give birth to another child out of wedlock. But she felt too sick with misery to pursue the matter further at the moment. At least he'd said he *would* marry her, in his own time.

'Let's discuss it again later, Walter, when I feel better. I'm too tired now, anyway. Goodnight,' she said with forced calm, leaving the room.

The days and weeks dragged and Mary became more and more bitter about her situation. She felt so exhausted and depressed, she was becoming irritable and short-tempered with the children, and even with Walter.

One morning at breakfast, Billie spilled his porridge.

'Can't you be more careful,' she yelled, grabbing the child from his chair and beginning to strip off his clothes.

'No . . . no!' Billie yelled and ran to Anne for comfort.

'He's just a bairn. There's no need to yell at him.' Walter scraped back his chair and stood up to leave, his face angry.

'Oh yes, and don't tell me you wouldn't yell at him if you had to clean him up.'

'I do my bit at work, and I'm going now. I get more peace there than I do in my own home nowadays.'

Mary bit her lip and kept her mouth shut. These episodes were becoming more and more frequent; she knew she was exacerbating the situation but she couldn't hide the fact that she felt ill and depressed. She'd never felt so low in her life, except when her mother had died. But nerve-shattering though that experience had been, she'd had Mrs Moynihan's constant love and attention to help her through the worst time and to comfort her with the belief that one day she would be happy again. Now that belief had crumbled and she could see nothing but blackness ahead – another illegitimate child and more disgrace.

'Anne,' she said, sitting down wearily and pouring herself a cup of tea. 'Would you mind changing Billie, please. There are some dry clothes in the airing cupboard.'

'All right,' Anne said, a touch of resentment in her voice. 'But I haven't finished my breakfast yet.'

'Then finish your breakfast first. You know I'm not well and I can't manage to do everything myself. I'm sorry, but you and Michael will have to pull your weight a bit more until I feel better.' She put her head in her hands and remained that way until the children had finished their porridge, when she got up wearily and began clearing the table. Her only pleasure in life was David. He was the only thing in the world that belonged to her in this house of strangers; fond of the children though she was, she had to remind herself that she was simply there to look after them. They belonged to Walter.

She'd received Joe's money again yesterday – at least he'd kept his word about that. This time he'd enclosed a casual note, telling her he was enjoying life in London and he hoped she was doing well. She hadn't told him about the baby. What was the point? She knew he had no intention of coming back to her and, besides, she'd already acknowledged Walter as the father. It would only mean more scandal if word got out about Joe. She would keep Joe out of this;

Walter, at least, had promised to marry her and be a father to the child. This was the only thought that kept her going.

It was Saturday and, as usual, Jane would be round the following day. She hadn't voiced her disapproval about the coming baby but Mary sensed it and resented it, thus further straining relations between the two women. Jane's only concern seemed to be for her sister's children, and Mary was becoming tired of her gentle interference; in fact, it was becoming less gentle since Mary had been depressed. This Saturday Jane came unexpectedly in the afternoon, while Anne was washing up and Michael filling the coal scuttle.

'Don't you think it's a bit much to expect o' these little bairns?' Jane asked tartly. 'That's grown-up's work; they need to get out more and play at their age.'

Mary, who was kneading bread dough on the kitchen table, was in no mood for criticism. 'I can't manage everything around this place by myself. Look at that pile of washing over there and those pots boiling on the stove. When I finish making this bread I've got to start on the washing, and it's damned hard work with that tub and poss-stick, not to mention that I have to do it two or three times a week or they run out of clothes. They'll simply have to learn to help out a bit more till the baby comes. I hate to do it, Jane, but I have to and, besides, they're quite old enough to help.'

'Were you doin' housework when you were their age?'

'No,' Mary said hotly, 'but that was different. My mother had paid help, and I'm the only so-called *paid* help around here. It's simply too much for me to cope with at the moment.' She stopped kneading the bread and covered her face with her floury hands, trying not to break down.

'You should o' thought o' that when you got yoursel' into it and then went and got yoursel' further in.' The woman nodded at Mary's growing belly. 'You chose it for yoursel', Mary, and don't take it out on these poor bairns. If you can't manage all the work, let some of it go, but bein' pregnant doesn't make you helpless. I was on me hands and knees scrubbin' the floor when both o' mine came.'

'Then you're lucky you carry babies so easily, Jane. I wish I were as strong as you . . . in every way.' She pushed her hair back from her face and kneaded the dough furiously. She must keep busy. She refused to break down in front of Jane.

'Aye, you do look bad, hinny,' Jane said, her voice softening, 'so I brought some boiled ham for supper. I boiled a big shank and had some left over, thought it would save you cookin' tonight. I'll do whatever I can to help, Mary.' She rummaged in her shopping basket and set a basin on the table. 'I've cut it up ready.'

'Thank you,' Mary said, touched. She mustn't argue with Jane. She was a kind woman; she simply didn't realise what it was like to feel ill during pregnancy. Jane was one of the lucky ones, and she'd been happily married to a devoted husband when she'd had her children; she couldn't know what it was like to give birth to two children out of wedlock and to feel rejected by the man in your life – or in my case *men*, Mary thought ruefully. That was even worse.

'But if you have to get Anne to do something,' Jane added, resuming her cool tone, 'why don't you get her to help you with the bakin' instead of washin' dishes? That's more like fun for a bairn. At least you can teach her to cook and you can do the other work yoursel'.'

Even though the suggestion was well intentioned, Mary had taken enough criticism for one day and couldn't help retaliating. 'Thank you for your advice,' she said, trying not to let her voice sound as icy as she felt. 'But I think I know best how to run my own house.'

'Oh, *your* house now, is it? I thought you just worked here,' Jane retorted acidly.

At the sound of her aunt's raised voice, Anne came in, pale, from the scullery. 'It's all right, Auntie Jane, I really don't mind doing the dishes. Please don't fight.'

'Aye, pet, I'm sorry; I shouldn't have raised me voice in front of you bairns. Don't get upset. I'm leavin' now, and I'll be back to look after you the morrow. I'll be here straight after church,' she addressed Mary, 'and you can have a rest then.'

Mary muttered under her breath after Jane had left. And then she sat down, laid her head on the table and sobbed. She knew Jane was right. She must try to pull herself together. It was her dearest wish to make this a comfortable, loving, and happy home for Walter and all the children. But she was failing miserably.

Chapter Thirty

Summer came and went, but the sun shed no rays in the blackness of Mary's mind, nor, when autumn arrived, did treading on the soft mattress of autumn leaves that padded the hard, well-worn paths in the park give her her usual pleasure. One day was like the rest, except that she was feeling heavier and more restless daily, and relations with Walter were deteriorating at the same rate. Matters came to a head one November Saturday afternoon when he gave her her allowance and housekeeping money. She'd heard the week before, when he'd brought some of his work-mates home from the pub, that the welders were getting a rise. But she'd kept quiet, waiting to see what he would give her.

'Here's your money,' he said, sitting at the table and carefully placing the few coins on the green oilcloth, pocketing the little brown envelope that contained the remainder of his wages.

'And what about my rise?' she asked sharply.

'What rise?' His voice was threatening.

'I know you got a rise this week and that's for the cost of living. It's for the family, not the damned pub.'

'I keep tabs on me own purse strings, and stop telling me what to do with me own money. You're better off than most women around here.'

'What would you know about the cost of food or clothing? You never go into a shop, you never go

anywhere but that blasted pub. All you know about
is the price of beer and whisky.'

'Aye, and that's gone up more than food. I work
damned hard to keep you and the bairns fed and
clothed and housed and I'm entitled to some
relaxation.'

'Well, I work hard too, cleaning the house and keeping your children clean and fed. Not a penny of your
money goes on David; I keep him. You've been pro-
mising me a rise since I started and I need it now,
especially with another child coming and the rent
going up by a shilling next week. I need more.' Her
voice was shrill now and her face flushed.

'You don't have to remind me about another bairn
comin'; I'm reminded every day by your belly.'
He thumped his hand on the table and averted his
gaze.

'And whose fault is that?' Not to be ignored, she
walked towards the table to face him.

'It takes two, so don't put all the blame on me.' His
voice was rising.

'Right! It takes two. But so far I haven't seen you
playing any part in it. I need more money for food and
baby clothes. It's just lucky for you that I didn't get
rid of David's pram or you'd have to fork out for that
as well. That really would hurt, wouldn't it? Getting
money out of you is like pulling your molars. I don't
know how your poor wife managed.'

'Keep her out of this.'

'Yes, don't speak of the dead. Well, she *is* dead and
you and your family and David and I are still alive and
I need more money to keep us going. And, speaking
of the dead, your wife will have been gone a year in
seven weeks. It's not too early to make arrangements
to announce the banns.'

'You must be crazy if you think I'd want to marry
a shrew.'

'Shrew! You didn't think I was a shrew when you got me pregnant.'

'Well, you weren't then, though I always sensed you had it in you. And anyway, how do I *know* I'm the father? You'd slept around before you came here. How do I know you weren't still up to it?'

'You bastard!' Mary was nearing hysteria now and the children, playing in the yard, heard the shouting. Anne told Michael to keep an eye on them and came in, her face white.

'Please don't shout,' she begged. 'David's cryin'. I think it was the shoutin' set him off.'

'Tell your child to go outside and play,' said Mary, now out of control, 'and tell her to send David in to me.'

'Tell her yourself,' Walter retorted angrily. 'She's your responsibility. You took on the job.'

'You're her father, *you* take charge of her. I have to take care of everything in this house. You never do a hand's turn.'

'Get out, Anne. Do as you're told,' he shouted at the child.

'And bring David in to me,' Mary repeated.

In tears, the girl turned and quickly reappeared with a crying David, whom Mary grabbed and clutched tightly.

'So it's your brat that gets all the attention and mothering around here. I'm sick to death of this. I'm going to the pub,' he shouted, flinging two more shillings on the table. 'That's all you're going to get.'

'Oh, yes! Disappear to the pub as usual; that'll solve all your problems.'

Mary buried her face in David's little neck and sobbed with him. Such scenes with Walter had been common recently, and the children were increasingly becoming part of them. How dared he say she didn't give his children any attention? She spent her life looking after them. She sat down on the sofa and cradled David to her, rocking him until his sobs subsided. He was such a solace to her; he was all she had in the world to call her own.

Two shillings! Well, it was better than nothing, which is what she would have got if she hadn't made a scene. It had been worth it. Walter was easier to manipulate than Joe, but she wished it didn't take a row every time to get him to see reason about money. She was tired of rows and tired of life. As she raised her head to dry her eyes, she saw Anne standing by the table, her eyes brimming with tears. Dabbing at her own eyes, Mary cursed herself inwardly for allowing Anne to witness another scene with Walter.

'Oh, poor Anne! I'm so sorry, sweetheart. Don't worry; we won't row so much when the baby comes and I feel better. It seems to be mostly my fault these days. Come and sit beside me and I'll dry your eyes. I know you love your dad, but sometimes he's very hard to deal with, especially about money.'

Anne sat down and Mary mopped the girl's tears with the by now damp handkerchief, putting her free arm round the little shoulders and holding David with the other. How much had Anne heard?

'It's all right,' Anne said. 'I just get frightened when I hear shouting. Him and me mam used to shout as well sometimes, but they kissed and cuddled a lot too.'

Mary laughed, despite herself. 'I suppose I'm just not very kissable or cuddlesome at the moment. But you know that most grown-ups who live together have *some* problems and, just now, what with being so worried about money and the baby coming and not feeling well, I get irritable sometimes. You'll understand when you're older.'

'I think when Mam used to fight with him it was because she wasn't feeling well, too, an' she was always worried about money.'

368

'Were the rows always about money?'

'I don't know. Sometimes they were, but sometimes I could only hear the shouting when I was in bed. And Mam sometimes cried, like you.'

'Well, you and Michael fight sometimes, don't you? Even people who love each other fight, you see. In fact, it's usually the ones we love that we fight with; the ones we don't love we're usually more polite to. It's part of life, a strange part I admit, but don't get upset about it; it always blows over quickly, doesn't it?'

'Yes, I suppose so.'

'And now, I'd better lay this sleeping boy down for his nap. You see! He fell fast asleep in my arms, so the shouting couldn't have upset him very much, could it?'

'I'll tuck him in,' said Anne rising and retrieving the old cot blanket that lived under the settee cushion in readiness for naps.

'Thank you, and while you're doing that I'll butter these fresh scones. I baked them for tomorrow's tea so Auntie Jane wouldn't have to bake, but you can all have one now for a treat. David can have his when he wakes up.'

'Oh yes, I'd love a scone. Crying must make me hungry,' she laughed.

Mary rose and picked up the tray of scones cooling on the table, offering one to Anne before she took them outside to the children. 'Why don't you play outside too, Anne; the sun's actually shining, and there's nothing more to be upset about. It's over.' She hated herself for having lost her temper within the children's hearing; it wasn't fair to upset them with her problems and, despite Walter's remark, she was fond of them. She put her hands on her hips and stretched backwards to relieve her aching back. Then she retrieved the zinc bucket from the scullery cupboard, half filling it with cold water and topping it up to hand temperature from the kettle, afterwards throwing in a bar of carbolic soap and a scrubbing brush. She usually gave the floors a second scrub for the week and generally cleaned up the house again on Saturdays; she wanted it sparkling clean so Jane would have no cause for complaint. Grunting, she eased her bulk down on to her hands and knees awkwardly; that was the worst part. Once she was down she could move in that position better than upright; it temporarily relieved the heavy downward pull of her belly.

As she scrubbed, she thought with pleasure of her free day tomorrow. She had written to Mrs Moynihan to announce her visit; she could use some of her friend's wisdom to help her solve her present predicament and, besides, she hadn't seen her since she'd first discovered her condition. Sunday – her favourite day, but a special treat tomorrow.

It was another sunny day, although the sunlight, filtered by the smoke, shed a slightly greyish hue on the countryside. As usual, the train ride relaxed Mary, and David chattered excitedly as he stood on her lap gazing out of the window and shouting 'dog', or 'tree', or 'house'. It was pleasant to be reminded that there was a more tranquil life outside the big, grey city.

'I'm here, Mrs M.,' Mary said, as she pushed open the scullery door.

'Why, hinny, nice to see you. Eey, you've got a right bump on you, I must say,' she said, patting Mary's belly. 'I'm glad you made it in time for dinner. I got a leg o' mutton special for you comin'.' Mrs Moynihan, as gaunt and lively as ever, swung David up in her arms. 'Give us a kiss then, and you can go out and play with the bairns while your ma and me has a chat.'

With David safely out in the yard with the other children, Mrs M. produced a half bottle of sherry from the sideboard. 'An' I got this special an' all. It's quite an occasion when you come to see us these days.' She poured two glasses and they sat down at the table.

'I wish I could come more often, but it's the train fare, and I have to pay for David now he's a toddler.'

'Aye, I know, hinny, money's short. How you been feelin' and how's that man o' yours treatin' you?'

'Well, I don't feel sick now and Walter's all right. We have our rows but, all in all, it's a lot better than being on my own like last time. And we're both equally to blame; we only row about money and occasionally the children. The money's his fault but the children are mine. Sometimes when I'm feeling low I'm impatient with them, but I don't mean to be, and he thinks I'm taking it out on *his* children and not David. But that's not true; I find myself shouting at David too. And I'm usually so mad at myself after I've shouted at them that I end up crying and that upsets them even more. I wish I had more control over my moods.'

'Aye, hinny, it's hard copin' with five bairns when you're tired an' feelin' rotten. Eey, by God! I should know,' she added, laughing.

'But it's not all bad,' Mary added hastily. 'When we're not fighting I enjoy being with him. I *am* fond of him and I've got a home and he provides for me in his fashion. But for him, I'd be in the workhouse.'

'Aye, you've had some rotten luck, that you have. Thank God your poor mam can't see you now. So when's the bugger goin' to marry you?'

'We had another fight yesterday and he says he's not, but I'm sure I can persuade him to change his mind again. I can do a lot more with him than I could with Joe. That's something else in his favour.'

'Aye, that one had a mind of his own, but I still don't like the sound of all these fights. Couldn't you manage him without rowin'?'

'Well, I admit blame for some of the rows, and I could probably even avoid the others if I used a little more tact, but I'm feeling so edgy and depressed, I have no self-control. And, as I say, between rows we get along pretty well. He could be a worse provider, and we have a good relationship in the bedroom and that's important.'

'You don't mean to say he's still manhandlin' you?' Mrs M. plunked her glass down in horror.

'No, not now, but it was all right until a couple of weeks ago. One thing I like about making love when you're pregnant is that you can't get any more pregnant. I'm too far on now though.'

'Aye, men! They never give up till the last minute. You know, Mary, when you was a little lass I never thought I'd hear you talkin' about things like this. Such a proper little thing you were. Life's certainly changed you.'

'Yes, I know. And I don't know that it's all for the better, but at least I've learned to fend for myself.'

'I know, hinny, you were too soft. But I miss that innocent little lass. Anyway, I suppose you're right,' she sighed, getting up from her chair. 'You can't stay a bairn for ever, though you certainly grew up in leaps and bounds. I'd better set the table now. Them bairns'll be starvin'.'

'I'll help,' said Mary, getting up heavily from her chair.

'No, lass, sit down and rest yoursel' while you can. You can chat while I'm busy.' She began wiping down the yellow and white chequered oilcloth and covering it with a freshly washed and starched white damask cloth. 'Nothing but the best for me little Mary.' She paused while scrambling in the dresser drawer for knives and forks. 'You know, luv, I can't help worryin' if you're doin' the right thing. If you're both fightin' now, I don't think it'll get any better after you marry him.'

'And if I don't marry him, what then? What sort of

life would I have as an unwed mother with two fatherless children? Who else would have me now? At least Walter can provide a home for me and the children and, anyway, in my experience, there's no such thing as a relationship without fighting and disagreements. I'd rather be a respectable married woman with a husband to provide for me than be out in the world on my own with two children, fights or no fights.'

'Aye, I suppose you're right, lass. That certainly wouldn't be no fun.' She continued setting the table with another sigh. 'Not much of a choice you have, is it?'

'None at all, really. I've learned my lesson about hanging around waiting for prince charming. Joe taught me that,' she added wryly.

'Aye, you've learned a lot, hinny. I'm just not sure that I like what the lessons are doin' to you. You're gettin' a bit hard-bitten fo' bein' so young still.'

'Better that than soft and beaten down the way I used to be.'

'But don't let yoursel' get too brittle, luv. You wouldn't be my Mary any more.'

'My feelings for you could never change, Mrs M.,' Mary said, rising with difficulty and putting her arms round the woman.

'Aye, I hope not, hinny.' She returned Mary's hug from her lofty five foot eight and, for a brief moment, Mary felt protected again, as she had within those bony arms as a child.

At that moment Molly arrived with the gang and whooped a greeting, falling on Mary and hugging her, closely followed by Jimmy, who did the same. The younger ones buzzed around, excited to be having such a special dinner – a leg of mutton and a white tablecloth.

Molly, quite a young lady now, had found a new job

with the local dairy and was walking out with the dairyman's son. Mary stroked the girl's shining blonde hair, smartly pinned up now with just a few wisps falling around her pale, pretty face, and thought of the straggling locks and grubby face she remembered from their first meeting. 'Take a lesson from me, Molly, and don't let your boy friend lay a finger on you till you've got him neatly tied up in wedlock.'

'Don't worry, Mary! I've had enough warnin's from me ma and, anyway, he respects me, treats me like gold. All he's ever done is give me a goodnight peck on the cheek.'

Jimmy, now the image of his father, was visibly embarrassed by Mary's condition and avoided looking at her belly as he chatted: 'Did you know I've left the pit and I'm lookin' for a better job, Mary?'

'No, I didn't, Jimmy. That's wonderful! What are you going to do?'

'Well, me ma won't let me go down the pits any more because she says it's too unhealthy. Bob James, one o' me mates, is poorly an' the doctor says he's got black lungs or somethin'. But that's where the money is. I don't know till I look around and see what I can get, though, an' I'll have to hurry up. Me ma's missin' me wage packet since I've been off work.'

'I know, Jimmy, it's wonderful to get your own wage packet every week. I miss my money from the factory.'

Mrs Moynihan cut in as she sliced the steaming joint and carefully placed two slices on each plate, 'Aye it's about time he earned his keep again. Wait till your bairns are old enough; you'll be all right then, hinny.'

Mary laughed. 'It'll be a long time before I can look to them for support, but they will eventually be a help. Money's the only thing that gives some comfort and security in life. I know I'll never be rich but I'll make sure my family never go without a roof over their heads and food in their bellies, plus a little spare to spend on fun now and then. That's important, too. If you don't have a good time occasionally, life's all drudge.'

'Aye, lass, you learned that lesson,' retorted Mrs Moynihan, hurling a spoonful of mashed potato at each plate to join the heaps of cabbage, while Molly ladled the gravy out of the meat tin and dribbled it over the mounds.

'Yes,' Mary said, 'and that reminds me, Walter's bringing his friends back from the pub for a drink and a sing-song tonight, and Jane's making the sandwiches. I have to get back in time to put the children to bed and then I'll join them for some fun. I always enjoy a sing-song.'

'Right! Good for you, lass! And now get some decent food down you to last till then,' said Mrs Moynihan, slapping the heaped plates on the table.

Chapter Thirty-one

A week later Mary was blackleading the stove when she heard a knock on the door. She gasped in astonishment when she opened it. There stood Joe. He gasped with as much astonishment when he saw her, his jaw dropping visibly. 'Good God, Mary! . . . I . . . I had to make an unexpected business trip and I thought I'd pop in and see you . . . I . . . I thought . . .' He was faltering awkwardly, staring at her belly, his expression now not so much one of astonishment as of dismay.

'Hello, Joe,' she said, not knowing what else to say, pushing her untidy hair off her face with a blackened hand, which left black smears on her forehead.

'Mary, I didn't know . . .'

'Of course you didn't know, because I didn't tell you. A fat lot of good it did my telling you last time.'

'May I come in for a minute?'

'I . . . I suppose so,' she said hesitantly. 'But the older children will be back from school in ten minutes. Whatever you have to say will have to be brief.' She shook as she led him down the hall to the kitchen. Good God! Could he still affect her this way after all he'd done to her? No! She'd had enough of Joe's ways; he was nothing but trouble and that she had plenty of at the moment.

'I'm sorry, Mary,' he muttered, looking at her belly.

He took it for granted it was his. Well, whether or not it was, let him think so; he deserved to know how his selfish ways affected others. 'Yes! And you were sorry last time too, weren't you? And you did everything you could to get me out of trouble, didn't you? Why do you think I should turn to you a second time? I've learned *that* lesson.' She didn't even ask him to sit down, but stood before him, trembling inside, not knowing where those harsh words were coming from.

'I don't know what to say, Mary,' he said, tousling his hair, perplexed.

'Well, how about *goodbye*. You're an expert at that.'

'All right! If that's what you want. I can see you're in no mood to talk to me.'

'What is there to say, Joe? We've been through this once before and I know what your answer was then; why should it be any different this time?' She was amazed she could keep her voice so cool when her heart was thumping so much.

'I'm sorry I've upset you, Mary. I'll go now then.'

'Don't you want to see how your son's getting on? He's playing in the back yard.'

'I . . . I'd better not disturb him. I'll just go, Mary. Goodbye now, and if you decide you want to talk to me, write, won't you?'

Moving closer, he took her hand and she left it there for a few seconds, amazed that she felt nothing at his touch and proximity. Then she pulled her hand away and answered bitterly: 'Oh, yes! And you'll reply with loving concern the way you did last time? Goodbye, Joe!'

She averted her head. She heard his footsteps thump down the hall and the door slamming. Then, groping for a chair, she sat at the table, head in hands and body now visibly trembling. Why was she trembling? His touch had left her cold, so he no longer had the same old physical power over her, thank goodness! But damn him all the same! Why did he have to come back into her life now and upset her again? Should she have been nicer to him? Maybe he would act differently this time. No! That was too much to expect. She must settle for reality. She was with Walter now and he was a better man and would be a better father to both her children. Tears of anger and dismay overtook her, and she had no idea how long she'd been sitting there with her head in her hands when she heard the back door open. Anne and Michael, back from school already. She mustn't let them see she'd been crying again, so she dragged herself up to her room; she would pull herself together, splash her face and tidy her hair before greeting them and serving their meal. Thank goodness she'd prepared it in advance.

By the time Walter had returned from work, she felt a little calmer, but her face still looked drained.

'Hello, Walter.' She tried to sound normal.

'Hello, lass. You feelin' all right?'

'No worse than usual. Why?'

'You're lookin' a bit wrung out, that's all.'

'What's new?' She forced a smile.

'Aye, you can say that again. I feel done in an' all. This new piecework's killin' me,' he said, removing his overalls and washing in the scullery.

Mary followed him. 'But you'll earn more in the long run.'

'Not at the rate I've been goin' today,' he said, wiping his face and hands on the clean white towel she always left ready for him. 'I think we'd be better off to go back to a flat wage. All it means is that we have to burst our guts every minute to make our wage packets up to normal. Piecework's designed for the bosses, if you ask me. They get more work out of us but it's slave labour.' He took his place at the table and glanced out of the window. 'Did you know those bairns are playin' in the water butt? I told them to stop it when I came in but they're at it again.'

'I'll see to them. Here's your dinner.' She placed a plate of boiled tripe and onions before him, and he looked at it distastefully.

'You know I don't care much for this stuff.'

'Well, it was the only thing I could afford today. Force yourself, it's good nourishment.' With that she hurried out to the yard to see to the children. She didn't need Walter to start complaining tonight.

She brought the children in, while Anne assured her: 'I tried to stop them, but they wouldn't listen.'

'It's all right, Anne; at least they didn't throw any dirt in, but I'll have to change them out of these wet clothes. Would you mind helping me? We can put them straight into their nightclothes and then that's one job over. I still have to do the dishes, clean their shoes, and start a pan of broth for tomorrow.'

'Yes, I'll help,' said Anne eagerly, and, rather daringly, 'Do you think our Michael could do the dishes tonight, then?'

Michael? Do the dishes? Mary had never thought of that – it wasn't a man's job.

'Aw, forget it,' grumbled Michael. 'That's woman's stuff. You can do them tomorrow.'

'No, we need them for breakfast,' said Mary, the idea appealing to her.

'Listen to them, Dad. I don't have to wash the dishes, do I?' Michael whined.

Walter, who had been listening, put down his paper. 'I don't see why not, for once. You can see they're both busy. Give them a hand then.'

'Well, what about you, Dad? You're not busy.'

'I'm resting after a hard day's work – you're not. But just this once I'll do them with you and show you how; then maybe you can help out a bit more in future. But I'm doing it just this once – do you hear?'

Mary couldn't believe her ears – Walter actually doing a woman's job in the house, and training Michael! He must be in a good mood tonight. Maybe she could tackle him about money for baby clothes; there weren't enough left of little Walter's. No, on second thoughts, she'd had a bad enough day. She couldn't stand the thought of another confrontation; she'd leave it till she'd got over Joe's visit.

The following day, she was ironing and thinking about Joe – how dared he think he could just drop in for an afternoon of passion – when the postman came. A letter from Doreen! How she missed her! Like Doris, she was always so warm and caring, especially when Mary was in trouble.

She opened it eagerly:

Dear Mary,

Good news! Dad's got a family pass from the railroads – the first he's had – and about bloody time. They're going to Newcastle this weekend to see some friends and I can go with them. We'll be staying with the Johnsons (our old next door neighbours at number 27) from Saturday afternoon till Sunday afternoon. Will you be able to come and see me or should I come to see you? I thought you might prefer to get away from the children for a while.

I hope you're feeling better; your time's getting close. I have some good news, but I'm going to save it to tell you in person.

Please drop me a line care of the Johnsons; I can see you either Saturday or Sunday (one day I have to see some friends of my parents) so you make the arrangements.

Much love, and dying to see you,

Doreen

Mary, delighted, grabbed a pen and paper from the box that sat on the window sill and replied immediately:

Dear Doreen,
I'm thrilled! I can see you on Sunday; Jane's coming over to help. It would be better to meet at your place; it's so bloody crowded here we'd have no chance to talk alone. I can be there by about ten o'clock. Expect me.
Love,

Mary

Hurriedly, she threw on her coat; she'd go to the post office and post it straight away. Then she'd stop off at Doris's on the way back to tell her she couldn't make it this Sunday and, of course, to discuss Joe's visit. She tucked up little Walter in the pram and strapped Billie and David into their reins. It was a fairly long walk to the post office and then to Doris's, but if they got tired, she could seat one at a time on the pram.

Doris was scrubbing the front step when Mary arrived, wearing her mobcap and 'dirty work' pinafore.

'Hello, Doris. Sorry to interrupt you but I just came to tell you I can't make it on Sunday, Doreen's coming.'

'Oh, that's nice, luv, an' you're not interruptin' nothin' I want to do.' She grinned and threw the brush into the bucket with a splash. 'I can do that later. 'Leave the pram outside an' bring the bairns in. I've just finished me bakin' an' I could do with a cup o' tea an' a break mesel'.'

Jimmy greeted his two visitors with delight, too much delight for Doris. 'All right, you brats, if you're goin' to make that much noise you can make it outside. Here's a piece o' rice cake each. Go out in the yard and play. You sit down, Mary, and rest that belly on your lap.' She giggled. 'My goodness, you look as if you're about to pop.'

Mary eased herself into the chair with a sigh. 'I feel as though I'm about to pop, but now I hope nothing happens until after Sunday.'

'That's nice that Doreen's comin'. I know she's your best friend.'

'Don't be silly, Doris. You're my best friend and you know it. Doreen's my best friend from afar, and you're my best friend here. I couldn't have two nicer friends.' She accepted the cup of tea Doris handed her and drew in a deep breath. 'And I've got some more news. You'd better sit down for this one: Joe came yesterday.'

'Good God!' Doris sat down abruptly. 'What the hell did he want? Crikey Moses!' she exclaimed, shaking with mirth. 'I wish I'd seen his face when he saw you. Eey, I'm sorry, luv, I didn't mean to make light of it.' She looked closely at her friend.

'Don't worry. And you're right, his face was a sight to behold, only I didn't feel like laughing at the time.'

'What did he want and what happened?'

'He was here on a business trip and thought he'd just drop by and see me, but more likely he thought he'd just drop by to go to bed with me.'

'So, go on, what *happened*? I'm getting impatient.'

'He asked me why I hadn't told him and I gave him a mouthful about that. He just took it for granted it was his, so I let him think it was. Whether it is or not, I'm not sure that it'll bother him that much, but I wanted to punish him for what he's done to me, Doris. Isn't that awful?'

'I think it's natural, luv. Don't lose any sleep over that. So, he just popped in for a bit o' fun, did he? Well, I'm glad you've finally decided he's not goin' to have no more fun at your expense. At least Walter's a bird in the hand, an' he's more reliable, even if you don't feel exactly the same way about him as you did about Joe.'

'Yes,' Mary sighed, 'but I do wish Joe hadn't come. It just got me all upset, yet the funny thing is when he took my hand I didn't feel the way I used to; I didn't go all wobbly inside.'

'Well, that's somethin', any rate.'

'What about you? How's Frank, and how are things going in that direction?'

Doris giggled. 'Well, funny you should ask that today, luv. He came over last night an' we finally made it.'

'Doris, you harlot! How was it?' Mary added, laughing.

'Bloody wonderful, luv, even better than it was with Harry. It just sort of happened; he hadn't planned it. We were just kissin' an' cuddlin' as usual and we simply got carried away. Bloody funny, though. Just after the first time, me da got up to go to the privy an' I was terrified he'd come into the kitchen for a bite, so Frank an' me grabbed our clothes an' hid out in the hall, all naked an' goosepimply, but luckily me da went straight back to bed. We went right back for more, shiverin' and gigglin', an' we kept it up until about four in the mornin'.'

'Doris, you don't mean you literally kept *it* up?'

Doris laughed almost hysterically, 'No, you daft bugger! He'd be dead by now after six hours solid.' She crumpled up again with laughter. 'Oh! I shouldn't have said solid or you'll twist my words again, you clever, educated bitch.'

'I don't twist your words, you nut; I simply know your dirty little mind too well.'

'Oh, Mary, there was nothing dirty about last night. In between makin' love we just cuddled and kissed till he got his motor runnin' again. It didn't take him long to get goin' each time neither; I've never known anything like it.'

'I hope you took sensible precautions, Doris. Take me as an example.'

'Well, we did the best we could last night because we didn't know it was goin' to happen, did we? But he said he'll get some o' them French things the day, even though he wouldn't mind if I did get pregnant, because – wait for this – he wants to marry me anyway.'

'Oh, that's wonderful, Doris! When?'

'Why, we were too busy enjoyin' ourselves last night to talk about dates, but he says he'd like it to be soon.'

'Well, it's too late for me to pretend to be a virgin bridesmaid, but if you don't mind a maid-of-honour instead . . . after I get rid of my bump, of course.'

'Of course, luv. I wouldn't have nobody else but you.'

'Well, I'd love to help you make the arrangements, but not now. I must get those boys in and take them home, and little Walter should be waking up any minute; he'll be hungry.' She went to the scullery door and stuck her head out: 'David, Billie, come in. Time to go now.'

'I'll stop by on Friday on me way to the fish shop, luv. Don't worry about Sunday, unless you'd like to bring Doreen over. I'd like to meet her.'

'I'll see what she's planned. Thanks, Doris.'

Three small heads poked round the door. 'Well, hello you monsters. That was quick. Say goodbye to Auntie Doris while I see to little Walter.'

Sunday arrived and Mary, despite her weariness, was excited; it would be wonderful to see Doreen again. At ten o'clock sharp she arrived at the house to see her friend's slim figure hurtling out of the door to greet her.

'I was watching for you coming,' she shouted, flinging her arms round Mary.

'Oh, Doreen, it's lovely to see you,' Mary gasped, returning her friend's hug. 'How are you? Let me look at you . . . Oh, you look marvellous!'

Indeed, Doreen had changed. Gone were the sad-eyed expression and pallor that had characterised her during her wartime bereavement. Now her brown eyes were radiant and her pale cheeks glowed.

'I am bloody marvellous, but how are you?' She held Mary at arm's length and scrutinised her. 'God! Mary, you're a size, even bigger than with David. How are you feeling?'

'As can be expected – heavy, in more ways than one.'

'Come on in, luv. I've got my own bedroom, so we can go up there and chat after you've said hello to my parents.'

Doreen's parents greeted her warmly. They had always treated her well, despite the bad example she was for their daughter, but the girls couldn't wait to be alone and retreated to Doreen's room as soon as they could politely make their exit.

'Here, you have the chair, luv; it'll be more comfortable for you,' said Doreen, sitting on the bed. 'Now, what's new since you last wrote?'

'Not much, except that Joe came to see me the other day.'

'Oh, my God! I thought he was in London.'

'He is, but he was here on a business trip and he thought he'd call in to see me and have a roll in the hay, so to speak. You should have seen his face when he saw me; his jaw dropped a mile.'

'I'll bet! What happened then?'

'I told him what I thought of him and sent him

packing. He thinks for sure it's his baby and I let him. Maybe he'll be more careful in future, before he gets another girl into trouble. The rest of my life is the same: Walter still won't marry me until the full year's up. But you said you've got some good news, Doreen. I don't want to go on about my woes, I'd rather hear about you. Don't keep me in suspense any longer.'

'Well, I never thought it could happen to me again, but it has. I'm in love, Mary.'

'Oh, that's wonderful! Who is it?'

'Well, would you believe it, it's my boss.'

'Your boss! At the flower shop? You mean you've not only fallen in love, but also with a man with his own business. Oh, Doreen, you'll be comfortable for the rest of your life.'

'Hold on a minute, he hasn't actually asked me yet; we've only been walking out for four weeks, but I'd always liked him anyway, and now I'm smitten with him . . . and he is with me. At the rate our relationship's progressing, he should be popping the question after a decent period of courting.'

'Fantastic! What does he look like? How old is he? What's his name? Tell me more.' In her eagerness, Mary leaned forward in her chair, until her belly reminded her she couldn't do that, and she groaned.

'Well, he's tall, slim and dark – not handsome but nice-looking – and he's thirty. His name's Ed and he was married for two years but his wife died from a still-birth. He says for a while he couldn't even look at other women, but he's finally over her loss. And he's got a lovely house with a real garden at the back, not a yard.'

'How wonderful!' Mary sighed. 'It sounds like heaven; I'm so happy for you, Doreen. If anyone deserves to be happy, you do, after all you've been through.'

'And what about all *you've* been through?'

'Oh, that's different! I brought on most of my misery myself, through my ignorance and stupidity, but I'm in charge of myself now, Doreen. I intend to make sure that my life goes right from now on and that David and the new one are happy. I'll stop at nothing for that.'

'But do you really love Walter?'

Mary sighed. 'I'm not sure. Sometimes I think yes, and then, when he has his bad moods, I think no. But then Joe had bad moods too and, despite the moods, Walter is a better person than Joe. We quarrel quite a bit, but half the time it's my fault. My emotions are so topsy-turvy at the moment, I'm never sure how I feel from one moment to the next. But we're going on about me again. Tell me more about your boy friend. How did he get round to asking you to walk out with him? I want to hear every detail.'

It seemed they had hardly begun their chat when they were called down for lunch, which was a jolly reunion. Doreen's father was in his element, telling his favourite anecdotes, which never failed to raise a laugh. Afterwards the girls returned to the bedroom to continue their chat, this time Mary lying down to rest her aching back. Time flew and she was horrified when she finally looked at the clock. 'My goodness! It's five o'clock already! I told Doris I might take you to meet her, but Frank's going there at five and I don't want to disturb them. I'll just have to introduce my two best friends next time. Will there be a next time, Doreen?'

'Why, I certainly hope so. Dad should be getting more passes now, and pretty soon I shall have enough money for the fare – after I get married, that is. I'll be sending you your fare to come to the wedding, when it happens.'

'I've never been to London. I'd dearly love to go anyway, but especially for your wedding. Ironical, isn't it? I'm the one in the family way, but it's my two best friends who are getting married.'

'You will, luv; don't worry. It's your turn for things to turn out right.'

'Maybe,' Mary sighed. 'Now tell me about Maggie and the girls. I didn't know you were going to see them yesterday, I haven't seen them for ages. I wouldn't look quite right on the dance floor at the moment, you see,' she smiled wryly.

'I thought I wouldn't have time to see them but I knew where they'd be last night, so after we left Mam and Dad's friends I thought I'd catch them at the pub before they went on to the dance. They never change, do they?'

'No! Especially Maggie,' Mary laughed. 'But she's helped me out a couple of times. Her intentions are good.'

They chatted until five thirty, when Doreen and her parents had to leave.

'This is not goodbye, luv,' Doreen said as they hugged at the door. 'See you again soon, either here or London.'

'Sounds wonderful! 'Bye, Doreen,' Mary said, her voice choked.

Chapter Thirty-two

Two weeks later Mary decided to tackle Walter about putting up the banns; they should be read for three weeks, so there was no time to be lost. She waited until the children were in bed before broaching the subject and poured Walter a nightcap of whisky to soften her approach.

'Walter, why don't we put up the banns next Sunday? By the time the three weeks are up your mourning period will be over.'

'I've told you, Mary. I don't feel like doin' it just yet; you'll have to wait till I'm ready, if at all.'

'What do you mean, if at all? You promised!'

'I didn't promise anything except that I'd see you all right and I'll still do that. Now stop goin' on about it, there's a good lass. I've had a hard day. Let me read the paper in peace.'

'Time was when you liked to talk to me before bed,' she said petulantly.

'Aye, and time was when you had somethin' better to talk about. I'm gettin' tired of bein' nagged about marriage and money and bairns.'

'Nagging, am I, because I ask for my rights? If I didn't ask, I'd never get anything from you.'

'Well, you can stop askin' about marriage because I'm not goin' to do anythin' about it . . . at least not just yet, and if you keep on the way you're goin', I won't be doin' anythin' about it at all. What man in his right mind would want to marry a naggin' woman?

If you're like this before we're married, I can't see it improvin' after, so you'd better learn to change your tune or hold your tongue if you don't want me to change me mind altogether. I'm makin' excuses for you at the moment because your nerves are in a bad way, and I can understand that, but if you don't snap out of it by the time the bairn comes, you can look elsewhere for a husband.'

Mary bit her tongue. She knew she hadn't been exactly pleasant to be around lately. 'All right, I'm going to bed. But you're not going to go back on your word, are you?'

'You'll tempt me to if you don't stop naggin',' he muttered, opening the paper again and burying his head in it. 'Goodnight, Mary.'

'Goodnight, then.'

During the next week she was careful to avoid all mention of marriage and tried, ill and miserable though she felt, to keep relations sweet. If she wanted to win this man she had to use all her guile but, as her time drew nearer, it was difficult to remain cheerful. Her back and her head ached, and it took her twice as long as usual to do everything. She felt on the verge of tears most of the time. Keeping up an act under such circumstances was a strain and one night, after she'd had a particularly trying day with the children, Walter came home late, having stopped at the pub on the way. Her patience snapped.

'How do you expect me to keep your dinner hot for two hours? It's ruined and it's your own fault.' She thumped a plate of dried up ox-tail stew on the table. 'I need someone to look after *me* at the moment and all I do is wait on others.'

He put his arm round her jovially. 'Come on, Mary, I just stopped off for a couple of drinks; I've had a hard day as well, you know.'

She burst into tears at his touch and put her head

on his chest. 'Oh, Walter, I think my time's coming on. It's terrible, I know, but I don't want this baby.'

'Aw, you're just feelin' rotten. If you don't feel any better tomorrow, get Jane to come and help,' he suggested kindly, looking distastefully at the congealed stew but knowing better than to complain about it. 'Why don't you have an early night and I'll get Anne to put the bairns to bed.'

'Little Walter's been crying all day; I'll see to him and David myself. Anne can see to Billie. They're outside playing in the back lane, and it's too dark for them to be out anyway.' She picked up the crying baby from the settee, where David was patting the tiny back as he'd seen his mother do, and she trudged up the stairs with David at her heels. It would be wonderful to have an early night. She would put the baby in Anne's room so she could sleep undisturbed.

The next morning her pains were coming regularly and she trudged to Anne's room at six o'clock. Shaking the sleeping figure gently, she said urgently: 'Anne, it's my time. Be a good girl and go to Auntie Jane's and ask her to come . . . and to get the midwife.'

Anne, speechless, was out of bed and into her clothes before Mary had returned to her room. At least she could have this one in the comfort of her own home, she thought, as she sank back into bed.

It seemed hours later, yet it was only twenty minutes, before she heard Jane's voice: 'Just relax, hinny! I'm here. How far apart are the pains?' She was leaning over the bed and stroking Mary's damp forehead.

'I think about five minutes but I'm not sure. They're so bad I lose count,' Mary gasped. She'd never been so glad to hear Jane's calm voice.

'Well, I sent Anne for the midwife and came straight on. I can see to things till she gets here,' she soothed, wringing out the towel she'd dipped into the cold water in the bowl and placing it on Mary's forehead. 'I'm just goin' down to get some hot water and some sheets and towels, luv, an' I'll get Michael to look after the bairns till Anne gets back. Walter will just have to make the breakfast an' be late for work. I'll be right back,' she called over her shoulder as she reached the door.

'Thank you, Jane, I'm glad to have you,' Mary called after her gratefully as she lay gasping and timing her pains – about three minutes now. This one was going to be quicker than David, thank heaven.

When Jane returned, Mary was frightened. 'Where can the midwife be, Jane? I think it's coming . . . Oh God, it is! My water's are starting.'

'Anne's back, luv. The midwife was out on a call, but no need to worry; it's not the first time I've had to bring a bairn into the world. You just relax now and push when I tell you.'

Mary did as Jane told her, but it seemed hours before she heard the woman shout triumphantly: 'It's a girl, and she's a beauty!'

Mary sank back on her pillow in relief. 'Oh, thank God,' she whispered, 'and thank you, Jane. You were marvellous.'

'All in a day's work, hinny,' she said wrapping the slippery creature in a towel and then placing her in Mary's arms. 'I've just washed her face and now I'll go and get the water ready for her bath. What do you think, then?'

'Oh, she's perfect,' Mary cried, unwrapping the towel, her eyes greedily devouring the tiny form. 'I have a beautiful daughter!' She carefully examined the delicate features, the shock of dark hair, and the beautiful, rosebud mouth. Did she resemble Walter? Yes, she had that high forehead and those deep, almond-shaped eyes. Mary heaved a sigh of relief and gazed at the infant fondly – a daughter to love and to love her, to form that very special bond that she and her mother had had. She was glad it was a girl this time; she would call her Elizabeth after her mother.

She fell into a happy, deep sleep, waking periodically to feed and hold her new precious bundle. She felt exhausted, but it was her happiest day since she had first discovered she was pregnant. 'How could I have been so out of my mind that I thought I didn't want you,' she murmured to the suckling child.

Anne came up after school to see the new arrival. 'I've got a little baby sister,' she whooped joyfully as she gazed adoringly at the infant. 'Can I pick her up?'

'Of course, as soon as she wakes up you can hold her, but she's not quite your sister yet, although she will be soon.'

'She will be when you and Dad get married, won't she?'

'Yes, she will,' Mary said, gazing at the newborn face and wondering again if that were really true. Yes, thank God, she was undeniably like Walter. She then took Anne's hand and addressed her in a confidential tone: 'While Auntie Jane's getting supper ready, would you mind going to church and asking Father Donnelly if he could come over this evening?'

'Yes, I'll go now,' said Anne, her eyes widening. Whatever did Mary want to see the priest for? To bless the baby?

Mercifully, Walter was late and Mary had the chance she wanted, to speak to the priest first.

'Father, can you talk him into doing the right thing? He didn't want to do it too soon after his wife's death, but now it's been a year.'

'Well, I'll do what I can, but I know from experience he's stubborn, though not a bad man.' Father Donnelly gazed intently at the infant through his gold-rimmed spectacles, his shock of white hair falling over his lined, careworn face. 'I'll try to persuade him to start the banns this Sunday. The little ones come into this world with enough sin on their souls,' he sighed. 'Another one for the flock,' he said, making the sign of the cross over the child.

'Would you talk to him before he comes up, Father? That sounds like his voice downstairs now.'

'All right, child. I'll see what I can do, but I can't make any promises. Is there anywhere downstairs I can talk to him in private?'

'Yes, Father, the front parlour.'

'I'll be going down then, and I'll send him up to you when I've spoken to him. And I hope to see you both at Mass in future. You can't bring up children in the fear of God without setting them a good example.'

'Yes, Father,' Mary said, lowering her eyes. If only Father Donnelly could talk Walter into marrying her, she *would* go back to church; she would be eternally grateful.

Half an hour later, Walter came up to see the baby. 'Aye, she's a pretty one,' he murmured, looking into the cot.

'She's your daughter, Walter,' Mary said, confidently. 'Has Father Donnelly talked to you?'

'Aye, that he has. Puttin' pressure on me, eh? Well, I suppose it's the right thing to do.'

'Oh, thank you, Walter.' Mary took his hand and pulled him down on the bed beside her. 'We can make a new start.'

'Aye, we can. I've been thinkin' about that, but we'll talk about it tomorrow when you're feelin' better. You get some rest now.'

Mary snuggled down happily under the blankets. At last, everything would be all right. She'd be a respectable married woman, and she had a beautiful new daughter.

The next morning she awoke feeling cheerful and rested and reached happily into the cot to hold and feed her new little girl. Amidst the clatter of pots and pans, she could hear Jane and Walter talking downstairs. It was nice to be taken care of and to know the family were being well looked after. Then she heard the stairs creak and Walter appeared, carrying a tray with a mug of tea, two slices of toast and a boiled egg. 'Mornin', how are you feelin'?'

'Wonderful,' Mary said, sitting up.

'Jane sent this up,' he said, placing the tray on her lap. 'She's takin' the bairns to their granny's today so you can have a bit of peace. She's had to run now to pick her own two up before her old man goes to work, but Anne's stayin' behind to keep you company and get you what you need. I've told her not to bother you unless you shout for her, and Jane's left a pot of stew and some cold meat and pickles, so there's nothin' to do. They'll be back about six and the bairns'll have had their tea there.'

'Oh, that's nice of her. It'll be lovely to have a nice quiet day.' Mary sipped the tea and took a bite of toast. She felt hungry.

'Mary, I've got somethin' to say to you,' he said, sitting heavily on the bed. 'I've been awake all night thinkin' about it and I have a proposition to make. There's been a new development. Life would be a lot easier if we had fewer mouths to feed, and it would be less work for you.' He paused and ran his fingers through his hair. 'Jane's cousin and her husband are lookin' to adopt; they've just found that they can't have any of their own, so they've offered to adopt little Walter and the new one.'

Mary sat upright, the tea slopping on to the tray as she almost threw it to the side of the bed. 'Walter, you can't mean what you're saying!' Her voice was shrill in disbelief.

He ran his fingers through his hair again. 'Aye, I had to give it a lot of thought, but I do. It'll lighten the load on us, but most of all it'll be better for the bairns in the long run. The couple have money and can give them a decent life and a good education, so at least two of them will have the chance we both lost.'

'Give up my baby!' Mary screamed. 'You must be out of your mind. How could you even think of parting with your own children?'

His voice was determined. 'I've told you, Mary; it'll be better for them.'

'No, never! It's too much to ask. Have you *no* fatherly feelings?' she yelled.

'Aye, I have, Mary,' he said quietly, 'and it wasn't an easy decision. Do I have to keep tellin' you? It'll be better for them and us. Those are my terms; the choice is up to you.'

'You mean you won't marry me unless I give my baby away?' Mary's voice was horrified and her face white.

'If you want to put it that way. I just can't work hard enough to feed eight mouths and, I'm tired of tellin' you, it's in the bairns' best interest, for the ones left at home, too. There'll be more to go round for everybody.'

'And what if I won't?' Mary's voice was adamant, her eyes still staring in astonishment at Walter.

'All right, if you're goin' to be that stubborn about it, then we don't get married. That's my price, Mary. You've burdened me with two extra bairns, and I'm tired of havin' no peace in the house and no money in me pocket. If we're goin' to be married, we need to have some peace and harmony in our lives. We haven't had much of either this past six months, and there's not much chance of it with six bairns to bring up.'

'But I'd rather have the extra work and keep my family together – and yours. They'll be my family too after we're married.'

Walter looked exasperated and thumped his fist on

the bed. 'Look, Mary! I'm not goin' to change me mind now; it took me all night to make it up. That's my choice and that's that.'

'You're giving me no choice,' Mary shouted. 'If I don't do what you say, you know I couldn't possibly manage on my own. What would life be like for me with two illegitimate children? I could never hold up my head again, whether I stayed or whether I left. And if I left, where could I go with two? I'd end up in the workhouse.' Her voice broke and she turned her head, sobbing into her pillow.

'For God's sake, don't be so melodramatic and try to be a bit more practical.' He rose angrily. 'I've got to go to work now and I'll expect your answer when I get back.' Then he stalked out.

Mary slumped back into her pillow. Oh, God! She must think what would be best for the baby and David. She had no power over what Walter did with his youngest boy, but she had the right to chose her own children's lives. Would keeping them be selfish? She would be depriving her daughter of a better life with a loving, well-off family and – Walter was right in a way – David's life would also be easier with a smaller family to keep. By keeping the baby she would condemn both her children to a life of poverty and disgrace without a father. No! She couldn't possibly give up her baby. Whatever it took, she was going to keep her family together, no matter what. She had no rights over Walter's child, but he couldn't take hers from her. How could he be so cold and practical? He was no better than Joe after all. She'd always thought he had a warm streak behind his cool exterior but she'd been wrong. How could she have been so stupid not to see through him? She felt a stab of pain as she thought of leaving him. She hadn't realised just how much a part of her life he had become. Had she been so bound up in her old feelings for Joe that she hadn't realised that this man had a place in her heart as well as her body? How could she have loved two such worthless men, both callous enough to want her to give up her children? Damn all men! Whatever the cost, she'd be in charge of her own life from now on.

The baby whimpered and she picked her tenderly out of the cot and held her to her breast, her mind in turmoil. She must be practical. What could she do? She would go to Mrs Moynihan's as soon as she felt strong enough. While she was looking for another job in town she could stay there. The fares back and forth would be heavy but she wouldn't be paying rent. She would try for another housekeeping position, with a married couple or an old man this time. Walter would have to give her a good reference, so surely someone would take her on, even with the children. Failing that, she'd take another factory job and leave the children with a baby-minder. She'd done it before with one. She could do it again with two.

But then she remembered the pain of leaving David all day long with a stranger. It would be twice as bad with two. And what would happen when David started school? How could she arrange to have him taken there and picked up? She would be at work at those times. Dear God! And then she cried aloud: 'Oh, Mother, tell me what to do. Could you have given me away for my own good?' The tears trickled slowly down her cheeks as she clutched the baby at her breast. She knew the answer. No! 'I'll make you happy, my little one, and your big brother,' she sobbed to the infant, stroking the downy black head. 'I'll try hard to find a housekeeping job and keep you both with me. And if I can't find a job, I'll find a flat and take in washing the way Mother did. You'll get to know and love your own brother and your own mother. No stranger is going to bring you up. I can teach you all the lessons I've learned. Who else could do that, my little one?'

She smothered the baby in tear-damp kisses before laying her back in her cot and falling back, exhausted, on her pillow. She had her answer ready for Walter. Oh, Walter! At the thought of leaving him, pain spurted from her like blood from a fresh wound. How could she have been so blind to her own feelings? And Walter's children! She hadn't realised how fond of them she'd grown. God! How stupid could she be! She'd been so consumed by old, sad memories of Joe and guilt at the thought that it might not be Walter's child she was carrying that she hadn't realised what was happening in the present. And now she knew it too late, just when she was losing him. But it was his fault. If he weren't so stubborn, he wouldn't insist on going through with this. He isn't only giving up his children, he's also giving up me, she thought sadly. He couldn't possibly feel anything for me or he wouldn't do it. What is it about me that makes men want me only in bed? Is that all I'm good for? she thought for the umpteenth time in her life. Tears of self-pity started, but this time she bit her lip to stem them. No, not any more. No man will ever get into my heart or my bed again. I'm not wasting my love on any more men who don't love me. When Walter came home, she'd tell him what she thought about that too.

Dreading it, yet eager to get the inevitable scene over, she glanced at the clock. Eleven o'clock! Oh, God! Six seemed years away. She dried her face on the white sheet and smoothed back her hair. She needed some clean nappies from the airing cupboard and she mustn't let Anne see her upset again. She must compose herself. She called the girl's name and heard her light steps racing up the stairs. 'Yes, Mary,' she said breathlessly. 'I've been waiting all mornin' for you to call.'

'I was asleep, Anne,' Mary lied, not looking the child in the eye. 'Would you mind bringing me up some clean nappies from the airing cupboard?'

'Yes, I will, but can I see the baby first?' she asked eagerly.

'Of course,' Mary said, trying to stop the tremor in her voice.

'Ooh! Isn't she lovely?' Anne exclaimed, peeking into the cot. 'Can I take her out in the pram when she's old enough?'

Mary winced, but tried to keep her voice normal. 'Certainly you can.' There was no point in upsetting the child yet; it would come soon enough. Anyway, she couldn't deal with Anne's grief as well as her own at the moment. She must be alone until she faced Walter. 'I'm very tired today, Anne, so why don't you just go downstairs and read or draw or something. Just relax and enjoy your day off. I promise I'll shout if I need anything.'

'All right!' Anne tore her eyes away from the baby and picked up the barely touched breakfast tray. 'But you didn't eat hardly anythin'. Didn't you like it?'

'Yes, it was fine. I'm just not hungry yet. I need to sleep some more. I'll let you know if I get hungry later.'

'I'll put the stew on to warm now so it'll be hot for when you want it. Have a good sleep,' the child said, looking at Mary closely. 'You look tired . . . at least, your eyes look red.'

'I was awake most of the night with the baby, that's all. Thank you, Anne, for looking after me,' Mary said, forcing a smile. But as soon as she heard the footsteps trail away at the bottom of the stairs, she buried her head under the blankets to muffle the sound and sobbed until she could sob no more.

Lying in a sort of torpor, she waited. Three o'clock.

She must eat something to keep her strength up. 'Anne,' she called again.

The child appeared at the doorway.

'I think I'll have some of that stew now if it's still hot.'

'I had to take the pan off the stove 'cause it was goin' all mushy, but I'll put it back on for you now. It'll only take a few minutes,' she said, turning and galloping down the stairs.

Ten minutes later Anne returned with a steaming bowl on a tray. 'Here you are. It's nice and hot now. Can I hold the baby while you have your stew?'

'Yes, just lift her out gently without waking her, if you can.' Mary took the tray, her stomach turning as she looked at the mushy mess. She must eat it, for the baby's sake. 'This looks lovely, Anne. Thank you.'

'Oh, I love her already,' Anne said, rocking the baby gently. 'Have you decided yet what you're goin' to call her?'

'Elizabeth, after my mother,' Mary said, forcing herself to swallow a spoonful of stew. That's one down, now for one more, she thought.

'Elizabeth, that's a pretty name. I don't know anyone called Elizabeth. Elizabeth . . . Elizabeth,' she cooed to the baby, while Mary turned away, afraid she was going to cry again.

'I think I've had enough to eat now, Anne.'

'But you haven't even finished half,' said Anne, peering into the bowl.

'I know, but that's all I need for the moment. I'll have some more later. I just want to have another sleep now, if you don't mind.'

'No, I'll take the tray,' Anne said, gently laying the baby back in her cot. 'Mam was up the next day after she had Billie, but she never got up at all after little Walter. You will be getting up tomorrow, won't you?' She looked anxiously at Mary.

'Yes, of course I will. It's just that Elizabeth was a big baby so it made me extra tired. I'll be fine tomorrow, don't worry.'

Anne looked relieved. 'I'll go now then. Just shout when you want some more stew.'

'I promise,' Mary said, forcing another smile until Anne had left, then burying her head in the pillow and moaning, 'Oh, Walter! What are you doing to all of us? Poor little Anne! She's been through enough, losing her mother. They all have. Please, please don't do this.' But she knew Walter would never change his mind once he'd made it up – that much she'd learned about him.

She looked at the clock. Four o'clock. God! Two more hours. She hadn't seen David all day and longed to hold him in her arms, but he was better off with Jane today than with his mother in this state. She lay staring at the ceiling, her mind and body numb, until the baby cried and jerked her out of her stupor. Glancing at the clock, she picked her up to feed and change her. Five thirty, almost time. She trembled at the thought. But six o'clock came, then seven o'clock. Damn him, she thought. He's gone straight to the pub, the swine! And where are the children? Jane was supposed to bring them back at six thirty.

Just then she heard the back gate opening and childish voices. Thank God, she thought, at least I can talk to Jane. I know she'll be on my side; she could never give her own children away. But it was Walter's voice she heard coming from the kitchen, and then his footsteps on the stairs.

'You're late,' she said accusingly, as he entered the room.

'Aye, I know. I'm sorry. I went straight to pick up the bairns. I wanted to talk to Jane.' He sat on the bed, still in his dirty overalls.

'I'm not giving my baby up. I don't care what

happens. I'm leaving you,' she cried.

'Well, I've been doin' some thinkin' all day and you needn't worry your head. It sounded like a good idea at first. I mean, you told me yourself you didn't want the baby and then I was surprised when you seemed to have changed your mind. I suppose I should have reacted quicker than I did, but it took me all night long to make the decision, and you know I don't change me mind easily. I still thought it was the best choice for all of us, but now I'm not sure I want to farm me own bairns out either, especially if *you* don't want to. God knows I never asked for six, but you were right, Mary; their place is with their own folks, poor or not.'

'Oh, Walter! You *do* care about your children,' she cried, relief in her voice and tears in her eyes.

'Aye, I suppose I do. I didn't know it so much till I thought about givin' them away – and no more rubbish about leavin'. The bairns need you and so do I.'

'Do you just need me or do you love me, Walter?' Mary inquired, breathlessly waiting for his answer.

'I suppose I must love you,' he smiled.

'And *I suppose* that's the closest I'll ever get to hearing you say it?' she smiled back.

'Well, why do I have to tell you something you already know? Be logical, woman!'

'Then if you need me and you love me, why don't you want to marry me?'

'It seems I'll not get any peace till I do, especially now you've got the priest on me back.' He smiled and his dark eyes gazed down at her as he added, 'Do you always get your own way, Mary, or is it only with me?'

She leaned forward eagerly and grabbed both his calloused hands. 'Oh, Walter, you won't regret it. I'll be a good wife and mother and we'll be a whole family. We can make a new start,' she sobbed, letting the tears of joy flow.

Just then Anne poked her nose round the door.

'I've got them all ready, but David's cryin' and he won't go to bed.'

'Bring him up, Anne, and I'll tell him a bedtime story,' Mary said, quickly wiping her tears with the back of her hand. 'In fact, why don't you all come up and listen? And you can nurse your new little sister again.'

'Ooh, yes! I'll get them all except little Walter, 'cause he's already asleep and he wouldn't know what you're talkin' about anyhow.' Anne skipped from the room and was back in seconds with the others. She lifted the whimpering David into his mother's arms and Mary cradled him beside her. Michael and Billie took an uninterested peek at the baby before climbing on to the bed and sitting cross-legged, waiting, while Anne picked up the little bundle lovingly and sat in the bedside chair, rocking her new sister.

David was still whimpering as Mary patted his back. 'It's all right, David, no need to cry any more,' she said, fondly stroking his hair. 'And did you boys have a nice day with Auntie Jane and Granny?'

'Aye,' said Michael, nodding, 'and we had fish and chips for tea.'

'Aye,' repeated Billie, nodding like his brother.

Walter rose from the crowded bed and stretched. 'Well, I'll leave you to it and go down and get some of that stew. I'll pop up and see you before I go to bed.'

'Can we set the date then?' asked Mary hesitantly.

'Aye, I suppose we can.'

'Do you mean the date to get married?' Anne asked excitedly, as her father left the room.

'That's right, Anne,' Mary said, bestowing on the child the first genuine smile she'd given her that day.

'Oh, goody, and then you'll be called Dolan, same as us.'

'Strange, I hadn't even thought of that. I shan't be Mary Maddison any more.'

Mary closed her eyes for a minute before she could speak, her head swimming with relief and happiness.

'Well, now, which story shall I tell you? Let me see, how about "Rumpelstiltskin"?'

'Yes, Rumblesilsin,' attempted David, his tears stemming, while his brothers and sisters nodded agreement.

More Compelling Fiction from Headline:

Rosie Edwards

A delightful
family saga from

– HILDA McKENZIE –

Wesley Street was built in the nineteenth century
when Cardiff was beginning to emerge as an
up-and-coming industrial town. Now in 1928 it
looks drab and cheerless, but Number 42 has a
newly painted front door and the knocker and
letter-box glow from a recent application of
Brasso and elbow grease. Inside the Edwards are
a caring, close-knit family – though Mam is
considered by Grandma Hughes to have married
beneath her.

Tragedy strikes when Mam dies having her
seventh child and young Rosie takes over the role
of mother for her anguished father and six
brothers. Though forced to give up her
scholarship to the grammar school Rosie keeps
the family together through hardship and illness.
But she dreams always of a better life.

ROSIE EDWARDS is a nostalgic and evocative
family saga in the great tradition of Catherine
Cookson and Marie Joseph.

FICTION/SAGA   0 7472 3574 0

A selection of bestsellers from Headline

FICTION

GASLIGHT IN PAGE STREET	Harry Bowling	£4.99 □
LOVE SONG	Katherine Stone	£4.99 □
WULF	Steve Harris	£4.99 □
COLD FIRE	Dean R Koontz	£4.99 □
ROSE'S GIRLS	Merle Jones	£4.99 □
LIVES OF VALUE	Sharleen Cooper Cohen	£4.99 □
THE STEEL ALBATROSS	Scott Carpenter	£4.99 □
THE OLD FOX DECEIV'D	Martha Grimes	£4.50 □

NON-FICTION

THE SUNDAY TIMES SLIM PLAN	Prue Leith	£5.99 □
MICHAEL JACKSON The Magic and the Madness	J Randy Taraborrelli	£5.99 □

SCIENCE FICTION AND FANTASY

SORCERY IN SHAD	Brian Lumley	£4.50 □
THE EDGE OF VENGEANCE	Jenny Jones	£5.99 □
ENCHANTMENTS END Wells of Ythan 4	Marc Alexander	£4.99 □

All Headline books are available at your local bookshop or newsagent, or can be ordered direct from the publisher. Just tick the titles you want and fill in the form below. Prices and availability subject to change without notice.

Headline Book Publishing PLC, Cash Sales Department, PO Box 11, Falmouth, Cornwall, TR10 9EN, England.

Please enclose a cheque or postal order to the value of the cover price and allow the following for postage and packing:
UK & BFPO: £1.00 for the first book, 50p for the second book and 30p for each additional book ordered up to a maximum charge of £3.00.
OVERSEAS & EIRE: £2.00 for the first book, £1.00 for the second book and 50p for each additional book.

Name ....

Address ....

....

....